Turbo Pascal 5.0/6.0
for Engineers

Brian D. Hahn

British Library Cataloguing in Publication Data

Hahn, Brian, D.
Turbo pascal 5.5/6.0 for engineers.
I. Title
005.133

ISBN 1-85554-081-9

First published in 1991 by:

NCC Blackwell Limited, 108 Cowley Road, Oxford, OX4 1JF, England.

Editorial Office: The National Computing Centre Limited, Oxford House, Oxford Road, Manchester M1 7ED, England.

Typeset in 10pt Palacio by Scribetech Limited, Bradford
and printed and bound in Great Britain by
Biddles Limited, Guildford and King's Lynn

ISBN 1-85554-081-9

To four very special people:
Cleone, David, André and Lyndall

Contents

Preface

Turbo Pascal is one of the most widely used language systems for microcomputers. This book explores the problem solving potential of the most recent versions: 5.0, 5.5 and 6.0.

The approach taken is one developed over many years of teaching programming, in FORTRAN, Pascal and various versions of BASIC, to first-year university students with no computing experience. It can therefore be used as a "teach yourself" guide by anyone wishing to learn Turbo Pascal, and who has access to a computer and the Turbo Pascal software.

The computer is presented as a tool for solving interesting, real-world problems and examples from many areas, as wide apart as business and biology, but particularly science and engineering, are discussed. The technicalities of each new programming construction are therefore generally presented only after a motivating example. Since the objective of this book is to enable you to solve problems using Turbo Pascal, the earlier chapters are in a sense a preparation for later ones, where you will be introduced to some modern computer applications, such as simulation, modelling and numerical methods. There are also a large number of exercises, taken from a variety of areas, and developed from experience gained by teaching hands-on programming courses for beginners. Solutions to most of the exercises are provided. Some of those for which solutions have not been given have been successfully used as class projects in teaching situations.

In keeping with modern concepts of structured programming, procedures are introduced as soon as possible, with formal definitions coming later.

It must be stressed that this book is not a technical reference manual, but rather an exposition of how to use Turbo Pascal to solve problems, so new constructions are generally introduced as the problems presented require them. All the details of particular statements and standard functions and procedures will not therefore always be found in the same place. However, there are summaries of statements and standard functions and procedures in the appendices. A complete description of the language may be found in the *Turbo Pascal User's Guide* and *Reference Guide*.

No specialised mathematical background is needed to follow most of the examples. There are occasional forays into first-year university mathematics, but these are self-contained and may be glossed over without loss of continuity (you may even find them interesting!).

All the programs in this book can be run with Turbo Pascal 5.5 or 6.0. With the exception of those in section 12.3, they can all be run with version 5.0. Version 5.5 introduced the new object type, discussed in this section, and version 6.0 develops it further (to make full use of version 6.0 you need to be an experienced programmer, well grounded in object-oriented programming and pointers).

If you become a serious Turbo Pascal programmer, you may like to consider joining the Turbo User Group (TUG). It publishes a bimonthly journal with articles and letters of interest to users of all Borland products (Turbo Pascal, Turbo C, Turbo Basic, Turbo Prolog, etc). Their address is P.O. Box 1510, Poulsbo, WA 98370, USA.

It is hoped that this book will give you some insight into the ways that computers in general, and Turbo Pascal in particular, may be used to solve real problems, and that after working through it you will be better equipped to solve problems for yourself.

I wish to thank my wife, Cleone, for her continual love and support over the years, and particularly during the writing of this and other books, and my children, Lyndall, André and David, for their interest and encouragement. I want to acknowledge a debt to present and past students and colleagues in the Departments of Applied Mathematics at the University of the Witwatersrand, Johannesburg, and at the University of Cape Town, for providing the stimulating environment required to produce a book of this nature.

Brian D. Hahn
Department of Applied Mathematics
University of Cape Town
Rondebosch 7700
South Africa
October 1991

1 Getting Going

1.1 INTRODUCTION

The first computer I programmed, 20 years ago, was called an ICT 1301 and occupied a large room. Only one person could use it at a time and programs had to be punched on cards. It could remember about 240 different numbers in its fast memory and a few thousand in its slow memory, which was on a rotating drum that you could hear ticking as it spun. It was very slow!

The computer you use most likely sits on a desk, displays information on a video monitor (in colour if you are lucky), can remember many thousands of numbers instantaneously and is much faster and easier to use. Computer technology has advanced so much during this time that the personal computer is now firmly entrenched in almost every walk of life in the Western world, and affects most careers, particularly those in scientific and engineering fields. Apart from the mere interest factor, anyone who is computer literate is far better equipped for a wide range of occupations than someone who is not.

You may not have used a computer before, but you are probably familiar with using a calculator of some kind. The simplest sort can only do basic arithmetic and display the answer. The next step up is one with a single **memory location,** where an intermediate result may be stored, and with function keys, such as sin, log, etc. Even smarter calculators may have more memory locations, so that a number of intermediate results may be stored during a long and involved calculation.

If you have to perform the same sequence of arithmetic operations on a calculator many times for different sets of data, it can become extremely tedious. So more sophisticated calculators allow you to store, in some suitable coded form on a magnetic card, the sequence of operations (or **instructions**) needed to calculate the solution of the problem. This sequence of instructions is called a **program.** To carry out the entire set of calculations you need only load the program into the calculator, press the run key, provide the necessary data (which may also be on the magnetic card), and sit back while the machine churns through the calculations. A calculator like this is called **programmable.** A computer, whether it is a micro (or personal computer) like the IBM PC, or a large impersonal mainframe like a VAX, is really only an advanced programmable calculator, capable of storing and executing sets of instructions, called programs, in order to solve specific problems.

1.2 PASCAL

The particular set of rules or conventions for coding instructions to a computer is called a **programming language.** In the same way that there are many spoken languages, there are also many computer languages, for example Pascal, True BASIC, FORTRAN, COBOL, etc. Some operations look almost the same in many languages (for example assigning the value 1 to the variable X) whereas others (for example printing a message) look a little different, as you can see in Table 1.1.

Pascal	*True BASIC*	*FORTRAN*
X:= 1; **Writeln('Hi');**	**LET X = 1** **PRINT "Hi"**	**X = 1** **PRINT*, 'Hi'**

Table 1.1 Three ways of saying the same thing.

The programming language called Pascal was designed by a computer scientist, Niklaus Wirth, of the Technical University of Zurich, who had become frustrated with the languages available for teaching his students. It was published in 1971 and named after Blaise Pascal, the seventeenth century French philosopher and mathematician. The original version ran only on mainframe computers and was used mainly by computer scientists at universities and polytechnics.

Machine	*Language*	*Time (secs)*
ZX-80	**BASIC interpreter**	**30**
Apple IIe	**MSBASIC interpreter**	**24**
IBM PC	**MSBASIC interpreter**	**16**
Apple IIe	**MSBASIC compiler**	**8**
Olivetti M24	**GWBASIC interpreter**	**6.7**
Olivetti M24	**True BASIC compiler**	**1.5**
Olivetti M24 (with 8087)	**True BASIC compiler**	**0.81**
Olivetti M24 (with 8087)	**Turbo Pascal 3.0**	**0.81**
Olivetti M24	**Turbo Pascal 5.5**	**0.73**
80286 (AT) (with 80287)	**True BASIC compiler**	**0.54**
Olivetti M24 (with 8087)	**Turbo Pascal 5.5**	**0.19**
80386	**Turbo Pascal 5.5**	**0.12**
VAX 6230 mainframe (batch)	**FORTRAN 77**	**0.0003**

Table 1.2 Benchmark test

In the early 1980s Borland International Inc. produced a version called Turbo Pascal which ran on personal computers. The language then began to enjoy much wider usage. In a recent advertising brochure Borland claim that over one million copies of Turbo Pascal are in use. I have designed my own benchmark test for comparing different languages and computers, and have found that Turbo Pascal is certainly one of the fastest compilers available and produces the fastest code. For those who are interested in such things, the test is to compute the first 1000 terms in the Taylor series for cos(x), and is listed at the end of Appendix E. Some typical results are shown in Table 1.2.

There are very few *differences* between Turbo Pascal and Standard Pascal, although Turbo Pascal has many *extensions.* These differences and extensions are listed in the various Turbo Pascal reference manuals. The aim of this book is to enable you to learn to solve problems in a variety of areas using Turbo Pascal 5.0/6.0.

1.3 RUNNING TURBO PASCAL PROGRAMS

Your ultimate aim will be to write your own program coding for whatever problem you want to solve, and you will be keen to achieve this objective as soon as possible. However, the greatest hurdle facing you at the moment, especially if you are a computer novice, is actually getting the computer to do anything at all. The examples in the rest of this chapter are therefore very easy, and are given without much explanation (this will follow in Chapter 2). You should run these examples, and the exercises at the end of the chapter, on your computer as soon as possible. Do not stop trying until you have succeeded!

Starting up

Seat yourself comfortably in front of the computer. It is assumed that Turbo Pascal has been correctly installed on your computer, and that you have access to the Turbo Pascal's User's Guide and Reference Guide. If your machine does not have a hard disk with Turbo Pascal installed on it, insert your Turbo Pascal disk into drive A. (For simplicity it is assumed that the Turbo Pascal disk is in drive A and that your program disk is in drive B.) Switch the computer on. It should eventually display the DOS system prompt

A>

which means that it is waiting for you. To start Turbo Pascal, type the word **TURBO** and press the **Enter (Return)** key. If your machine has a hard disk, get into the Turbo Pascal directory and call up Turbo Pascal by typing **TURBO**. If something goes wrong and the computer hangs up on you, **reboot** the system by holding down the **Ctrl** and **Alt** keys simultaneously with the fingers of one hand (preferably the left) while pressing **Del** briefly with any free finger (preferably on the right hand). Incidentally, you can't damage the computer by pressing the wrong keys, so don't worry!

After a few seconds, the Turbo Pascal Environment, as it is called, will appear, as shown in Figure 1.1. The Hello box in the middle will disappear as soon as you press any key. The screen is divided into two **windows.** The **Edit** window is where you will type your programs. The **Watch** window will be used later when we discuss debugging. You can get the Hello box back at any time by pressing **Shift-F10** (this can be helpful if you've forgotten which version of Turbo Pascal you are in).

At the top of the Environment screen are the words **F**ile, **E**dit, **R**un, etc. These represent menus containing sets of commands. To select a particular menu, type the highlighted initial letter and press **Enter.** Alternatively use the arrow keys to move the highlight box to the correct menu and then press **Enter.** These two methods only work from the top line itself. If you are *anywhere* in Turbo Pascal, the **Alt** key plus the initial letter of the menu will invoke the menu, for example **Alt-F** invokes the **File** menu. These special key combinations are called **hot keys** (shortcuts).

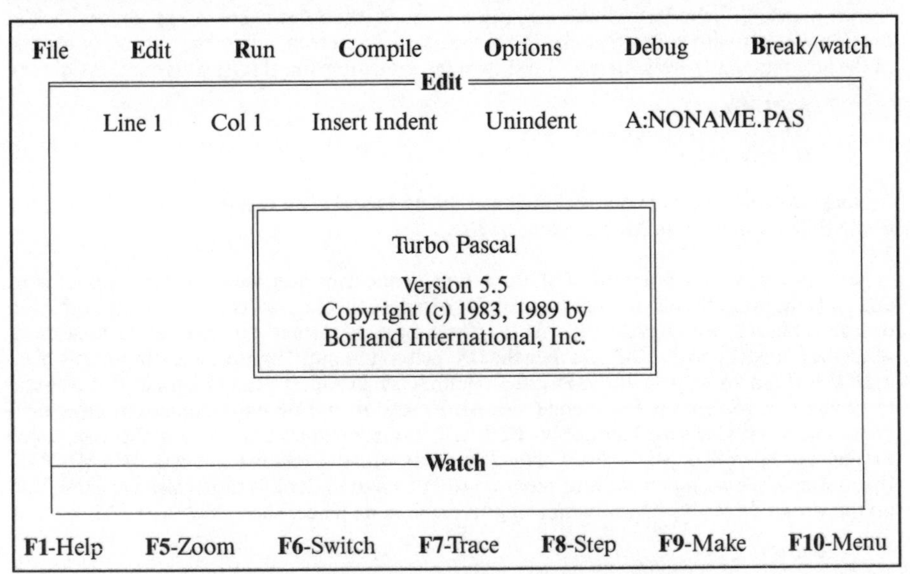

Figure 1.1 The Turbo Pascal Environment Screen

To enter your first program, type **Alt-E** to invoke the editor. The cursor will move into the Edit window. Note that the position of the cursor is indicated at the top of the window. Type the following eight-line program exactly as it stands (leaving out any semi-colons will cause an error!). Use the **Shift** key to get uppercase letters. Press **Enter** to get a new line, or to enter a blank line. If you make a mistake, use the arrow keys to position the cursor and then use **Backspace** or **Del** to correct the mistake.

```
program First;
var Name: string;

begin
   Write( 'What is your name? ' );
   Readln( Name );
   Writeln( 'Hi there, ', Name );
end.
```

If you miss out an entire line, move the cursor to the extreme right of the line *after which* you want to insert the new line, press **Enter,** and a blank line will appear. If you want to delete an entire line, position the cursor anywhere in the line to be deleted and press **Ctrl-Y.** If you delete part of a line by mistake and want to get it back, **Ctrl-QL** will restore the line. Unfortunately this won't work if the *whole* line has been deleted – it's gone forever.

When you are reasonably sure that the program is correct, the great moment has come to run it. One way is to select the **R**un menu with **Alt-R.** The **R**un menu then pops up in front of your program. To select commands in this menu (and the others) move the highlight bar up and down with the arrow keys, and press **Enter** to invoke the highlighted command. Alternatively enter the initial letter of the selected command (**R** for **R**un in this case, to run the program). However, one needs to run programs so often that there is a special hot key for it: **Ctrl-F9** (ie hold the **Ctrl** key while pressing the **F9** function key on the left). The hot keys, incidentally, are indicated on the right in the menus.

Run the program, by whatever way you like. The response, after a momentary flash of colour, should be the question

What is your name?

on a different screen. Type your name in response, and press **Enter.** At this stage, a rather irritating feature appears. Turbo Pascal makes a response which is too fast to see, and puts you back in the Edit window with your program. To see the Execution screen (where the output, or results, of the program went) press **Alt-F5.** You should see something like this (if your name is Caesar):

```
A>TURBO
What is your name? Caesar
Hi there, Caesar.
```

Note that your original command to enter Turbo Pascal is on this screen also. To get back to the Edit window press **Alt-F5** again, or **Esc.**

At this stage if there is a power failure, or if someone trips over the computer's power cord and pulls the plug out, all your hard work will be lost, so the time has come to save the program on a disk. Place a *formatted* disk in drive B. (If you forgot to format your disk before the session, select the **F**ile Menu with **Alt-F** and then the **OS** shell command. This puts you temporarily back in **DOS** without losing your Turbo Pascal program. Format your disk and return to Turbo Pascal by typing Exit.) Select the **F**ile menu (with **Alt-F**), and then the **S**ave command by entering **S** (you could instead have used the hot key **F2** directly from the Edit window). A smaller box, called the **dialogue box** will pop up in front of the **F**ile menu, with the default name **A:NONAME.PAS.** If you simply press **Enter** now, your program will be saved under this rather strange name, and on the wrong drive. Type a more meaningful name in its place, like

B:greet

(you won't need to delete the name in the box – as soon as you touch a key it will conveniently disappear). Press **Enter** and note that the red light next to drive B should go on for a few seconds. The program has been saved on the disk in drive B as a **file** with the name **GREET.PAS.** To check that it is there (one should never trust computers too much!), select the **D**irectory command in the **F**ile menu. Type

B:*.*

in the dialogue box which appears and press **Enter.** The names of all the files on the disk in drive B should appear. Press **Esc** to return to the menu (**Esc** always returns you to where you came from).

How can we load the saved program back from the disk into the Edit window? First clear the Edit window with the **New** command in the **File** menu (this isn't strictly necessary, but makes it easier to see what happens). Then use the **Load** command in the **File** menu (hot key **F3**). Type **B:GREET** in the dialogue box and press **Enter.** The original program should reappear in the Edit window, with its name on the right of the top line.

Now try the following exercises. Remember you will need to press **Alt-F5** to see the output (Execution) screen.

1. Replace the word **Write** in line 5 with the word **Writeln.** Run the changed program (**Ctrl-F9**) and see what difference it makes.
2. Run the program again, but give a different name in response to the question.
3. Add the following line at the end of your program, just before the end statement, and run the new program:

   ```
   Writeln( 'Have a nice day, ', Name );
   ```

4. To avoid having to press **Alt-F5** each time to see the output screen, you can try this trick. Add the following line at the end, just before the end statement, and run:

   ```
   Readln;
   ```

   Turbo Pascal will freeze the output screen and wait for you to press **Enter** before returning to the Edit window. This is because Readln makes the program wait for something from the keyboard.
5. If you would like your output to go onto a clean screen each time, you could try the following (the two highlighted lines are new):

   ```
   program First;
   uses Crt;
   var Name: string;
   begin
     ClrScr;
     Write( 'What is your name? ' );
     Readln( Name );
     Writeln( 'Hi there, ', Name );
     Writeln( 'Have a nice day, ', Name );
     Readln;
   end.
   ```

6. You may be wondering how to get output on the printer at this stage, and how to print your program on the printer. There are a number of ways of doing this. You can always print whatever is on the screen (program or output) by pressing **Shift-PrtSc** (as long as there is a printer properly connected to your computer). This is called a **screen dump.**

   You have probably guessed by now that the statements Write and Writeln produce output on the screen. These statements can send output to the printer instead as follows (changes have been highlighted):

   ```
   program First;
   uses Printer;
   var Name: string;
   begin
     Write( 'What is your name? ' );
     Readln( Name );
     Writeln( Lst, 'Hi there, ', Name );
   Writeln( 'Have a nice day, ', Name );
   Readln;
   end.
   ```

The easiest way to print the program on the printer at this stage is probably to select the **OS** shell command in the **File** menu, and then in DOS to type the command

copy b:greet.pas prn

Get back to Turbo Pascal with Exit.

A more efficient way of printing a program on the printer is as follows. Move the cursor to the first character in the program. Press **Ctrl-KB.** Now move the cursor to the last character in the program and press **Ctrl-KK.** The program should appear highlighted on the screen. Now make sure the printer is connected and ready, and press **Ctrl-KP** to print the program. To remove the highlighting press **Ctrl-KH.** By the way, the highlighted, or **marked** block can be moved, deleted, copied, etc. See section 2.15 for more details.

7. If you have got this far without making any mistakes, congratulations! To see how Turbo Pascal reacts to errors in the program, try removing any semi-colons from your program, and attempt to run it.

When you have saved any changes you want to with the **F2** hot key you can leave Turbo Pascal with the **Q**uit command in the **F**ile menu (**Alt-X** hot key).

AIDS cases

It was recently reported that the number of accumulated AIDS cases $A(t)$ in the United States in year t can be represented by the formula

$$A(t) = 174.6(t - 1981.2)^3$$

The following program computes $A(t)$. You can use the **L**oad command (hot key **F3**) in the **F**ile menu, and type the new program name (**B:AIDS**) in the dialogue box. The cursor will then move to the Edit window for you to enter the program (there must be no spaces between **:** and **=** in the line **A:=** .. below).

```
program Aids;
var A  : real;
    T  : integer;
begin
   Readln( T );
   A:= 174.6 * (T - 1981.2) * (T - 1981.2) * (T - 1981.2);
   Writeln ( 'Accumulated AIDS cases in US by year ', T, ':', A );
   Readln;
end.
```

When you run the program it will pause until you type in a value for t. Try 2000 (remember to press **Enter** after typing the number). The output screen should contain the following:

2000
Accumulated AIDS cases in US by year 2000: 1.1601597313E+06

Note that the answer is given in scientific notation. E+06 means multiply the preceding number by 10^6, so the output represents about 1.16 million cases. Using trial and error run the program repeatedly to find out when there will be about 10 million accumulated cases.

Try typing a mistake in the value for t to see how Turbo Pascal responds, for example 2,000.

Remember to save the program if you want to keep it.

Compound interest

Suppose you have $1000 saved in the bank, which compounds interest at the rate of 9% per year. What will your balance be after one year? You must obviously be able to do the problem in principle yourself, if you want to program the computer to do it. The logical breakdown, or **structure plan,** of the problem is as follows:

1. Get data (initial balance and interest rate) into computer
2. Calculate interest (9% of $1000, ie $90)
3. Add interest to balance ($90 + $1000, ie $1090)
4. Print out new balance.

Enter the following program in the Edit window (under the name B:MUNNY):

```
program Munny;
var
   Balance : real;
   Interest : real;
   Rate     : real;
begin
   Balance:= 1000;
   Rate:= 0.09;
   Interest:= Rate * Balance;
   Balance:= Balance + Interest;
   Writeln( Balance );
   Readln;
end.
```

Run the program, and observe that no input (from the keyboard) is required now (why not?). The output should be 1.0900000000E+03. The format of the output is difficult to read. You can tidy it up by changing the **Writeln** as follows:

```
Writeln( Balance: 6:0 );
```

This prints the value of **Balance** over a field **6** columns wide with **0** decimal places. Save the program for further use.

1.4 EDITING

By this stage you should be able to enter a short Pascal program (designed by someone else), run it and save it on disk. So far, editing the program has been limited mainly to the use of **Backspace.** Load a program into the Edit window to experiment with the following useful editing features.

Cursor movement keys

Ctrl-S or **Left arrow**	left one character
Ctrl-D or **Right arrow**	right one character
Ctrl-E or **Up arrow**	up one line
Ctrl-X or **Down arrow**	down one line
Ctrl-A or **Ctrl-Left arrow**	left one word
Ctrl-F or **Ctrl-Right arrow**	right one word
Ctrl-W	scroll up
Ctrl-Z	scroll down
Ctrl-R or **PgUp**	page up
Ctrl-C or **PgDn**	page down
Ctrl-QS or **Home**	beginning of line
Ctrl-QD or **End**	end of line
Ctrl-QE or **Ctrl-Home**	top of window
Ctrl-QX or **Ctrl-End**	bottom of window
Ctrl-QR or **Ctrl-PgUp**	top of file (program)
Ctrl-QC or **Ctrl-PgDn**	end of file (program)

Editing keys

Ctrl-N	insert new line
Ctrl-Y	delete line
Ctrl-QY	delete to end of line
Ctrl-H or **Backspace**	delete character to left of cursor
Ctrl-G or **Del**	delete character above cursor
Ctrl-T	delete word to right of cursor

Ctrl-QL restore line (unless deleted)
Ctrl-V or **Ins** insert mode off/on

1.5 HANDLING PROGRAM FILES ON DISKS

As we have seen, a program may be saved on the disk in drive B with the **Save** command in the File menu (hot key **F2**). The entity in which it is saved is called a **file.** The filename may be up to eight characters long, with an **extension** of up to three characters. The following characters may be used for filenames and extensions:

- the letters of the alphabet;
- the digits 0 to 9;
- the following special characters: ! @ # $ % & ( ) – _ { } '

Note that the space is not a valid character. If an extension is used it must be added after the filename and separated from it with a period, for example:

Name.Ext

Lowercase characters are automatically translated into uppercase. If you do not specify an extension, Turbo Pascal assumes .PAS for an extension. If you specifically do not want an extension, type a period after the filename, for example,

```
─────────────── Rename NONAME ───────────────
b:plonk.
```

If you want to save a program on a disk under a filename which already exists, use the **W**rite command in the **F**ile menu to indicate the disk file name. The dialogue box

```
═══════════════ Verify ═══════════════
        Overwrite JUNK.PAS? (Y/N)
```

will appear. The response Y in upper- or lowercase will cause the previous contents of JUNK.PAS to be lost and replaced by the current program. The response N will protect the disk file from being overwritten.

To delete a file (B:JUNK.PAS) from a disk get into DOS (**F**ile/**OS** shell) and use the command

del b:junk.pas

We have already used the **L**oad command in the **F**ile menu, which calls up a file from the disk into the Edit window. Note that **L**oad will delete the current contents of the Edit window before loading the required program. However, the copy of the file on the disk remains intact.

NB: When entering (or editing) a long program (ie more than about 20 lines) it is wise to save it after every 20 lines or so. This way your work is saved on the disk in case of power failure, or even a voltage drop, which may cause your computer to hang up.

NB: It is wise to make frequent backup copies of all your important programs on a separate backup disk to guard against disk failure, damage or loss. There are at least two ways of doing this. Once you have saved the current program on the master disk (ie your usual working disk), remove the master disk from drive B, and insert the backup disk, remembering to lock the drive. Then use **S**ave to make a copy of the current program on the backup disk. Alternatively, you can make a backup copy of a file as follows: call it up from the master disk with **L**oad, replace the master disk with the backup disk, and use **S**ave.

NB: NEVER touch the disk in a drive when the red drive light is on. ALWAYS wait for the red light to go off before removing the disk. Removing the disk while the light is on is like removing a record from a gramophone turntable while the needle is still in the groove! You can corrupt disk files in this way.

SUMMARY

- You can get into Turbo Pascal with **TURBO.**
- A program is a set of statements for solving a particular problem.
- Programs are entered in the Edit window.
- A program may be run with the **Ctrl-F9** hot key.
- A program may be saved as a file on a diskette (with **F2**), and subsequently loaded back into the editing window (with **F3**).
- **Alt-F5** toggles between the Edit window and the output (execution) screen.
- An up-to-date backup disk of all important files should be kept at all times.
- Apart from cursor movements and editing, the following key combinations are useful:

Ctrl-Alt-Del	Reboots system.
Ctrl-Break **Ctrl-Scroll Lock**	Stops execution of program.
Ctrl-NumLock	Suspends execution. Press any key to continue.

EXERCISES

1.1 Write a Turbo Pascal program to compute and print the sum, difference, product and quotient of two numbers A and B (supplied by you). The symbols for subtraction and division are the hyphen (−) and forward slash (/) respectively. Use this example to discover how Turbo Pascal reacts to being asked to divide by zero.

1.2 The energy stored on a condenser is $CV^2/2$, where C is the capacitance and V is the potential difference. Write a program to compute the energy for some sample values of C and V.

Solutions to most exercises are given in Appendix F.

2 Fundamentals of Turbo Pascal

By now you will be wanting to write your own programs and so we are going to start looking in detail at how to write Turbo Pascal programs to solve particular problems. There are two essential requirements for successfully mastering this art:

1. The precise rules for coding instructions must be learnt;
2. A logical plan for solving the problem must be developed.

This chapter is devoted mainly to the first requirement: learning some coding rules. (Appendix A has a quick reference to TURBO PASCAL syntax.) Once these are mastered we can go on to more interesting problems.

2.1 COMPOUND INTEREST AGAIN

In Chapter 1 you ran the program MUNNY to compute compound interest:

```
program Munny;
var
   Balance     : real;
   Interest    : real;
   Rate        : real;
begin
   Balance:= 1000;
   Rate:= 0.09;
   Interest:= Rate * Balance;
   Balance:= Balance + Interest;
   Writeln( Balance );
   Readln;
end.
```

We will now discuss exactly what each line in the program means. When you enter a program, the program lines (code) are stored in part of the computer's **random access memory** (RAM). When the program is executed, a different part of this memory is used to store the numbers (data) that are generated by the program. This part of the memory may be thought of as a bank of boxes, or memory cells, or memory locations, each of which can hold only one number at a time. These memory locations are referred to by symbolic names in the program statements. So the Turbo Pascal statement

```
Balance:= 1000;
```

means put the number 1000 into the memory location named **Balance**. Since the contents of **Balance** may be changed by the program, it is called a **variable**. The statements in our compound interest program between the special words **begin** and **end** can now be interpreted as follows:

1. Put the number 1000 into memory location **Balance**
2. Put the number 0.09 into memory location **Rate**
3. Multiply the contents of **Rate** by the contents of **Balance** and store the answer in **Interest**
4. Add the contents of **Balance** to the contents of **Interest** and store the answer in **Balance**
5. Write the contents of **Balance** on the screen
6. Stop.

When the program is executed, most of the memory locations are initially set to zero by Turbo Pascal. The program statements are then executed in order from the top down. After execution, a snapshot of the memory will show the contents of the variables used as follows:

Balance	:	**~~1000~~/1090**
Interest	:	**90**
Rate	:	**0.09**

Note that the original contents of **Balance** (1000) is *lost*.

The four lines of the program before **begin** are also very important (in fact the program won't run without them).

program Munny announces and names the program.
var starts the section in which the names of all memory locations to be used as variables are declared. Variables can have different **types** as we shall soon see, and ours have all been declared with type real. This basically means they are ordinary numbers which may or may not have decimal parts.

The words **begin** and **end** enclose the executable program statements (ie the statements that do the actual computing).

Exercises

1. Run the program as it stands.
2. Change the first executable statement to read
   Balance:= 2000;
   and make sure you understand the answer when you re-run the program.
3. Leave out the line
   Balance:= Balance + Interest;
   and re-run. Can you explain the answer?
4. Rewrite the program so that the original contents of Balance is *not* lost.

A number of questions immediately arise, for example:

- What names may be used for memory locations?
- How can numbers be represented?
- What happens if a statement won't fit on the screen?
- How can we organise the output more neatly?

These questions, and many more, will be answered in the following sections.

2.2 PROGRAM LAYOUT

The general structure of a simple Turbo Pascal program is as follows:

PROGRAM *Name;*

declarations

BEGIN

  statements

END.

Declarations and statements are separated (delimited) by semi-colons. It looks neater to have only one statement on a line, although this is not strictly necessary.

Spaces between words in a line may be used to improve the readability of a program, and blank lines may be used to separate logical sections of a program. The program MUNNY can be compressed somewhat, but it's rather hard to read:

```
program Munny;var Balance:real;Interest:real;Rate:real;begin
Balance:=1000;Rate:=0.09;Interest
:=Rate*Balance;Balance:=Balance+
Interest;Writeln(Balance);Readln;end.
```

There must be a period after the final **END.** **end** is a special delimiter word so the statement immediately before **end** never needs a semi-colon after it, although Turbo Pascal won't mind if you put it in. So

```
    Readln;
  end.
```

and

```
    Readln
  end.
```

are both correct.

Long lines

A program line may not be longer than 126 characters. The cursor position at the top of the Edit window shows you how long a line is.

Comments

Anything between the symbols { and } or between (* and *) is a comment for the user's instruction and is ignored by Turbo Pascal. The MUNNY program can be made more readable with comments:

```
program Munny;
{ calculates compound interest }
var
  Balance    :  real;
  Interest   :  real;
  Rate       :  real;
begin
  Balance:= 1000;                    { opening balance }
  Rate:= 0.09;                       { interest rate }
  Interest:= Rate * Balance;
  Balance:= Balance + Interest;      { new balance }
  Writeln( Balance );
  Readln;
end. { Munny }
```

A comment inside braces { .. } may contain a comment inside (* .. *), and vice versa, for example:

```
{ this is (* also *) a comment }
```

In this way a whole section of code, including comments, can be commented out:

```
M:= 1;
(* C:= 297600;
E:= M * C * C { Einstein } *)
```

You should develop the habit of using comments wherever possible to make the logic of your programs clearer to anyone else reading them. You will also find them helpful yourself, because after a month or so you will have forgotten how a particular program worked.

2.3 IDENTIFIERS

An **identifier** is the symbolic name used to represent items in a Pascal program. The name **Rate**, which represents the interest rate in the program MUNNY, is an identifier. There are rules about constructing identifiers, which must be adhered to.

An identifier must begin with a letter and may not contain spaces. Apart from letters, the only other characters allowed in an identifier are the ten digits and the underscore character (_). An identifier may be of any length, but only the first 63 characters are significant. You can use upper- or lowercase letters in identifiers.

Turbo Pascal has 48 special **reserved words** which may not be used as identifiers, although they may be embedded. We have already come across some: **program, var, uses, begin** and **end**. The complete list is in Appendix D.

Valid identifier	*Invalid identifier* (why?)
X1	**$5**
R2D2	**HP41−C**
AMA_104W	**M. Thatcher**
endofthemonth	**2a**
	Shadow Fax

2.4 NUMBERS

An ordinary (decimal) number may be expressed with or without a sign, and with or without a decimal point. If it has a decimal point it is called a **fixed point** number. The following are all valid numbers:

0
1.0
−12345.6789
+0.00023

If an integer (whole) number is prefixed with a $ symbol it is interpreted as a hexadecimal (base 16) number. For example, the ordinary (decimal) value of the number $10 is 16 (see section 2.16).

A decimal number may also be expressed in **floating point** or **scientific** (engineering) notation in two parts: the **mantissa**, which may have a decimal point, and the **exponent**, which must be an integer (signed or unsigned). Mantissa and exponent must be separated by the letter e. The mantissa is multiplied by the power of 10 indicated by the exponent. For example:

2.0e2	**(= 200)**
+2e2	**(= 200)**
4.12e+2	**(= 412)**
−7.321e−4	**(= −0.0007321)**

A number may not start with a decimal point. If necessary, insert a leading zero, for example, type 0.1234 and not .1234. The allowable range of a number depends on the type of variable it is stored in. This is discussed in the next section.

2.5 VARIABLES

A **variable** is a memory location whose value can be changed by a program. A distinctive feature of a Pascal variable is that it must be **declared** to be of a certain **type** in the declaration part at the beginning of a program. Turbo Pascal allows a bewildering number of types.

We have already seen variables of type **real**. Real variables can be positive or negative and can have decimal parts. They are allowed to range (in absolute value) between 2.9e−39 and 1.7e38 and they have about 11 significant digits.

Another type is **integer**. Variables of this type will be in the range −32768 to 32767 inclusive and are declared like this:

```
var
   Number : integer;
```

Warning! If an integer variable is increased above 32767 in a calculation its value cycles. For example, if the variable has the value 32767 and is increased by 1, its new value is −32768. This can cause apparently inexplicable errors!

Turbo Pascal variables are *not* automatically initialised to zero when a program begins executing.

We will come across many more types later in the chapter.

To promote good programming style, it is suggested that every variable declared in a program be described in a comment. Most of the examples in this book follow this practice.

2.6 VERTICAL MOTION UNDER GRAVITY

From the laws of dynamics one can show that if a stone is projected vertically upward with an initial speed u, its vertical displacement s after a time t has elapsed is given by the formula

$$s = ut - 0.5gt^2,$$

where $g = 9.8\ \text{m/s}^2$, the acceleration due to gravity. Air resistance has been ignored (the effect of air resistance is discussed in Chapter 16). We would like to compute s, given u and t. Notice that we are not concerned here with how to derive the formula, but how to compute its value. The logical preparation of the problem is very simple:

1. Get values of g, u and t into the computer
2. Compute the value of s according to the formula
3. Output the value of s
4. Stop.

The program is as follows:

```
program Vertical;
{ vertical motion under gravity }
const
  G = 9.8; { acceleration due to gravity }
var
  S : real; { vertical displacement of stone in metres }
  T : real; { time in seconds }
  U : real; { initial velocity in metres/second }
begin
  Writeln( 'Time      Displacement' );
  Writeln;
  U:= 60;
  T:= 6;
  S:= U * T - G / 2 * T * T;
  Writeln( T:4:1, S:10:2 );
  Readln
end. { Vertical }
```

Note that **G** has been declared as a **constant**, since it is not likely to change. It has this value throughout the program. The declaration part of the program has been extended to cater for the constant declaration. From time to time we will add different sorts of declarations to this part. Run this example as an exercise. Note that **T** is displayed over 4 columns with 1 decimal place, while **S** is displayed over 10 columns with 2 decimals. This example is discussed further in Exercise 2.19 at the end of the chapter.

2.7 PROGRAMMING STYLE

Programs that are written any old how, while they may do what is required, can be difficult to follow when read again a month or two later. Throughout this book, therefore, attention has been paid to what is called **programming style,** by which is meant an emphasis on neat and clear physical and logical layout of programs. Guidelines for good style are laid out in the Epilogue.

2.8 ARITHMETIC EXPRESSIONS

An arithmetic expression is a formula combining numbers, variables and functions (like square root), using arithmetic operators. It specifies a rule for computing a value.

Arithmetic operators

There are six arithmetic operators, as follows:

Operator	*Meaning*	*Example*
+	Addition	**A + 6.9**

–	Subtraction	**X – Y**
	or negation	**– Z**
*	Multiplication	**2 * A**
/	Real division	**B / DELTA**
div	Integer division	**10 div 3** (= 3)
mod	Remainder	**10 mod 3** (= 1)

In addition, parentheses (round brackets) may be used to control the order of evaluation (see below). The result of a real division (/) is real even if both operands are integers.

Warning! You need to be careful when using integer arithmetic that the intermediate value of an expression does not go out of range. The value cycles as mentioned above, giving meaningless results. Suppose **K** is an integer variable, and **X** is real. The statements

```
K:= 256;
X:= K * K;
```

will leave **X** with the value zero, because of the way the integer value of the expression **K * K** cycles. (Try it!) To correct it, either replace the expression for **X** with

```
X:= 1.0 * K * K;
```

(since the expression is evaluated from left to right, the 1.0 ensures that the calculation is done in real mode) or (which is probably better) declare **K** with type real in the first place. Rearranging this statement as

```
X:= K * K * 1.0;
```

causes the original problem because the **K * K** is evaluated first, in integer mode, so the damage is done before the 1.0 is noticed.

This is a general rule. If both operands are integer, the result of the operation is integer, whereas if one or both operands are real, the result of the operation is real. Operators may not be juxtaposed. **A * – B** is therefore not allowed. Write **A * (– B)** instead.

You may have noticed that there is no exponentiation (raise to the power) operator. This is because Pascal was invented by a computer scientist. He never imagined that anyone would want such an operator. However, if you've heard of logarithms and the exponential function, we can easily use them to get around this minor irritation.

Suppose we want to calculate a^b. Call the answer x. So we want to find:

$$x = a^b.$$

Take the natural logarithm of both sides of this equation:

$$\log(x) = b\log(a).$$

Now take the anti-logarithm of both sides (ie exponentiate):

$$x = e^{b \log(a)}.$$

The righthand side is what we are after, and we can use the Turbo Pascal standard functions **Exp** and **Ln** to compute it. So a^b is computed as **Exp(b * Ln(a))**. Note that a must be non-negative, since the logarithm of a negative number is undefined.

It is suggested that spaces be typed on either side of an operator, to make programs more readable. This is done throughout this book.

Precedence of operators

Since an expression may contain many operators, it is necessary to know in what order Turbo Pascal evaluates operations. The order of precedence is as follows:

Order	*Operation*
1st	Parentheses
2nd	Negation (sign inversion)

3rd	Multiplication and division
4th	Addition, subtraction

When operators with the same precedence occur in the same expression, an ambiguity could arise. For example, does **A / B * 3** mean **A / (B * 3)** or **(A / B) * 3**? To resolve this, operations with the same precedence are always evaluated from left to right. So this expression is in fact evaluated as **(A / B) * 3**.

Turbo Pascal constants

The vertical motion program in section 2.6 used a constant declaration to define the acceleration due to gravity, g, as 9.8. Any identifier may be declared a constant – it will retain this value throughout the program, and any attempt to change it will cause an error.

Turbo Pascal also allows **constant expressions,** involving +, –, * and / to be declared. Such expressions may not include variables. For example:

```
const
   Pi = 3.1415927;
   Pi2R = 1 / (2 * Pi);
   Message = 'Hi there!';
```

2.9 ASSIGNMENT

An assignment statement enables you to assign a value to a variable, usually after computing the value of an expression. Its general form is:

ident:= *expr*;

where *ident* stands for a suitably declared variable.

The := character combination (no spaces between : and =) does *not* have the same meaning as the equal sign in mathematics, and should be read as "becomes". So the statement

```
X:= A + B;
```

should be read as "**X** becomes **A** plus **B**" or more literally "The contents of **X** becomes the contents of **A** plus the contents of **B**".

In this way, the assignment statement

```
N:= N + 1;
```

is meaningful, and means "Increase the contents of **N** by 1", whereas the mathematical *equation*

$$n = n + 1$$

is not generally meaningf

Examples

The formulae

$$F = GME/r^2,$$
$$C = \sqrt{(a^2 + b^2)}/(2a),$$
$$A = P(1 + r/100)^n$$

may be translated into the following Turbo Pascal statements:

```
F:= G * M * E / (R * R);
C:= Sqrt( A * A + B * B) / (2 * A);
A:= P * Exp( N * Ln( 1 + R / 100 ) );
```

Note the use of the standard function **Sqrt** to find a square root. More standard functions are discussed in Chapter 4.

Assignment compatibility

If **I** is an integer variable, and **X** is any real expression, the statement

```
I:= X;
```

will cause error 26 (Type mismatch). The standard functions **Round** or **Trunc** may be used to convert **X** to an integer type before assignment. **Round** rounds up (**Round**(1.5) is 2), while **Trunc** chops off the decimal part (**Trunc**(1.5) is 1). For example:

```
var
  I, J : integer;
  X    : real;
...
I: =  Round( X );
J:=  Trunc( Sqrt( 10 ) );
```

The reverse assignment is allowed, ie

```
X:= I;
```

because integers are a subset of reals.

More formally, in the context of reals and integers, a value of type *T2* is **assignment compatible** with a value of type *T1* (ie *T1*:= *T2* is allowed) only if one of the following is true:

- *T1* and *T2* are either both real types or both integer types;
- *T1* is real type and *T2* is integer type.

There are more rules for types other than real and integer.

2.10 BASIC INPUT AND OUTPUT

This section describes the simplest ways of getting numbers neatly into and out of Turbo Pascal programs.

Write and Writeln

Write and **Writeln** are two standard Turbo Pascal **procedures,** ie pre-written sections of code that perform particular tasks. To help you discover how they work, load the compound interest program MUNNY discussed at the beginning of this chapter, and carry out the following experiments (make the suggested changes and run).

1. Replace the **Writeln** statement with

   ```
   Writeln( Interest, Balance );
   ```

2. Now try

   ```
   Write( Interest );
   Writeln( Balance );
   ```

   and see if this makes any difference.

3. Next try

   ```
   Writeln( 'Interest: ', Interest:4:2, 'Balance:':12, Balance:8:2 );
   ```

4. Try **Writeln(' ':10, Balance);**

5. Try the following group:

   ```
   Writeln( Balance:10 );
   Writeln( Balance:11 );
   Writeln( Balance:12 );
   ```

6. Now insert the statement

   ```
   uses Crt;
   ```

   before the **var** declarations, and replace **Writeln** by the three statements

   ```
   ClrScr;
   GoToXY( 40, 20 );
   Writeln( Balance );
   ```

Simple rules for Write *and* Writeln

1. Basically, the difference between **Writeln** and **Write** is that the cursor moves to the beginning of a new line on the screen after **Writeln** has been executed, whereas after **Write** it remains at its current position. Technically, **Writeln** sends an **end-of-line marker**

to the screen. Everything else that follows applies equally to **Write** and **Writeln**.

2. The arguments (things in the parentheses) of **Write** may be messages enclosed in single quotes (these are also called **strings**), and/or variable names, and/or expressions, all separated by commas. All of these will be referred to as *items*.

3. The string **'plonk'** in

   Write('plonk':*n*);

   is written over *n* columns and right-justified (ie blanks are filled in from the left). Note that the construction

   ' ':*n*

   can be used to write *n* blanks.

4. The real variable represented by *ident* in

   ident:n:m

   is written over *n* columns, with *m* decimal places. Remember to leave room for the decimal point and a possible minus sign. This process is called **formatting**. Find out what happens if you don't leave room, or if $n < m$.

5. *ident:n*

   writes a real variable in scientific notation over *n* columns. Remember to leave 4 columns for the exponent, one for the decimal point, and one for a possible minus sign. An integer variable is written over *n* columns, right-justified.

6. The predeclared procedure

   GoToXY(*X, Y* **);**

   moves the cursor to column *X* and row *Y* on the screen (numbered from the left and top respectively). It is collected with a number of other predefined procedures and functions in a standard Turbo Pascal **unit** called **Crt**, which has been precompiled. The procedures and functions in a unit are accessed by referencing the unit name in the **uses** part of the declarations. **ClrScr** is also in the **Crt** unit. (You may have guessed that **Crt** stands for cathode ray tube because this unit involves the monitor.) Units are discussed in more detail in Chapter 8.

Sending output to the printer

We have already seen some ways of doing this in Chapter 1. The standard unit **Printer** declares a special variable **Lst** (it's actually a text file variable, but more about that later), which enables you to print directly on the printer:

```
uses Printer;
. . .
Writeln( Lst, 'Rhubarb rhubarb on the printer' );
```

Read and Readln

In the compound interest program MUNNY the data for the program were supplied with two assignment statements:

```
Balance:= 1000;
Rate:= 0.09;
```

This is a somewhat inflexible way of supplying data, since to run the program for different balances or interest rates you would have to change these statements, and there may be many such assignment statements in a more complicated program. The **Readln** statement, however, which we saw in Chapter 1, allows you to supply the data while the program is executing, rather than before execution, as in the case of the assignment statement. Replace these two statements with the single statement

```
Readln( Balance, Rate );
```

When you run the program Turbo Pascal will wait (forever, if necessary!) for you to type in the values of **Balance** and **Rate** at the keyboard. This must be done with at least one space separating them. The numbers may be on the same line, or on different lines. Turbo Pascal simply waits patiently until you have typed two numbers.

If you make a mistake with the input, like typing a letter instead of a number, or separating the numbers with commas as in BASIC, the program will crash and an error message will be displayed. Try it! You can use **Backspace** to correct a number before entering it.

The general form of **Readln** for keyboard input is

Readln(*list of variables separated by commas* **);**

The difference between **Read** and **Readln** is that **Readln** skips to the beginning of the next line after reading the value of its last variable.

Read *and* **Readln** *Reading data from a text file*

It often happens that you need to test a program by reading a lot of numbers. For example, you may be writing a program to find the average of 10 numbers. It becomes a great nuisance to have to type in the 10 numbers every time you run the program (since programs seldom work the first time!). The following trick is very useful.

The idea is to store the numbers in a separate file which is stored on a disk. The program then reads the numbers from the file each time it is run, instead of from the keyboard. As an example use the Turbo Pascal Editor to store the following line in the file B:DATA.TXT:

```
12.34     -0.02     1.2e2
```

Then use the following program to read these three numbers from the file and display them on the screen:

```
program ReadData;
var
   X, Y, Z: real;
   ReadFile: text;
begin
   Assign( ReadFile, 'B:DATA.TXT' );
   Reset( ReadFile );
   Readln( ReadFile, X, Y, Z );
   Writeln( X:8:2, Y:8:2, Z:8:2 );
   Readln;
   Close( ReadFile );
end.
```

ReadFile is a Turbo Pascal **text file** variable (which exists only for the duration of the program execution). **Assign** relates it to the physical file DATA.TXT on the disk in drive B. **Reset** opens an existing file, and **Close** closes it. In general,

Readln(*Ident, list of variables* **);**

reads the list of variables from the text file *Ident*, instead of the keyboard. To change the data, simply edit the disk file.

There are more details of text files in Chapter 11.

Prompts with Readln

When **Readln** is used to get input from the keyboard, it helps to prompt the user with a **Write** statement. Change the MUNNY program to include the following, and run it:

```
Write( 'Old balance: ' );
Readln( Balance );
Write( 'Interest rate: ' );
Readln( Rate );
```

The prompts **Old balance:** and **interest rate:** will appear on the screen. Each time, the program will wait for your response.

2.11 for LOOPS

So far we have seen how to read numbers into a Turbo Pascal program, how to do some arithmetic with them, and how to output them. In this section we look at a new feature: repetition.

Run the following program:

```
program Count;
var
   I: integer;
   Sum: real;
begin
   for I:= 1 to 20 do
      Write( I:3 );
   Readln
end.
```

Now replace the **Write(I:3)** with **Write('*')**.

To get some random numbers replace **Write(...)** with **Writeln(Random)**. Every time you run this program you will get the same 20 random numbers, which is rather boring. Immediately after **begin** insert the statement **Randomize**. Each time you run the program you will get different random numbers.

For a change try the following:

```
for I:= 97 to 122 do
   Write( Chr( I ) );
```

To get them backwards replace the **for** statement with

```
for I:= 122 downto 97 do
```

The **for** loop is one of the most powerful constructions in any programming language. In general:

for *I*:= *J* **to** *K* **do**
  statement;

where *I* is a variable of any ordinal type (see section 2.17) and *J* and *K* may be numbers, variables, or expressions. *I* is called the **control variable**. The *statement* following **do** will be repeatedly executed. The numerical values of *J* and *K* determine how many repeats are made. On the first loop, *I* is given the value of *J*, and is then given its next value at the end of each loop (in effect *I* is increased by 1). Looping stops once *I* has passed the value of *K*, and execution proceeds with the next statement. The *Turbo Pascal Reference Guide* states that the control variable *(I)* is undefined after completion of the loop (it may have the final value, but it may not).

The operation of the **downto** version is the reverse of the above.

Now let's try something slightly more adventurous (if you leave out the **NoSound** statement below you will need to press **Ctrl-Break** a few times to stop the noise):

```
program Noise;
uses Crt;
var
   I: integer;
begin
   Randomize;
   for I:= 1 to 10 do
   begin
      Sound( Round( 1000 * Random ) );
      Delay( 500 );
      Nosound
   end
end.
```

The important thing to notice here is that if a *group* of statements is to be repeated by a **for** loop they must be enclosed with a **begin-end** pair immediately after the do. Such a group is called a **compound statement.**

Sound(*I* **);**

causes the computer speaker to emit a sound of frequency *I* hertz (where *I* must be integer) *until switched off by* **NoSound**.

Delay(*I* **);**

delays execution by approximately *I* milliseconds (to enable the sound to be heard).

These three procedures are all in the **Crt** unit.

Danger!

The following example illustrates the dangers lurking in integer arithmetic mentioned above. It is well known that the sum of the reciprocals of the squares of the whole numbers converges to a limit, ie the sum

$$1/1^2 + 1/2^2 + 1/3^2 + 1/4^2 + \ldots 1/n^2$$

gets closer and closer to a fixed number, called the limit, as *n* gets bigger and bigger. Run the program below for some values of *n*, between 10 and 200:

```
program Limit;
var I, N: integer;
     X: real;
begin
   X:= 0;
   Readln( N );
   for I:= 1 to N do
      X:= X + 1 / (I * I);
   writeln( X:8:6 );
   readln;
end.
```

The sum is obtained by repeatedly updating the value of **X**. Note that **X** must be set to zero initially in the program – Turbo Pascal does not automatically do this. In other words, if the statement

```
X:= 0;
```

is left out, there is no guarantee that the running total for **X** starts at zero.

For *n* greater than about 181 something strange happens: the sum begins to get *smaller.* And for $n = 256$ a division overflow error occurs. This is because **I * I** moves past the maximum size of an integer, and begins to cycle from the minimum value. See if you can correct the program to give the right answer for $n = 256$: 1.641035.

Square-rooting with Newton

The square root *X* of any positive number *A* may be found using only the arithmetic operations of addition, subtraction and division, with Newton's method, which is explained more fully in Chapter 16. The structure plan of the algorithm, and the program with sample output for $A = 2$, is as follows:

1. Input *A*
2. Initialise *X* to 1
3. Repeat 6 times (say)
   3.1. Replace *X* by $(X + A / X) / 2$
   3.2. Write *X*
4. Stop.

```
program Newton;
{ Square rooting with Newton }
```

```
var
  I   :  integer;  { iteration counter }
    A  :  real;        { number to be square rooted }
    X  :  real;        { approximate square root of A }
  begin
    Write( 'Enter number to be square rooted: ' );
    Readln( A );
    Writeln;
    X:= 1;
    for I:= 1 to 6 do
    begin
      X:= (X + A / X) / 2;
      Writeln( X:16:12 )
    end;
    Writeln;
    Writeln( 'Turbo Pascal''s value: ', Sqrt( A ):16:12 );
    Readln
  end.
```

Output:

```
Enter number to be square rooted: 2

    1.50000000000
    1.41666666670
    1.41421568630
    1.41421356240
    1.41421356240
    1.41421356240

Turbo Pascal's value:        1.41421356240
```

The values of *X* converge to a limit, which is the square root of *A*. Note that it is identical to the value returned by Turbo Pascal's standard **Sqrt** function. Most computers and calculators use a similar method internally to compute square roots and other standard mathematical functions. Note also that to write an apostrophe (') in a string the apostrophe must be repeated ('').

Money again

The next program outputs a balance over a number of years with interest compounded each year. Run it for a period of about 10 years, and see if you can follow how it works. Save it under the name GROWTH for use in Exercise 2.29 at the end of the chapter.

```
program Invest;
{ compound growth of an investment }
uses Crt;
var
  Bal    :  real;       { balance }
  Rate   :  real;       { interest rate }
  Num    :  integer;    { period of investment }
  Year   :  integer;    { year counter }
begin
  ClrScr;
  Write( 'Initial balance: ' );
  Readln( Bal );
  Write( 'Period of investment (years): ' );
  Readln( Num );
  Write( 'Rate: ' );
  Readln( Rate );
  Writeln;
  Writeln( 'Year', 'Balance':10 );
  Writeln;
  for Year:= 1 to Num do
  begin
```

```
Bal:= Bal + Rate * Bal;
Writeln( Year:4, Bal:10:2 )
   end;

   Readln
end.
```

The next program is a variation on the compound interest problem. Suppose we have to service four different savings accounts, with balances of, say, $1000, $500, $758 and $12750 respectively. We want to compute the new balance in each of them after 9% interest has been compounded. Try it out.

```
program Savings;
uses Crt;
var
   Acct    : integer;     { counter }
   Line    : integer;     { cursor position (row) }
   NewBal  : real;        { new balance after interest }
   OldBal  : real;        { original balance }
   Rate    : real;        { interest rate }
begin
   Rate:= 0.09;
   ClrScr;
   Line:= 1;

   for Acct:= 1 to 4 do
   begin
      GoToXY( 1, Line );
      Write( 'Old balance: ' );
      Read( OldBal );
      NewBal:= OldBal + Rate * OldBal;
      GoToXY( 30, Line );
      Write( 'New balance: ', NewBal:8:2 );
      Line:= Line + 1;
      Readln
   end;

   Readln
end.
```

Line is a counter representing the row on the screen where the output must go. It is increased by 1 in the loop. **GoToXY** then ensures that **NewBal** appears on the same line as **OldBal** for each account. Remove the two **GoToXY**s if you want to see why this is necessary.

Note that good programming style requires that statements inside a **for** loop be indented to the right a few columns. The Editor's Autoindent feature helps with this. You may have noticed when editing a program that the cursor always returns to the starting column of the previous line. **Ctrl-OI** toggles this feature on and off. **Ctrl-KI** can be used to indent a block of statements (see section 2.15).

Differential interest rates

Most banks and building societies offer differential interest rates. Suppose in the above example that the rate is 9% only for balances less than $5000, but 12% otherwise. We can easily amend the program to allow for this by deleting the statement **Rate:= 0.09** and inserting a new statement after **Read(OldBal)** as follows:

```
if OldBal < 5000 then
   Rate:= 0.09
else
   Rate:= 0.12;
```

Try this out with sensibly chosen data to verify that it works. For example, $4000 will grow to $4360 whereas $5000 will grow to $6000.

2.12 DECIDING WITH if-then-else

We will discuss the **if-then-else** statement introduced above more fully in this section.

Final course mark

The final course mark of students attending a university course is calculated as follows. Two examination papers are written at the end of the course. The final mark is either the average of the two written papers, or the average of the two papers and the class record mark (all weighted equally), whichever is the higher. The following program computes and writes each student's final mark, with the comment PASS or FAIL (50% being the pass mark).

```
program Final_Marks;
{ Final mark for course based on class record and exams }
uses const
   N        = 15;              { column width of output }
var
   CRM    :  real;             { class record mark }
   ExmAvg :  real;             { average of two exam papers }
   Fin    :  real;             { final mark }
   P1     :  real;             { mark for paper 1 }
   P2     :  real;             { mark for paper 2 }
   Stu    :  integer;          { student counter }
   DFile  :  text;             { data file of marks }
begin
   Assign( DFile, 'B:MARKS.' );
   Reset( DFile );
   ClrScr;
   Writeln( 'Class Record':N, ' Exam Average':N, ' Final Mark':N );
   Writeln;

   for Stu:= 1 to 3 do
   begin
     Read( DFile, CRM, P1, P2);
     ExmAvg:= (P1 + P2) / 2;
     if ExmAvg > CRM then
       Fin:= ExmAvg
     else
       Fin:= (P1 + P2 + CRM) / 3;
     Write( CRM:N:0, ExmAvg:N:1, Fin:N:1 );
     if Fin >= 50 then
       Writeln( ' PASS' )
     else
       Writeln( ' FAIL' )
   end;

   Readln;
   Close( DFile )
end.
```

As explained above, the data are stored in a disk file to make reading more efficient. For example, for a sample class of three students, the data could be:

```
40 60 43
60 45 43
13 98 47
```

ie the first student has a class record of 40 with exam marks of 60 and 43. His final mark should be 51.5 (class record not used), whereas the second student's final mark should be 49.3 (class record used). Run the program as it stands.

The if-then-else Statement

In the above example we see a situation where the computer must make decisions: whether or not to include the class record, and whether to pass or fail the student. The programmer cannot be sure which of these possibilities will occur when writing the program, so it must be designed to allow for all of them. We need a **conditional branch** statement, which is another of the most powerful facilities in any programming language. Its general form is

if *condition* **then** *s*1 **else** *s*2;

where *condition* is a **Boolean expression** having a truth (Boolean) value of either True or False, and *s*1 and *s*2 are any statements (including compound statments and other **if** statements). If the condition is true, *s*1 is executed (and not *s*2), otherwise *s*2 is executed (and not *s*1). The **else** part of the statement is optional, and may be left out. Execution continues in the normal sequential way with the next statement after the **if**.

The condition may be formed from arithmetic expressions with the **relational operators** (<, <=, etc., with no spaces between juxtaposed characters like < and =), and from Boolean expressions with the **Boolean operators** (**NOT, AND, OR**). These are all discussed fully in Chapter 5.

For example, suppose we wanted to write the class (grade) of each student's final mark in the above program. We could replace the statement

```
if Fin >= 50 then
   Writeln( ' PASS' )
else
   Writeln( ' FAIL' )
```

by the following

```
if Fin >= 75 then
   Writeln( ' 1' );
if (Fin >= 70) and (Fin < 75) then
   Writeln( ' 2+' );
if (Fin >= 60) and (Fin < 70) then
   Writeln( ' 2-' );
if (Fin >= 50) and (Fin < 60) then
   Writeln( ' 3' );
if Fin < 50 then
   Writeln( ' FAIL' )
```

The **Writeln** in each statement is executed only if all the conditions are true. The temptation is to write something like

```
if Fin >= 70 and < 75 then . . .
```

since this is how we tend to say it in English. But this is wrong since **and** must join two Boolean expressions, and "< 75" is not a Boolean expression (it doesn't have a truth value). Note also that when the condition consists of more than one Boolean expression each expression must be in parentheses.

2.13 SIMPLE AND STRUCTURED STATEMENTS

The time has come for some more definitions. Turbo Pascal has two main types of statements: **simple statements** and **structured statements.**

A simple statement is one that doesn't contain any other statements, like **X:= 23** or **Writeln(X, Y).**

The structured statements that we have seen so far are constructs composed of other statements which are executed in sequence (**compound** statements – enclosed in **begin-end**), conditionally (**conditional** statements – **if-then-else**), or repeatedly (**repetitive** statements – **for**).

2.14 STRINGS

A glaring omission in the final mark program above is that the students' *names* are not output. To remedy this, we introduce the concept of a **string.** Make the following changes to the final mark program in section 2.12 (changes have been highlighted).

Insert in the variable declaration part of the line

```
Name     : string[N];     { student name }
```

Change the first **Writeln:**

```
Writeln( 'Name', ' ':N-4, 'Class Record':N, ...
```

Change the **Readln:**

```
Readln( DFile, Name, CRM, P1, P2);
```

Change the **Write**:

```
Write( Name, CRM:N:0, ExmAvg:N:1, Fin:N:1 );
```

Finally change the data file B:MARKS by inserting the following names (allow at least 15 columns for the names):

```
ABLE, E.R.     40 60 43
BAKER, M.D.    60 45 43
TUTU, A.B.     13 98 47
```

If you run the amended program you should get output like this:

Name	Class Record	Exam Average	Final Mark
ABLE, E.R.	40	51.5	51.5 PASS
BAKER, M.D.	60	44.0	49.3 FAIL
TUTU, A.B.	13	72.5	72.5 PASS

Character strings

A **character string** is a sequence of characters from the ASCII character set (see Appendix C) enclosed by apostrophes. Turbo Pascal distinguishes between lower- and uppercase letters only in the case of character string. So 'pascal' is not the same as 'PASCAL'. A character string may not be longer than one program line. Note that the string '007' is not the same as the number 7 (or 007 for that matter).

The null (empty) string has no characters in it: ''. However, the space (blank) is different from the null string, and spaces in character strings are significant: ' '. An apostrophe may be included in a character string by typing it twice:

```
'He said, ''Follow me.'''
```

(Typing an apostrophe twice is not the same as typing one double quote!)

A **control character** may be embedded in a character string if its ASCII code is preceded by a # character. For example:

```
Writeln( #7#7'Error!'#7#7 )
```

will sound the character with ASCII code 7, known as BEL, when writing the message.

String types

Variables of type string may be declared and have values assigned as follows:

```
var
  John 8_32  :  string;
  Name       :  string[15];
. . .
John 8_32:= 'You will know the truth and the truth will make you free';
```

This declares **Name** to have a maximum length of 15 characters, as in the final mark program above. That is why at least 15 columns had to be reserved for the student names in the disk file B:MARKS. The default length of a string is 255 characters (or **bytes**), which is the maximum length of **John8_32.**

Concatenation of strings

The only string operator is +, which concatenates (joins) strings. For example:

```
var
    X, Y, Z: string;
begin
   X:= 'Pilate said, ';
   Y:= '''What is truth?''';
   Z:= X + Y;
   Writeln( Z )
end.
```

produces the output

```
Pilate said, 'What is truth?'
```

There is more about strings in Chapter 10.

2.15 ADVANCED EDITING

In this section we discuss some of the more advanced features of the Turbo Pascal Editor. You should try out the commands described below on a test program, as they will increase your programming skill and enjoyment no end. To test the commands that move blocks of lines around, it is suggested that you enter a dummy program with the integers 1, 2, 3, . . . on separate lines, and nothing else. You will then easily be able to see what happens to the lines when you move them.

Block commands

A block of text may be **marked**. Once marked it can be moved, indented, printed, copied, deleted, or written to a disk file.

Ctrl-KB marks the beginning of a block (the next character to the right is the first character in the block). Nothing is visible until the end of the block is marked with **Ctrl-KK**, when the block is displayed with a different intensity or colour (the character immediately to the left is the last character in the block). (To remember this, think of the **B** and **K** in the two commands as the first and last letters of **BLOCK**.)

Ctrl-KT marks a single word (the one above or to the left of the cursor), where a word is defined as a sequence of characters delimited by one of the following

space <> , : . () [] ^ ' * + − / $

Ctrl-KP prints the marked block on the printer.

Ctrl-KC copies a marked block to the current cursor position. The original is unchanged and unmarked and markers are placed around the copy.

Ctrl-KY deletes a marked block. *There is no provision for restoring a deleted block, so be careful!*

Ctrl-KH alternatively **hides/displays** the highlighting of a marked block. Commands which operate on a whole block (copy, delete, etc.) only work if the block is displayed.

Ctrl-KV moves a marked block from its original position to the current cursor position.

Ctrl-KR reads a disk file into the text at the current cursor position. The Editor prompts you for the name of the file. The text thus read is marked as a block.

Ctrl-KW writes a copy of a marked block to a disk file. The Editor prompts you for the name of the file.

Ctrl-KI indents a marked block one column.

Ctrl-KU moves a marked block one column to the left (**unindent**).

Extended movement commands

Ctrl-QB moves the cursor to the beginning of a marked block, even if it is not displayed.

Ctrl-QK moves the cursor to the end of a marked block, even if it is not displayed.

Ctrl-QP moves to the position of the cursor before the last command.

Ctrl-QW moves to the last error position. The error message is redisplayed.

Miscellaneous editing commands

Ctrl-U aborts an operation which prompts you.

Ctrl-OI or **Ctrl-QI** switches **autoindent** on/off. The indentation may be changed with **Space bar** and **Left arrow**.

Ctrl-KD or **Ctrl-KQ** quits the Editor without saving and returns to the main menu.

Ctrl-QF (Find) searches for a string of up to 30 characters, from the current cursor position. The Editor prompts for the search string and asks for options (which may be combined): **B** (searches backwards from the current position), **G** (globally searches the whole file), **L** (locally searches the marked block), *n* (searches for the *n*th occurrence of the search string), **U** (ignores upper- or lowercase distinctions), **W** (searches for whole words only).

Ctrl-L repeats the last Find command.

Ctrl-QA (Find and replace) searches for a string and replaces it with a given string (after asking for permission). The options are the same as for Find, with the following additions: **N** (replaces without asking), *n* (replaces the next *n* occurrences of the search string).

Ctrl-Kn (where n is from 0 to 3) **sets a place marker**. Up to four positions in the text may be marked.

Ctrl-Qn finds a place marker.

Tab or **Ctrl-I** moves the cursor to the right 8 columns. This is the default tab size, and it may be changed in the Options/Environment menu.

Ctrl-OT or **Ctrl-QT** toggles the tab on/off. When it is off, **Tab** moves the cursor to the beginning of each word in the previous line.

Ctrl-OU toggles **unindent** on/off. In both cases **Backspace** deletes the character immediately left of the cursor. When it is On, **Backspace** in a blank line moves the cursor under the left most character of the line above.

A handy way of loading a file into the Edit window is as follows. Use the **File/Directory** command to display the current directory on the screen. Use the cursor movement keys to highlight the file you want to load, and press **Enter**.

All the editing commands are summarised in Appendix A.

Turbo Pascal 6.0 Editor

The version 6.0 editor allows multiple, resizable windows on the screen, which means you can edit more than one file at a time. This is ideal for moving chunks of code from one program to another using the "cut and paste" facilities. Files of up to 1 megabyte can be edited.

2.16 ODDS 'N ENDS

This section contains various items of information which may be helpful at this stage of your programming development.

Representation of information in a computer

The basic unit of information inside a computer is the bit: something which has only two possible states, usually described as on and off. Electronically this is very easy to represent, as a current can be either on or off, or a magnetic field can be orientated either clockwise or counterclockwise. The binary digits 0 and 1 can therefore be used to represent these two states mathematically (hence the term **digital** computer). The word bit is a contraction of **binary digit.**

Numbers in a computer's memory must therefore be represented in **binary code**, where each bit in a sequence stands for a successively higher power of 2. The decimal numbers 0 to 15, for example, are coded in binary as follows:

Decimal	*Binary*	*Hexadecimal*	*Decimal*	*Binary*	*Hexadecimal*
0	0000	0	8	1000	8
1	0001	1	9	1001	9
2	0010	2	10	1010	A
3	0011	3	11	1101	B
4	0100	4	12	1100	C
5	0101	5	13	1101	D
6	0110	6	14	1110	E
7	0111	7	15	1111	F

A **byte** is the amount of computer memory required for one character, and is eight bits long. Since each bit in a byte can be in two possible states, this gives 2^8, ie 256, different combinations.

Hexadecimal code (see the above table) is commonly used because it is more economical than binary. Each hexadecimal digit stands for a power of 16. For example:

$$2A\ (hex) = 2\times16^1 + 10\times16^0 = 32 + 10 = 42.$$

One byte can be represented by two hexadecimal digits. Turbo Pascal interprets a whole number prefixed with a $ symbol as a hexadecimal number, so $2A is a (hexadecimal) constant with the value 42.

Microcomputer memory size (and disk capacity) is measured in bytes, so 64K, for example, means slightly more than 64000 bytes (since 1K means 1024). This chapter takes up 105053 bytes on a disk because it has that many characters (including word processor control characters) in it. Microcomputers are sometimes referred to as 8- 16- or 32-bit machines. This describes the length of the units of information handled by their microprocessors, or chips. The longer these units, the faster the computer.

Compilers

Since the computer can only understand binary code, all instructions to it must ultimately be translated into this form. A **compiler** is a sophisticated program which translates your Turbo Pascal program statements into a machine readable form called **machine code**. This is collected together into a single entity, and stored in the memory. You may notice a slight delay after you press **Ctrl-F9** before the results come onto the screen. This is the time taken to compile the program. If you don't change the program, and run it again, it runs that much faster, because it doesn't need to be recompiled. This is much more noticeable with larger programs. Turbo Pascal has one of the fastest compilers on the market. Borland claim that version 5.5 compiles more than 34000 lines of code a minute, although this rate obviously depends on the type of computer you have. Compiling and executing are therefore two entirely different processes. When a program does not work, it is very important to know whether the error (or bug) occurred during compile- or run- time. This should be clear from the error messages generated by Turbo Pascal. There is more about errors in Chapter 7.

Operating systems

The operating system is a special program which controls the whole show while you are using the computer. It sits in the system tracks of the system disk (or hard disk) you are using, and is automatically loaded into memory when the computer is booted up. The operating system you are using is probably MS-DOS, which stands for **M**icro**S**oft **D**isk **O**perating **S**ystem, often simply called DOS. All commands typed in response to the system prompts **A>**, **B>**, **C>**, etc are commands to DOS. So when you type TURBO to start Turbo Pascal, DOS searches the disk for a command file called TURBO.EXE, and loads it into the RAM (random access memory). When you enter a program, DOS puts it into another part of the RAM, together with all the variables generated by the program. You therefore have indirect control of the RAM.

The ROM (read-only memory) on the other hand contains special programs, like the BIOS (**B**asic **I**nput-**O**utput **S**ystem), which is responsible for all the built-in support of the PC's input-output devices, such as the monitor and the disk drives. As its name implies, you have no control over ROM.

DOS also controls all the file handling and printing facilities.

Useful DOS commands

You can enter DOS directly from Turbo Pascal through the **File/OS** shell command. The following are some useful DOS commands:

COPY A: *oldfile* **B:** *newfile*	Copies *oldfile* from drive A into *newfile* in drive B. If *newfile* is omitted *oldfile* is used as the target filename.
COPY A:*. PAS B:	Copies all the .PAS files from drive A into files of the same names in drive B.
COPY A: *filename* **PRN**	Prints the file on the printer.
DEL A:*filename*	Deletes the file.
DEL A:*.*	Deletes all files on the disk after a warning (careful!).
DIR A:	Lists all files in drive A.
TYPE A: *file*	Displays the file on the screen. The file README on the Turbo Pascal disk provides a much more powerful display facility (for example, paging and searching) if used with a filename, for example: **README** *filename* This is a little known feature!

Memory matters

It is sometimes useful to know the actual **machine address** in memory. An address consists of two 16-bit parts: the **segment** and the **offset**. The segment part of the address points to regions of memory 16 bytes apart (the street name, if you like), whereas the offset part is the distance in bytes into one of the segments (the number in the street). The segment and offset together can specify each one of the 1048576 separate memory locations. This arrangement is due to the architecture of the 8086 processor used in most personal computers.

The standard functions **Seg** and **Ofs** return the segment and offset of machine address of a variable, for example, **Ofs(X)**. (Standard functions are discussed in Chapter 4.)

Normally, when you compile a program, Turbo Pascal decides on the addresses of all the variables and data. You can, however, specify a particular address for a variable with the **absolute** clause:

```
var
  Special : integer absolute $004A:$00FF;
```

This places the variable **Special** at segment $004A and offset $00FF (in hexadecimal). (Incidentally, the **D**ebug/**E**valuate command can be used to evaluate a hexadecimal number.)

The clause **absolute** can also be used to declare one variable on top of another:

```
var
  N : integ   X : real absolute N;
```

This means that **X** will start at the same address as **N** (although it will take up more memory). Since **absolute** interferes with the way Turbo Pascal manages a program's memory it should be used with great care.

If you want to see the machine addresses of the variables in a program, you can generate a **memory map** of the program with the **O**ptions/**L**inker/**M**ap File menu. If you choose a value other than **O**ff in the **M**ap File menu a file with the extension .MAP is generated with the memory map. The **C**ompile/**D**estination must be set to **D**isk. The .MAP file will be in your .EXE directory (**O**ptions/**D**irectories/**E**XE).

2.17 SIMPLE TYPES

This chapter concludes with a brief discussion of types.

Every variable in a Turbo Pascal program must be declared with a type. We have already met integer, real and string types. Types in Turbo Pascal may be divided into five main classes: simple, structured, string, pointer and procedural. We are going to look at simple types here.

Simple types basically define ordered sets of values. There are two categories of simple type: ordinal types and real types.

Ordinal types

The distinguishing feature of ordinal types is that each possible value of a given ordinal type is associated with an **ordinality** (position in the set) which is a whole number. Except for type integer, the first value of every ordinal type has ordinality 0, the next has ordinality 1, and so on. An integer type's ordinality is the value itself. The standard function **Ord** returns the ordinality of an ordinal type. **Pred** returns the predecessor in the set, and **Succ** returns the successor. There are seven predefined ordinal types in Turbo Pascal: integer, shortint, longint, byte, word, boolean, and char. There are also two other classes of user-defined ordinal types: enumerated and subrange.

Integer types

There are five predefined integer types, all with different ranges as shown below:

Type	*Range*	*Length*
shortint	128 .. 127	8 bits
integer	−32768.. 32767	16 bits
longint	−2147483648.. 2147483647	32 bits
byte	0 .. 255	8 bits
word	0 .. 65535	16 bits

The predefined constant **MaxInt** has the value 32767, and the predefined constant **MaxLongInt** has the value 2147483647.

When two variables of different integer types are involved in an arithmetic operation their values are both converted to their **common type** before the operation. The common type is defined as the predefined integer type with the smallest range that includes all possible values of both types. For example, the common type of integer and word is longint. The type of the result of the operation is the common type.

Boolean type

Boolean type values may be either **True** or **False**, these two identifiers representing the only boolean constants. Since **Ord(False)** has the value 0 and **Ord(True)** has the value 1, the expression **False < True** is true. Boolean values may be written with **Write** and **Writeln**.

Char type

The set of values of char type are the single characters ordered according to the ASCII set (Appendix C), as opposed to string type, which allows sequences of characters. This ordering implies, for example, that the expression **'A' < 'B'** is true. The constants of this type are string constants of length 1. A character can be generated from its ASCII code with the standard function **Chr**. For example, **Chr(90)** returns 'Z'.

Enumerated types

These are rather exotic, and are what makes Pascal different from most other programming languages. Enumerated types enable the user to define the values of the type and their associated identifiers. For example:

```
type
  suit = (club, diamond, heart, spade);
var
  card : suit;
```

Card is variable of type suit, and can take on one of four possible values: **club, diamond, heart,** or **spade.** These values may be assigned **(Card:= diamond)** but not output with **Write**. There are other ways of writing, however:

```
if card = club then
  Write( 'club' );
```

The standard functions **Ord**, **Pred** and **Succ** can be used on variables of an enumerated type. For example, **Ord(Card)** will return the value 1 if **Card** has been assigned the value **diamond**, and **Succ(heart)** will return the value **spade.**

Subrange types

This is a range of values from an ordinal type called the **host type.** The smallest and largest values must be specified in the type definition. For example:

```
type
  Mark = 0..100;
  Letter = 'A'..'z';
```

If a variable of a subrange type takes on a value outside the range during execution an error occurs. This is where subranges are useful. They provide a way of checking that variables don't take on meaningless values during a calculation.

Real types

There are five real types: real, single, double, extended and comp, as follows:

Type	*Range*		*Significant digits*	*Size in bytes*
real	2.9E-39	1.7E38 ..	11-12	6
single	1.5E-45	3.4E38 ..	7-8	4
double	5.0E-324	1.7E308 ..	15-16	8
extended	3.4E-4932	1.1E4932..	19-20	10
comp	$-2^{63}+1$	$2^{63}-1$ ..	19-20	8

Comp type holds only whole numbers in its range, which is approximately −9.2E18 to 9.2E18. If a comp variable is to be output with **Write** it must be formatted in the same way as a real variable.

Single, double, extended and comp types have been designed to make use of the 8087 **numeric co-processor.** The **{$N+}** **compiler directive** in a program before the variable declarations makes Turbo Pascal check whether your machine has a co-processor. If it doesn't, special software which emulates it is loaded. So you can use these types whether or not you have an 8087 chip, as long as your code contains the **{$N+}** compiler directive:

```
program Smart;
{$N+}
var
  X: double;
...
```

See Appendix E for more details.

Typed constants

A variable may be initialised at compile time by declaring it as a **typed constant**, for example:

```
const
  Balance : real = 1000;
  John8_12 : string = 'I am the light of the world';
```

Because typed constants are variables they may be changed in a program. However, being variables, they may not be used in places where only constants are allowed, for example, in a type declaration. So the following is not allowed:

```
const
  Min : integer = 0;
  Max : integer = 100;
type
  Mark : Min..Max;
```

Range checking

A constant may not be assigned to a variable if it is out of range. For example, the statement:

```
N:= 40000;
```

where **N** is integer type will cause error 76 (Constant out of range) during compilation. However, if **N** is of type longint, assigning it to a variable of integer type will *not* cause a compilation error, although the result will be garbage. The problem is that during execution the longint bit pattern is poured into the integer variable, resulting in a value which is far from correct, causing havoc in any subsequent calculations.

To prevent this, **range checking** may be switched on. This is done either with the **O**ptions/**C**ompiler/**R**ange-Checking command or by including the {**$R+**} compiler directive in your program before the code which must be checked. Note that range checking does not detect *intermediate* values in an expression which may cycle. It is generally best to use word type for integer calculations, since negative values will then be trapped. If you want even larger numbers, define a subrange type:

```
type
  PosLongInt = 0 .. MaxLongInt;
```

Type conversion

A value of a specific type may be converted to one of a different type by using a **transfer function** or by **type casting.** There are four standard transfer functions, which we have already seen: **Chr, Ord, Round** and **Trunc**. You should be aware that values may also be transferred between incompatible types by means of type casting. This is an advanced topic, so it is not dealt with here. You should consult the *Turbo Pascal Reference Guide* for details.

SUMMARY

- Successful problem solving with a computer requires knowledge of the coding rules and a sound logical plan.
- Turbo Pascal statements are generally separated by semi-colons.
- All variables must be declared with a type.
- Types are either predefined or user-defined.
- Statements are either simple or structured.
- Simple statements contain no other statements (for example, the assignment statement).

- Structured statements are either compound, conditional or repetitive.
- Comments may be enclosed in {..} or (*..*) and should be used liberally to explain what is going on in a program, and to describe variables.
- The value of a constant may not be changed in a program, but the value of a typed constant may be changed.
- Numerical expressions may be formed from numbers and variables with the six arithmetic operators (and parentheses), which operate according to strict rules of precedence.
- Real values may not be assigned to integer variables.
- **Write** and **Writeln** are used to output numbers and strings.
- Data may be entered from the keyboard while a program is running in response to **Read** and **Readln**.
- Data may also be read from a disk file.
- A **for** loop is used to repeat a set of statements.
- **if-then-else** enables a program to decide between alternatives.
- Units contain predefined procedures and functions.
- The **ClrScr** procedure in the **Crt** unit clears the output screen.
- String constants are strings of characters enclosed in apostrophes.
- Concatenation is the only string operation.

EXERCISES

2.1 Evaluate the following Turbo Pascal expressions, given that A = 2, B = 3, C = 4 (answers in parentheses):

A / 2 * B	(3, not 1/3)
A / (B * B)	(2/9)
A + B * C – 4	(10)
A * A * B / C + 3	(6)
A * B + C	(10)
17 div 5	(3)
4 div 3 div 4	(0)
4 div (3 div 4)	(division by zero)
17 mod (4 mod 3)	(0)

2.2 Decide which of the following numbers are not acceptable in Turbo Pascal, and state why not:

(a) 9.87	(b) .0	(c) 25.82	(d) 12,68
(e) 3.57*e2	(f) 3.57e2.1	(g) 3.57e+2	(h) 3,57e–2

2.3 State, giving reasons, which of the following are not acceptable Turbo Pascal identifiers:

(a)A2	(b) 2A	(c) X$	(d) A
(e) for	(f) MIN*2	(g) A+1	(h) pay day
(i) MIxeDuP	(j) U.S.S.R.	(k) r2d2!	(l) final_mark

2.4 Find the value of the following expressions by writing short Turbo Pascal programs to evaluate them (answers in parentheses):

(a) $\sqrt{2}$ (1.41421)
(b) the sum of 5 and 3 divided by their product (0.53333)
(c) the cube root of the product of 2.3 and 4.5 (2.17928)
(d) the square of 2π (39.4784 – take π = 3.1415927 or use the standard function Pi)
(e) $2\pi^2$ (19.7392)
(f) $1000(1 + 0.15/12)^{60}$ (2107.18 – the balance when $1000 is deposited for 5 years at 15% p.a. compounded monthly)

2.5 Translate the following expressions into Turbo Pascal expressions:

(a) $p + \frac{w}{u}$ (b) $p + \frac{w}{u + v}$ (c) $\dfrac{p + \frac{w}{u+v}}{p + \frac{w}{u-v}}$ (d) x^2

(e) $x^{2.5}$ (f) $x^{0.5}$ (g) x^{y+z} (h) $(x^y)^z$

(i) $x^{(y^z)}$

(j) $x - \dfrac{x^3}{3!} + \dfrac{x^5}{5!}$

2.6 Translate the following into Turbo Pascal statements:

(a) Add 1 to the value of I and store the result in I.
(b) Cube I, add J to this, and store the result in I.
(c) Set G equal to the larger of the two values E and F.
(d) If D is greater than zero, set X equal to minus B.
(e) Divide the sum of A and B by the product of C and D, and store the result in X.

2.7 Write a program to calculate petrol (gas) consumption. It should assign the distance travelled (in kilometres) and the amount of petrol used (in litres) and compute the consumption in km/litre as well as in the more usual form of litres per 100 km. Write some helpful headings, so that your output looks something like this:

Distance	Litres used	Km/L	L/100Km
528	46.23	11.42	8.76

2.8 Write a program to calculate x, where

$$x = \frac{-b + \sqrt{(b^2 - 4ac)}}{2a}$$

and $a = 2$, $b = -10$, $c = 12$ (use **Read** to get the data in). (Answer 3.0)

2.9 There are eight pints in a gallon, and 1.76 pints in a litre. The volume of a tank is given as 2 gallons and 4 pints. Write a program which reads this volume in gallons and pints and converts it to litres. (Answer: 11.36 litres)

2.10 If C and F are Celsius and Fahrenheit temperatures respectively, the formula for conversion is

$$F = 9C/5 + 32 .$$

(a) Write a program which will ask you for the Celsius temperature and display the equivalent Fahrenheit one with some sort of comment, for example: **The Fahrenheit temperature is: ...**

Try it out on the following Celsius temperatures (answers in parentheses): 0 (32), 100 (212), −40 (−40!), 37 (normal human temperature: 98.6).

(b) Change the program to use a **for** loop to compute and write the Fahrenheit equivalent of Celsius temperatures ranging from 20° to 30° in steps of 1°.

2.11 Write a program that displays a list of integers from 10 to 20 inclusive, each with its square root next to it.

2.12 The following program segment will write 5 asterisks on the same line:

```
for I:= 1 to 5 do
```

```
  Write( '*' );
Writeln;
```

(a) Change it to write 10 asterisks.

(b) Now change it to read an integer variable *N* and write *N* asterisks on the same line.

(c) Change it to produce the following effect (about 5 rows of output with an asterisk shifted one column to the right each time):

```
*
 *
  *
   *
...
```

2.13 Write a program to find and display the sum of the successive integers 1, 2, ..., 100. (Answer: 5050)

2.14 Write a program to find and display the sum of the successive even integers 2, 4, ..., 200. (Answer: 10100)

2.15 Write a program to find the sum of the squares of the first 256 integers:

$1^2 + 2^2 + 3^2 + ... + 256^2$

The answer is 5625216 (be careful!).

2.16 Ten students in a class write a test. The marks are out of 10. All the marks are entered in a disk file MARKS. Write a program which will read all ten marks from the file and find and display the average mark. Try it on the following marks: 5 8 0 10 3 8 5 7 9 4. (Answer: 5.9)

2.17 The pass mark for the test in Exercise 2.16 is 5 out of 10. Change that program so it uses an **if-then** to find out how many students passed the test.

2.18 Write a program which generates some random numbers using **Randomize** and **Random** and counts how many of them are greater than 0.5, and how many are less than 0.5. Try increasing the number of random numbers generated. What do you expect?

2.19 This question refers to the vertical motion example in section 2.6.

(a) Run the program as it stands. Try to work out whether the stone is moving up or down.

(b) Re-run for different values of *t*. In particular, use the program to find out where the stone is after 20 seconds, and interpret your results physically.

(c) Rearrange the formula to compute when the stone returns to the ground.

(d) Rearrange the formula to compute when the stone is at any particular height, ie calculate *t*, given *u* and *s*. Interpret your results physically.

2.20 Write some lines of Turbo Pascal which will exchange the contents of two variables A and B, using only one additional variable T.

2.21 Try Exercise 2.20 *without* using any additional variables!

2.22 What are the values of X and A (both real) after the following program section has been executed?

```
A:= 0;
I:= 1;
X:= 0;
A:= A + I;
X:= X + I /A
A:= A + I;
```

```
X:= X + 1 / A;
A:= A + 1;
X:= X + 1 / A;
A:= A + 1;
X:= X + 1 / A;
```

2.23 Rewrite the program in Exercise 2.22 more economically by using a for loop.

2.24 Work out by hand the output of the following program:

```
program Mystery;
var
   S, X : real;
   N, K: integer;
begin
N:= 4;
S:= 0;
for K:= 1 to N do
begin
   X:= K;
   S:= S + 1 / (X * X);
end;
Writeln( Sqrt( 6 * S ):10:6 );
readln;
end.
```

If you run this program for larger and larger values of N you will find that the output approaches a well-known limit.

2.25 Try to spot the syntax errors (ie mistakes in coding rules) in this program before running it on the computer to check your answers with the error messages generated by Turbo Pascal:

```
program Dread.ful;
var
   A, B, X: real;
   X = 5;
   Y:= 6,67
   B:= X Y;
   Writeln( The answer is: ' B;
end
```

2.26 A student makes a regular deposit of $20 each month into his bank account. Interest is compounded at the end of each month, after the deposit has been made, at the rate of 1.5% per month. He starts with nothing in the account. Write a program which displays, under suitable headings, the interest and month end balance each month for two years. (Answer: final balance is $581.26)

2.27 The steady-state electric current I flowing in a circuit that contains a resistance, capacitance and inductance in series is given by

$$I = \frac{E}{\sqrt{[\, R^2 + (\, 2\pi FL - \frac{1}{2\pi FC} \,)^2 \,]}}$$

where E, R, L, C and F are the input voltage, resistance, inductance, capacitance and angular frequency respectively. Translate this formula into a Turbo Pascal statement.

2.28 Suppose Income Tax is calculated as follows:

Taxable Income	*Tax Payable*
less than $10000:	10% of taxable income
between $10000 and $20000:	$1000 + 20% of amount by which taxable income exceeds $10000
between $20000 and $40000:	$3000 + 30% of amount by which taxable income exceeds $20000
more than $40000:	$9000 + 50% of amount by which taxable income exceeds $40000

Write a program which neatly displays the taxable income and tax payable for the following taxable incomes: $5000, $10000, $15000, $22000, $30000, $38000 and $50000. You should use a for loop.

2.29 If you invest $1000 for one year at an interest rate of 12%, the return is $1120 at the end of the year. But if interest is compounded at the rate of 1% *monthly* (ie 1/12 of the annual rate), you get slightly more interest in the long run. Adapt the program GROWTH in section 2.11 to compute the balance after a year of compounding interest in this way. The answer should be $1126.83. Evaluate the formula for this result separately as a check: $1000(1.01)^{12}$.

2.30 A plumber opens a savings account with $100000 at the beginning of January. He then makes a deposit of $1000 at the end of each month for the next 12 months (starting at the end of January). Interest is calculated and added to his account at the end of each month (*before* the $1000 deposit is made). The monthly interest rate depends on the amount A in his account at the time when interest is calculated, in the following way:

$A \leq$ 110000: 1%
110000 $<$ $A \leq$ 125000: 1.5%
$A >$ 125000: 2%

Write a program which displays, for each of the 12 months, under suitable headings, the situation at the end of the month as follows: the number of the month, the interest rate, the amount of interest and the new balance. (Answer: the last row of output should be 12 0.02 2534.58 130263.78).

2.31 Write a program which will read a person's name and address from a disk file and use the data to write a form letter with a special offer to paint his house. The data in the file should be in the form

Jones
31 Campground Rd,
Rondebosch.

If this data is used, the program output should be:

Dear Mr *Jones,*
We will paint your house with Sloshon at half price! You can have the smartest house in *Campground Rd,* if not in the whole of *Rondebosch*. The *Jones* family will be able to walk tall again. Your neighbours at number *33* will be amazed!

The items in italics are read from the file as data. You can use any other name and address with the same format, obviously.

3 Program Preparation

The examples in this book so far have been very simple logically, since we have been concentrating on the technical aspects of writing Turbo Pascal statements correctly. However, real problems are far more complex, and to program successfully we need to understand the problem thoroughly, and to break it down into its most fundamental logical stages. In other words, we have to develop a systematic method or **algorithm,** for solving the problem. There are a number of methods which assist in this process of algorithm development. In this chapter we outline two: flowcharts, and structure plans, which have already been mentioned briefly.

3.1 FLOWCHARTS

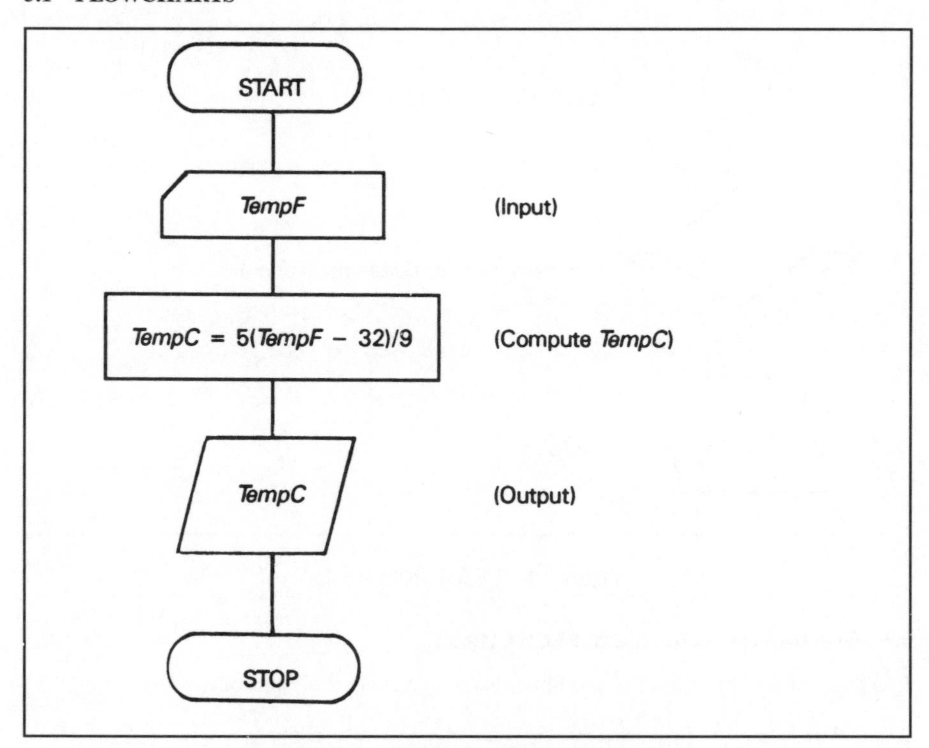

Figure 3.1 Celsius to Fahrenheit Conversion

This approach is rather old-fashioned, and tends to be frowned upon in with it computing circles. However, engineers often prefer this visual method, so for that reason, and for historical interest, some examples are given here.

Suppose we want to write a program to convert a temperature on the Fahrenheit scale (where water freezes and boils at 32°F and 212°F respectively) to the more familar Celsius centigrade scale. The flowchart for the problem is in Figure. 3.1.

The main symbols used in flowcharts, and their meanings, are:

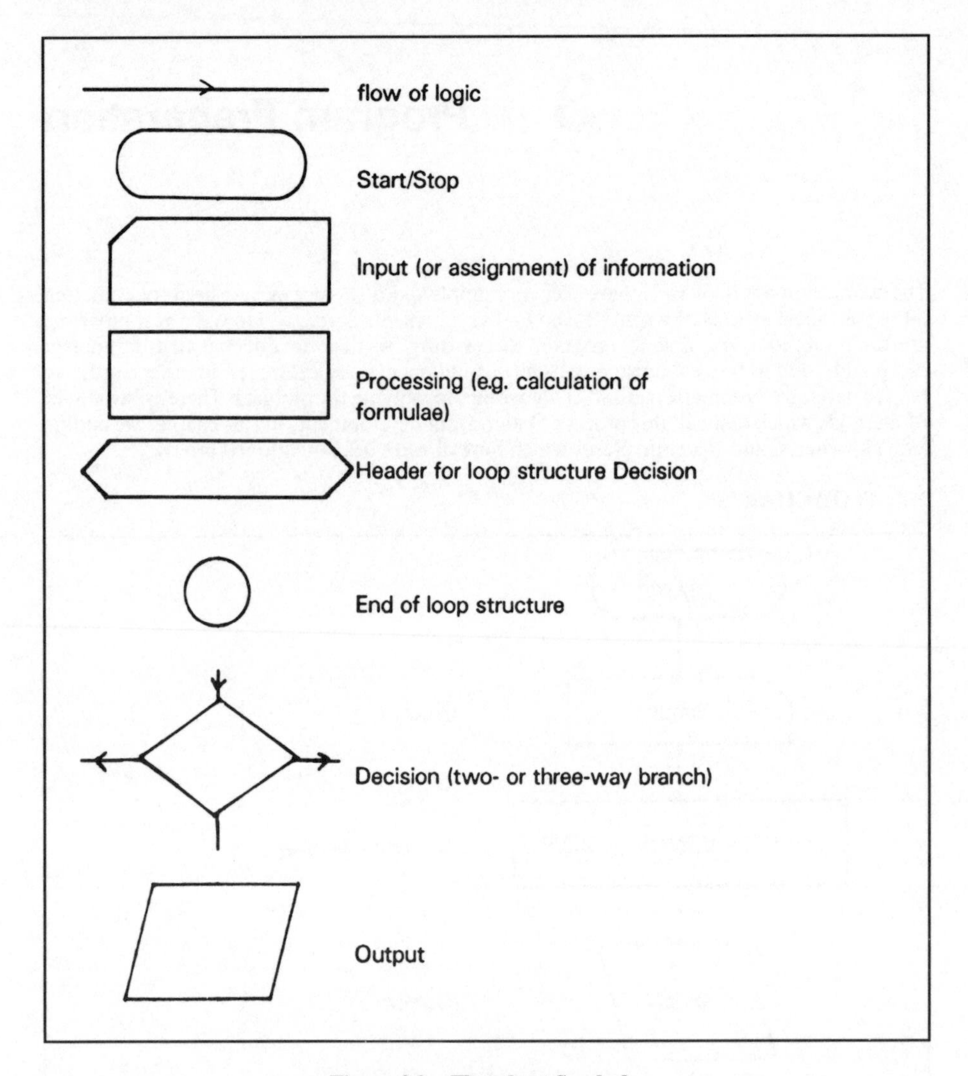

Figure 3.2 Flowchart Symbols

3.2 QUADRATIC EQUATION: FLOWCHART

Every schoolchild must have solved hundreds of quadratic equations of the form

$$ax^2 + bx + c = 0 .$$

The complete algorithm for finding the solution *x*, given *a*, *b*, and *c*, is flowcharted as follows:

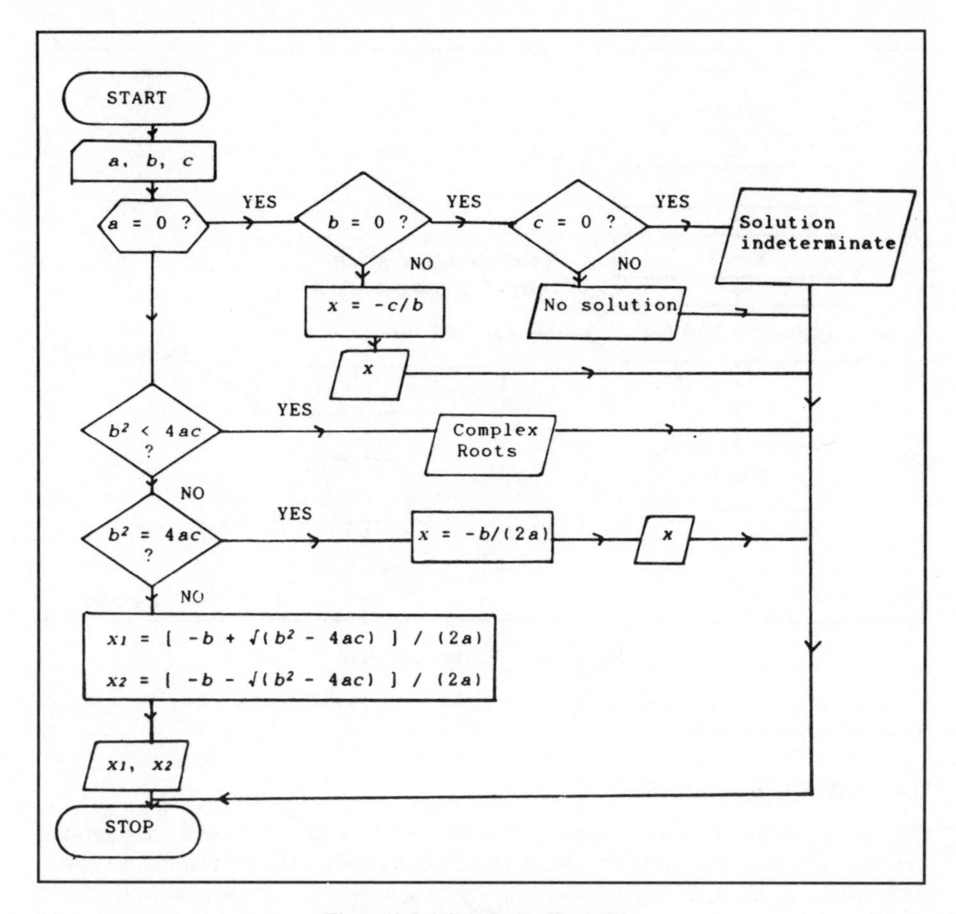

Figure 3.3 Quadratic Equation

3.3 NEWTON'S METHOD: FLOWCHART

In Chapter 2 we wrote a program to find square roots with Newton's method, the main part of which was:

```
  Write( 'Enter number to be square rooted: ' );
  Readln( A );
  WriteX:=
    Writeln;
    X:= 1;
for I:= 1 to 6
  begin
    X:= (X + A / X) / 2;
    Writeln( X:16:12 )
  end;
```

There is no universally accepted way of flowcharting a **for** loop, but one way is to use the elongated diamond to give the conditions under which the body of the loop is executed, with a small circle to mark the end of the loop, as follows:

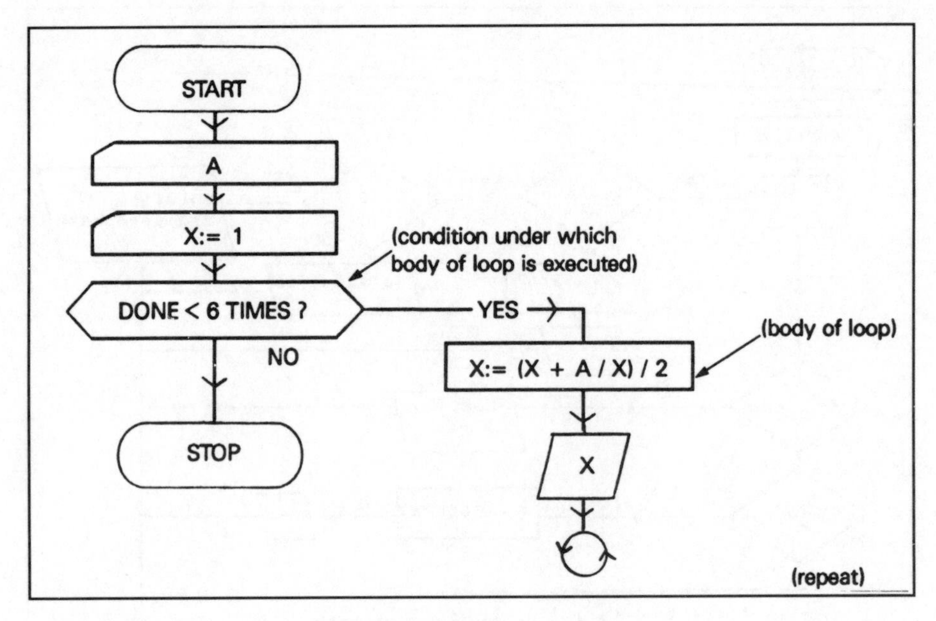

Figure 3.4 Newton's method

Note that the contents of the boxes can be either Turbo Pascal statements, or more general mathematical statements.

3.4 STRUCTURE PLANS

This is an alternative method of program preparation, which has advantages when the equivalent flowchart gets rather big. It is an example of what is called **pseudo-code.** The plan may be written at a number of levels, of increasing complexity, as the logical structure of the program is developed. For example, a first level plan of the temperature conversion problem above might be a simple statement of the problem:

1. Read Fahrenheit temperature
2. Calculate and write Celsius temperature
3. Stop.

Step 1 is pretty straightforward, but step 2 needs elaborating, so the second level plan could be something like this:

1. Input Fahrenheit temperature (*TempF*)
2. Calculate Celsius temperature (*TempC*):
   2.1. Subtract 32 from *TempF* and multiply by 5/9
3. Write the value of *TempC*
4. Stop.

There are no hard and fast rules about flowcharts and structure plans, and you should use whichever method you prefer (or even a mixture). The essential point is to cultivate the mental discipline of getting the logic of a program clear before rushing to the computer. The top down approach of flowcharts or structure plans means that the overall structure of a program is clearly thought out before you have to worry about the details of syntax (coding), and this reduces the number of errors enormously. The way Pascal has been designed, with variable and procedure declarations needed at the beginning of a program, forces you to plan in this way.

3.5 QUADRATIC EQUATION: STRUCTURE PLAN

The equivalent structure plan for the quadratic equation problem flow-charted above is as follows:

1. Start
2. Input data (a, b, c)
3. If $a = 0$ then
   3.1. If $b = 0$ then
      3.1.1. If $c = 0$ then
         3.1.1.1. Write "Solution indeterminate"
         Otherwise
         3.1.1.2. Write "There is no solution"
      Otherwise
      3.1.2. $x = -c/b$
      3.1.3. Write x (one root: equation is linear)
   Otherwise
   3.2. If $b^2 < 4ac$ then
      3.2.1. Write "Complex roots"
      Otherwise
      3.2.2. If $b^2 = 4ac$ then
         3.2.2.1. $x = -b/(2a)$
         3.2.2.2. Write x (equal roots)
         Otherwise
         3.2.2.3. $x_1 = [\ -\mathrm{b} + \sqrt{}\ (b^2 - 4ac)\ ]\ /\ (2a)$
         3.2.2.4. $x_2 = [\ -\mathrm{b} - \sqrt{}\ (b^2 + 4ac)\ ]\ /\ (2a)$
         3.2.2.5. Write x_1, x_2

4 Stop.

Details of how best to code the *If-then* blocks are discussed in Chapter 5. There are many more examples of structure plans throughout the book.

3.6 STRUCTURED PROGRAMMING WITH PROCEDURES

Many examples later in the book will get rather involved. More advanced programs like these should be structured by means of procedures, which are dealt with in detail in Chapter 8. A procedure is a self-contained section of code which can communicate with the main part of the program in specific ways, and which may be invoked or called by the main program. The main program will then look very much like a first level structure plan of the problem. For example, the quadratic equation problem may be structure planned at the first level as follows:

1. Read the data
2. Find and write the solution
3. Stop.

Using a procedure this may be translated directly into a Turbo Pascal main program:

```
Readln( A, B, C );
SolveQuadratic( X1, X2, A, B, C );
Writeln( X1, X2 );
```

The details of how to code this problem are left as an exercise in Chapter 8.

A Simple Procedure

To whet your appetite for procedures, here's a simple example which you should run.

```
program Main;
{------Stars------}
procedure Stars( N: integer );
{ writes a row of N asterisks on the same line }
var I: integer;
begin
  for I:= 1 to N do
    Write( '*' );
```

```
  Writeln
end; { Stars }

var
  I : integer;
begin
  Readln( I );
  Stars( I );
  Readln;
end.
```

As you may have guessed the procedure **Stars** displays a row of asterisks. The actual number of asterisks drawn is **I,** where **I** is read in the main program. Note that the procedure declaration, from the word **procedure** to the comment { **Stars** } is contained entirely in the program declaration part. In fact, a procedure is declared in the same sense that a variable is declared. The procedure itself looks just like a Turbo Pascal program, with three exceptions:

1. The word **procedure** is used instead of program.
2. The word **procedure** is followed by parameters in parentheses;
3. The procedure ends with a semi-colon instead of a period.

Note that the procedure has its own variable declaration: **I.** This name was used deliberately to stress that it has nothing to do with the variable of the same name in the main program. The procedure declaration is like a black box, which the main program can't see into, except through the window provided by its parameter list (**N** in this case). When the procedure is activated, or called, by referencing its name in the main program, the value of its parameter there **(I)** is copied into the corresponding parameter in its declaration **(N)**. This is the only communication between main program and procedure. Once the procedure is declared, it can be referenced wherever needed in the main program, so the same section of coding doesn't have to be repeated over and over.

SUMMARY

- An algorithm is a systematic logical method for solving a problem.
- An algorithm must be developed for a problem before it can be coded.
- A flowchart is a diagrammatic representation of an algorithm.
- A structure plan is a representation of an algorithm in pseudo-code.
- A procedure is a separate collection of Turbo Pascal statements defined to handle a particular task, and which may be activated whenever needed.

EXERCISES

The programs in these exercises should all be structure planned or flowcharted before being coded into Turbo Pascal.

3.1 This structure plan defines a geometric construction. Carry out the plan by sketching the construction:

1. Draw two perpendicular *x*- and *y*-axes
2. Draw the points *A* (10, 0) and *B* (0, 1)
3. While *A* does not coicide with the origin repeat:
   3.1. Draw a straight line joining *A* and *B*
   3.2. Move *A* one unit to the left along the *x*-axis
   3.3. Move *B* one unit up on the *y*-axis
4. Stop.

3.2 Consider the following structure plan, where M and N are Turbo Pascal integer variables:

1. Set $M = 44$ and $N = 28$
2. While M not equal to N repeat:
   2.1. While $M > N$ repeat:
      2.1.1. Replace M by $M - N$
   2.2. While $N > M$ repeat:
      2.2.1. Replace N by $N - M$
3. Write M
4. Stop.

(a) Work through the structure plan, sketching the contents of M and N during execution. Give the output.
(b) Repeat (a) for $M = 14$ and $N = 24$.
(c) What general arithmetic procedure does the algorithm carry out (try more values of M and N if necessary)?

3.3 Write a program to convert a Fahrenheit temperature to a Celsius one. Test it on the data in Exercise 2.10.

3.4 A builder is given the measurements of five planks in feet (′) and inches (″). He wants to convert the lengths to metres. One foot is 0.3048 metres, and one inch is 0.0254 metres. The measurements of the planks are: 4′ 6″, 8′ 9″, 9′ 11″, 6′ 3″ and 12′ 0″ (ie the first plank is 4 feet 6 inches long). Store the data in a disk file.

Write a program to display (under suitable headings) the length of each plank in feet and inches, and in metres, and to find and display the total length of planking in metres. (Answer: the total length is 12.624 metres)

3.5 Write a program to read any two real numbers (which you may assume are not equal), and write out the larger of the two with a suitable message.

3.6 Write a program to read a set of 10 numbers (from a disk file) and write out the *largest* number in the set.

Now adjust the program to write out the *position* of the largest number in the set as well.

3.7 Write a program to compute the sum of the series

$$1 + 1/2 + 1/3 + \ldots + 1/100 .$$

The program should write the current sum after every 10 terms (ie the sum after 10 terms, after 20 terms, ..., after 100 terms).

Hint: the statement N mod 10 will be zero only when N is a multiple of 10. Use this in an if statement to write the sum after every 10th term. (Answer: 5.18738 after 100 terms)

3.8 To convert the integer variable Min minutes into hours and minutes you would first use the div operator (Min div 60 gives the whole number of hours) and then the mod operator (Min mod 60 gives the number of minutes). Write a program which reads a number of minutes (use word type) and converts it to hours and minutes.

Now write a program to convert seconds into hours, minutes and seconds. Use word type again. Try out your program on 10000 seconds, which should convert to 2 hours 46 minutes and 40 seconds.

Also try to write structure plans for the following problems (don't try to write the programs until you've worked that far): Exercises 5.2, 5.3, 5.5.

4 Standard Functions and Procedures

So far you should be able to write a program which gets data into the computer, performs simple arithmetic operations on the data, and outputs the results of the computation in a comprehensible form. However, more interesting problems are likely to involve special mathematical functions like sines, cosines, logarithms, etc. Just as most calculators have keys for these functions, Turbo Pascal allows you to compute many functions directly. These functions are called **standard** functions.

4.1 PROJECTILE MOTION

We want to write a program to compute the position (x and y co-ordinates) and velocity (magnitude and direction) of a projectile, given t, the time since launch, u, the launch velocity, a, the initial angle of launch (in degrees), and g, the acceleration due to gravity.

The horizontal displacement is given by the formula

$$x = u \cos(a)t$$

and the vertical displacement by

$$y = u \sin(a)t - 0.5gt^2 .$$

The velocity has magnitude V such that

$$V^2 = \sqrt{}(V_x^2 + V_y^2),$$

where its horizontal and vertical components, V_x and V_y, are given by

$$V_x = u \cos(a),$$
$$V_y = u \sin(a) - gt,$$

and V makes an angle θ with the ground such that

$$\tan(\theta) = V_y/V_x.$$

The program is:

```
program Projectile;
{ projectile position and velocity }
const
  G = 9.8;
var
  A   : real;        { angle of launch in degrees }
  T   : real;        { time in flight }
  Th  : real;        { direction at time t }
  U   : real;        { launch velocity }
  V   : real;        { resultant velocity }
  Vx  : real;        { horizontal velocity }
  Vy  : real;        { vertical velocity }
  X   : real;        { horizontal displacement }
  Y   : real;        { vertical displacement }
begin
  Readln( A, T, U );
  A:= A * Pi / 180;                          { convert angle to radians }
  X:= U * Cos( A ) * T;
  Y:= U * Sin( A ) * T - 0.5 * G * Sqr( T );
```

```
    Vx:= U * Cos( A );
    Vy:= U * Sin( A ) - G * T;
    V:= Sqrt( Sqr( Vx ) + Sqr( Vy ) );
    Th:= ArcTan( Vy / Vx ) * 180 / Pi;
    Writeln( 'x: ', X:8:2, '        y: ', Y:8:2 );
    Writeln( 'V: ', V:8:2, Chr( 233 ):5, ': ', Th:8:2 );
    Readln
end.
```

If you run this program with the data as given you will see from the negative value of θ that the projectile is coming down.

The argument of a standard function may be any valid Turbo Pascal expression of appropriate type, including another function. So *V* could have been computed directly as follows:

```
V:= Sqrt( Sqr( U * COS( A ) ) + Sqr( U * SIN( A ) - G * T ) );
```

(The argument of **Sqrt** is always positive here (why?) so no problems can arise.)

Angles for the trigonometric functions must be expressed in radians, by default. To convert degrees to radians, multiply the angle in degrees by **Pi/180,** where **Pi** is a standard function with the well known value 3.1415926... If you want to impress your friends, however, you can cunningly exploit the mathematical fact that the arctangent of 1 is $\pi/4$, and use the **ArcTan** standard function:

```
MyPi:= 4 * ArcTan( 1 );
A:= A * MyPi / 180                              { convert angles to radians }
...
```

The standard function **Chr** with argument 233 enables you to write the Greek symbol θ on the screen (see below and Appendix C, which also describes how to get special characters directly on the screen). To print these special symbols on your printer, however, you will need to consult your printer manual for any additional control characters required, and you may also need a special font for your printer.

4.2 SOME USEFUL STANDARD FUNCTIONS

Brief descriptions of most of the standard functions supported by Turbo Pascal appear in Appendix B. A list of the more common ones is given here. The unit is given where appropriate. The unit name must be referenced in a **uses** statement. The name of a standard function may be used as an identifier, but then that function is unavailable to the program.

Functions and procedures in the **Graph** unit are all dealt with separately in Chapter 13.

Abs	Absolute value of real argument, e.g. **Abs(−2)** returns 2.
ArcTan	Arctangent in radians of real argument.
Chr	Character with ASCII code of integer argument.
Cos	Cosine of real argument.
Exp	Exponential of real argument, i.e. e^x.
Frac	Fractional part of real argument.
Int	Integer part of real argument (real result).
KeyPressed	Returns True if a key has been pressed on the keyboard, and False otherwise (**Crt** unit).
Length	Dynamic length of string argument, e.g. **Length('Abe')** returns 3.
Ln	Natural logarithm of real argument.
Ord	Ordinal number of ordinal type value.
Pi	Value of π (3.1415926 ...).
Random	Random number.
ReadKey	Reads a character from the keyboard (**Crt** unit).
Round	Rounds real argument to nearest longint type value.
Sin	Sine of real argument.

Sqr	Square of real argument.
Sqrt	Square root of real argument.
Tan	Tangent of real argument.
Trunc	Truncates real argument to longint type value.
UpCase	Converts character to uppercase.
WhereX	Horizontal position of cursor (**Crt** unit).
WhereY	Vertical position of cursor (**Crt** unit).

4.3 SOME USEFUL STANDARD PROCEDURES

A function returns a single value, which is associated with its name, for example **Pi**. A procedure, however, may return many values, through its parameters. Some interesting procedures are listed here. They, and many others, are described in Appendix B. An example of usage is given in the next section.

ClrScr	Clears screen (**Crt** unit).
Dec	Decrements a variable of ordinal type (faster than subtraction).
Delay	Delays a specified number of milliseconds (**Crt** unit).
GetDate	Returns the current system date (**Dos** unit).
GetTime	Returns the current system time (**Dos** unit).
GoToXY	Positions the cursor (**Crt** unit).
HighVideo	Selects high intensity characters (**Crt** unit).
Inc	Increments a variable of ordinal type (faster than addition).
LowVideo	Selects low intensity characters (**Crt** unit).
NormVideo	Selects normal intensity characters (**Crt** unit).
NoSound	Switches off the computer speaker (**Crt** unit).
Randomize	"Seeds" the standard function **Random** according to the system time.
SetDate	Sets the current system date (**Dos** unit).
SetTime	Sets the current system time (**Dos** unit).
Sound	Starts the computer speaker at the specified frequency (**Crt** unit).
Str	Converts a numeric value to its string equivalent.
TextBackground	Selects the background colour (**Crt** unit).
TextColor	Selects the foreground character colour (**Crt** unit).
Val	Converts a string to its numeric representation.
Window	Defines a text window on the screen (**Crt** unit).

4.4 A CONTINUOUS TIME DISPLAY

The following program illustrates some of the functions and procedures mentioned above. Don't worry about the details at this stage. The program displays the time continuously in the middle of the screen, until **Enter** is pressed. Note that two **Readln**s are needed to keep the time on the screen after the program has ended, because of the effect of using **KeyPressed**.

```
program TimeDisplay;
uses Crt, Dos;
var
   Hour, Min, Sec, Sec100 : word;
   Time : string;
   StrTime : string[2];
Begin
   ClrScr;
   HighVideo;
   repeat
      GoToXY( 35, 12 );                         { centre the output }
      GetTime( Hour, Min, Sec, Sec100 );      { system time }
      Str( Hour, StrTime );                      { hours }
      if Length( StrTime ) = 1 then
         Time:= '0' + StrTime + ':'
```

```
        else
          Time:= StrTime + ':';
        Str( Min, StrTime );                      { minutes }
        if Length( StrTime ) = 1 then
          Time:= Time + '0' + StrTime + ':'
        else
          Time:= Time + StrTime + ':';
        Str( Sec, StrTime );                      { seconds }
        if Length( StrTime ) = 1 then
          Time:= Time + '0' + StrTime + '.'
        else
          Time:= Time + StrTime + '.';
        Str( Sec100, StrTime );                   { hundredths }
        if Length( StrTime ) = 1 then
          Time:= Time + '0' + StrTime
        else
          Time:= Time + StrTime;
        Writeln( Time )
      until Keypressed;
      Readln;
      Readln
    end.
```

4.5 DEFINING AN EXPONENTIATION POWER FUNCTION

Pascal lacks an exponentiation operator, but a function to do this may easily be written. Chapter 8 describes in detail how to write your own functions, but an exponentiation function, **Power,** is given here without much explanation, because it is very useful in many scientific calculations. The function is shown below in use in a program:

```
program Check;

function Power( A, B : real ): real;
{ raises A to the power B }
begin
  Power:= Exp( B * Ln( A ) )
end; { Power }

var
  X, Y, Z : real;
begin
...
    Z:= Power( X, Y );                    { X to the Y }
    Writeln( Power( 2, 3 );               { 2 to the 3 }
    Readln
...
```

Save the function **Power** (from **function Power** to **end; {Power}**) as a separate file, and include it any program where you need it.

SUMMARY

Standard functions may be used to compute a variety of mathematical, trigonometric and other functions directly.

EXERCISES

4.1 There are 39.37 inches in a metre, 12 inches in a foot, and three feet in a yard. Write a program to read a length in metres (which may have a decimal part) and convert it to yards, feet and inches. You may need to use the Frac function. (Check: 3.51 metres converts to 3 yds 2 ft 6.19 in.)

4.2 Write some Turbo Pascal statements which will:

(a) Find the length C of the hypotenuse of a right-angle triangle in terms of the lengths A and B of the other two sides;

(b) find the length C of a side of a triangle given the lengths A and B of the other two sides and the size in degrees of the included angle *Theta,* using the cosine rule;

4.3 Translate the following formulae into Turbo Pascal expressions:

(a) $\log(x + x^2 + a^2)$

(b) $[e^{3t} + t^2\sin(4t)] \cos^2(3t)$

(c) $4 \tan^{-1} (1)$

(d) $\sec^2(x) + \cot(y)$

(e) $\cot^{-1} (|x/a|)$

4.4 A sphere of mass m_1 impinges obliquely on a stationary sphere of mass m_2, the direction of the blow making an angle a with the line of motion of the impinging sphere. If the coefficient of restitution is e it can be shown that the impinging sphere is deflected through an angle ß such that

$$\tan(ß) = \frac{m_2(1 + e)\tan(a)}{(m_1 - em_2) + (m_1 + m_2)\tan^2(a)}$$

Write a program to read values of m_1, m_2, e, and a (in degrees) and to compute the angle ß in degrees.

4.5 A bond (mortgage loan) of amount L is obtained to buy a house. The interest rate r is 15% (0.15) per annum compounded monthly. The fixed monthly payment P which will pay off the bond exactly over N years is given by the formula

$$P = \frac{Lr(1 + r/12)^{12N}}{12[(1 + r/12)^{12N} - 1]}$$

(a) Write a program to compute P if L = \$50000 and N = 20 years.
Hint: use the **Power** function defined above. You should get an answer of \$658,39.

(b) It's interesting to see how the payment P changes with the period N over which you pay the loan. Run the program for different values of N. See if you can find a value of N for which the payment is less than \$625.

(c) Now go back to having N fixed at 20 years, and examine the effect of different interest rates. (Remember that the interest rate is a decimal, ie 16% is 0.16). You should see that raising the interest rate by 1% increases the monthly payment by about \$37.

4.6 It's useful to be able to work out how the period of a loan repayment changes if you increase or decrease your monthly payment P. The formula for the number of years N to repay the loan is given by

$$N = (1/12) \log(P / (P - Lr/12)) / \log(1 + r/12)$$

(a) Write a new program to compute this formula. How long will it take to pay off the loan of \$50000 at \$800 a month if the interest remains at 15%? (10.2 years – nearly twice as fast as when paying \$658!)

(b) Use this program to find out by trial-and-error the smallest monthly payment that can be made to pay the loan off – ever. (Hint: it is not possible to find the logarithm of a negative number.)

5 Decisions

Apart from its ability to add numbers extremely quickly, a computer's other major attribute is to be able to make decisions, as we saw briefly in Chapter 2. It is this facility which gives the computer its great problem-solving power. The fundamental decision-making construct in Turbo Pascal is the **if** statement, of which the **case** statement is another form.

5.1 THE if STATEMENT

We have seen some simple examples of the **if-then-else** statement already. Further examples, which become more involved, are given in this section.

Bending moment in a beam

A light uniform beam $0 < x < L$ is clamped with its ends at the same level, and carries a concentrated load W at $x = a$. The bending moment M at any point x along the beam is given by two different formulae, depending on the value of x relative to a, viz.

$$M = W(L - a)^2[aL - x(L + 2a)]/L^3 \qquad (0 \le x \le a),$$
$$M = Wa^2[aL - 2L^2 + x(3L - 2a)]/L^3 \qquad (a \le x \le L).$$

The following program extract computes the bending moment every metre along a 10 m beam, with a load of 100 Newtons at a point 8 metres from the end $x = 0$:

```
L:= 10;
L3:= L * L * L;
L2:= L * L;
W:= 100;
A:= 8;
A2:= A * A;

for X:= 0 to Round( L ) do
begin
  if X <= A then
    M:= W * Sqr( L - A ) / L3 * (A * L - X * (L + 2 * A))
  else
    M:= W * A2 / L3 * (A * L - 2 * L2 + X * (3 * L - 2 * A));
  Writeln( X:2, M:10:2 )
end;
```

Top of the class

A class of students write a test, and each student's name and mark is entered in a data file, with at least 20 columns reserved for the name. Assume there are no negative marks. We want to write a program which writes out the name of the student with the highest mark, together with his/her mark. We are assuming that there is only *one* highest mark. The problem of what to do when two or more students share the top mark is discussed in Chapter 9.

A first level structure plan for this problem could be:

1. Start
2. Find top student and top mark
3. Write top student and top mark.

Step 2 needs elaborating, so a more detailed plan might be:

1. Start
2. Initialize *TopMark* (to get process going)
3. Repeat 50 times:
   3.1. Read *Name* and *Mark*
   3.2. If *Mark* > *TopMark* then
      3.2.1. Replace *TopMark* with *Mark*
      3.2.2. Replace *TopName* with *Name*
4. Write *TopName* and *TopMark*
5. Stop.

The program (for a sample class of 3 students) is:

```
...
const
  TopMark        : real = 0;          { top mark: can't be less than zero }
var
  I              : integer;           { student counter }
  Mark           : real;              { general mark }
  Name           : string[20];        { general name }
  TopName        : string[20];        { top student }
  Data           : text;
begin
  Assign( Data, 'MARKS.' );
  Reset( Data );

  for I:= 1 to 3 do
  begin
    Readln( Data, Name, Mark );
    if Mark > TopMark then
    begin
      TopName:= Name:
      TopMark:= Mark
    end
  end;

  Writeln( 'Top student: ', TopName );
  Writeln( 'Top mark:', TopMark:7:0 );
...
```

Work through the program by hand for a few turns to convince yourself that it works. Try it out on the following sample data:

```
ABLE, E.R.        40
BAKER, M.D.       60
TUTU, A.B.        13
```

Nested else-ifs

Recall the final mark example in section 2.12. To write the grade of each student's final mark we used the following code:

```
if Fin >= 75 then
  Writeln( ' 1' );
if (Fin >= 70) and (Fin < 75) then
```

```
   Writeln( ' 2+' );
if (Fin >= 60) and (Fin < 70) then
   Writeln( ' 2-' );
if (Fin >= 50) and (Fin < 60) then
   Writeln( ' 3' );
if Fin < 50 then
   Writeln( ' FAIL' )
```

This is a little inefficient on computer time. There are actually five separate **if** statements. The Boolean expressions in all five (for example **Fin >= 75**) have to be evaluated for each student, although we know that only one can be true: a student cannot get a first class pass and also fail! The following is a more efficient way of coding the problem. For good measure, we will also count how many passed in the first class, how many in the second class, and so on. The variables **Firsts, UpSeconds, LowSeconds, Thirds** and **Fails** represent the number of students in each of these respective classes.

```
if Fin >= 75 then
   begin
      Writeln( ' 1' );
      Firsts:= Firsts + 1
   end
else
   if Fin >= 70 then
   begin
      Writeln( ' 2+' );
      UpSeconds:= UpSeconds + 1
   end
   else
      if Fin >= 60 then
      begin
         Writeln( ' 2-' );
         LowSeconds:= LowSeconds + 1
      end
      else
         if Fin >= 50 then
         begin
            Writeln( ' 3' );
            Thirds:= Thirds + 1
         end
      else
      begin
         Writeln( ' FAIL' );
         Fails:= Fails + 1
   end;
```

The escalator indentation helps to follow the logic. Turbo Pascal stops going down the escaltor as soon as it finds a true Booelan expression. So if **Fin >= 75** is true it won't bother to check further.

In general the nested **else-if** structure is as follows:

```
if Boolean1 then
   Statement1
else
   if Boolean2 then
      Statement2
   else
      if ... then
         ...
         ...
      else
         StatementE;
```

The action is as follows. If *Boolean1* (a Boolean expression, which may be either true or false) is true, *Statement1* (which may be compound, conditional, repetitive, etc) is executed, and Turbo Pascal then branches to the statement after *StatementE*. If *Boolean1* is false, *Boolean2* is examined. If it is true, *Statement2* is executed, followed by the statement after *StatementE*. In this way, each Boolean expression is examined, until one that is true is found. As soon as a true one is found, no further Boolean expressions are examined. If none of the conditions is true, *StatementE* after the final **else** is executed. The Boolean expressions should be arranged so that only one of them will be true at a time.

It is very important that there should never be a semi-colon before an **else** inside an **if.** Adding a semi-colon would imply a statement starting with **else**, since the semi-colons are statement separators, and Pascal does not have such a statement. It is good programming style to indent statements inside successive **if**s.

You may prefer the following layout to the escalator indentation above:

```
if Boolean1 then
   Statement1
else if Boolean2 then
   Statement2
else if ... then
   ...
   ...
else
   StatementE;
```

In general, **else** belongs to the most recent **if**, so Turbo Pascal interprets the statement

```
if e1 then if e2 then s1 else s2
```

as

```
if e1 then
begin
   if e2 then
      s1
   else
      s2
end
```

Statements may be enclosed with **begin-end** to change this interpretation if necessary, but be careful! The next example illustrates the importance of the correct use of **begin-end.**

In programming the solution of the ubiquitous quadratic equation

$$ax^2 + bx + c = 0,$$

it is necessary to check if $a = 0$, to prevent a division by zero:

```
Disc:= B * B - 4 * A * C;
if A <> 0 then
   if Disc < 0 then
      Writeln( 'Imaginary roots' )
   else
   begin
      X1:= ( - B + Sqrt( Disc ) ) / (2 * A);
      X2:= ( - B - Sqrt( Disc ) ) / (2 * A)
   end;
```

Inserting an extra **begin-end** as shown below, however, makes a division by zero certain if $a = 0$, because the **else** is now forced to belong to the first **if,** instead of to the second one by default:

```
Disc:= B * B - 4 * A * C;
if A <> 0 then
```

```
begin
if Disc < 0 then
  Writeln( 'Imaginary roots' )
end
else
begin
  X1:= ( - B + Sqrt( Disc ) ) / (2 * A);
  X2:= ( - B - Sqrt( Disc ) ) / (2 * A)
end;
```

Boolean expressions

These were mentioned briefly in Chapter 2, but need to be tidied up. Boolean expressions can only have the values **true** or **false**, and can be formed in two ways. The first is from arithmetic expressions in combination with the six **relational operators** shown below:

Relational Operator	*Meaning*
<	less than
<= (not =<)	less than or equal to
=	equal to
>= (not =>)	greater than or equal to
>	greater than
<> (not ><)	not equal to

A space may not be typed between parts of the two-character operators, ie you may not type < =.

Examples of Boolean expressions thus formed are:

```
I = J
K <> M
X + 4 >= 5 * Y
A <= 1E-5
B > Sin( X )
W + X < A - B
```

Boolean expressions may also be formed from boolean type variables and other Boolean expressions using the three **Boolean operators NOT, AND, OR** and **XOR.** Parentheses must enclose expressions on either side of Boolean operators. Examples are:

```
(B * B = 4 * A * C ) and (A <> 0)
(Fin >= 60) and (Fin < 70)
(A = 0) or (B = 0) or (C = 0)
(not (A = 0) or (B = C)) and (D > E)
```

The effects of these operators on two Boolean expressions *B1* and *B2* are shown in the following truth table (T = true; F = false):

B1	*B2*	**not** *B1*	*B1* **and** *B2*	*B1* **or** *B2*	*B1* **xor** *B2*
T	T	F	T	T	F
T	F	F	F	T	T
F	T	T	F	T	T
F	F	T	F	F	F

not reverses the truth value. **and** returns True only if both operands are True. **or** returns False only if both operands are False. **xor** returns False only if both operands have the same Boolean value.

The precedence of the Boolean operators is: (1) parentheses, (2) **not**, (3) **and**, (4) **or** and **xor**. So if *B1, B2* and *B3* are Boolean expressions, the following two expressions are logically equivalent:

B1 **and not** *B2* **or** *B3* (*B1* **and** (**not** *B2*)) **or** *B3*

The following two expressions are also equivalent, and are false only when **A** = **B** = **C** = 0:

```
(A <> 0) or (B <> 0) or (C <> 0)
not( (A = 0) and (B = 0) and (C = 0))
```

It makes you think, doesn't it?

Turbo Pascal always short-circuits the evaluation of complex Boolean expressions once their truth value is known. For example, in

(1 = 1) or (3 + 2 = 6)

the truth value of **(3 + 2 = 6)** is not computed since **(1 = 1)** is true, and **or** makes the whole expression true whatever follows. A program can therefore often be speeded up by re-arranging the order of Boolean expressions. If complete evaluation is required, the {**$B+**} compiler directive must be used (see Appendix E).

Boolean variables may be output with **Write,** but not read in.

Logical or bitwise operators

The four Boolean operators **not, and, or** and **xor** may also operate on operands of all the integer types. In this context, the *Turbo Pascal Reference Guide* refers to them as **logical** operators. There are two additional logical operators: **SHL** (**SH**ift **L**eft) and **SHR** (**SH**ift **R**ight). These operators are also called **bitwise** operators because they act directly on the bit pattern of the operands.

shl and **shr** are the easiest to understand. They simply move the bits in the operand left or right the specified number of positions. Since shifting all the bits of an integer one position to the left multiplies it by 2, this provides a very fast means of multiplying by powers of 2. Conversely, shifting right divides by 2. For example,

I shl 4

moves all the bits in **I** (integer type) four positions to the left, ie multiplies it by 16.

not flips all the bits in its integer operand.

and, or and **xor** operate between corresponding bits of operands (ie first bit with first bit, second with second, etc) in the sense that 0 is False and 1 is True. So (in binary) 1001 **and** 1100 returns 1000.

Simulating a switching circuit

In the following program segment the boolean variables **S1** and **S2** represent the state of two switches (ON = True, OFF = False) and **L** represents the state of a light. The program simulates the circuits in Figure 5.1, where the switches are arranged either in series or in parallel.

```
...
var
  L, S1, S2 : boolean;
begin
  S1:= True;
  S2:= not S1;
  L:= S1 and S2;          { series }
  (* L:= S1 or S2;        { parallel } *)
  Writeln( L );
...
```

When the switches are in series, the light will be on only if both switches are on. This situation is represented by **S1 and S2.** When the switches are in parallel, the light will be on if at least one of the switches is on. This is represented by **S1 or S2.**

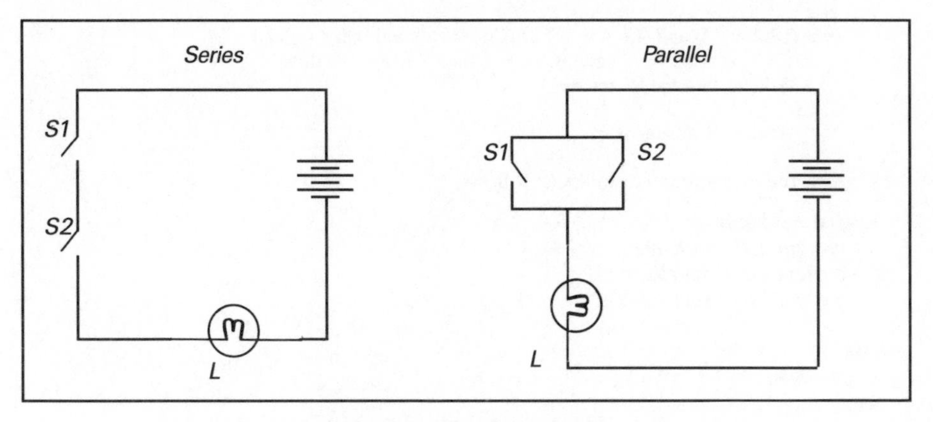

Figure 5.1 Switching circuits

5.2 THE case STATEMENT

The **case** statement is also conditional and enables a program to decide between a number of situations or cases based on a selector of ordinal type. In such cases, it is more convenient than **if.** Consider the following program segment:

```
var
   Ch : char;
begin
   readln( Ch );
   if Ord( Ch ) < 32 then
   Writeln( 'Control character' )
else
   case UpCase( Ch ) of
      'A', 'E', 'I', 'O', 'U': Writeln( 'Vowel' );
      '0'..'9': Writeln( 'Digit' );
      ' '..'/': Writeln( 'Special character' );
      ':'..'@': Writeln( 'Special character' );
      '['..'`': Writeln( 'Special character' );
      '{'..' ■ ': Writeln( 'Special character' );
   else
      Writeln( 'Consonant' )
   end;
...
```

It decides whether a character read at the keyboard is a control character (ASCII code of 31 or less), vowel, digit, consonant or special character (anything else). **UpCase** converts letters to uppercase and has no effect on any other characters.

Rewriting this with **if**s produces a lot more code, which is much harder to read:

```
Ch:= ReadKey;
Ch:= UpCase( Ch );
if Ord( Ch ) < 32 then
   Writeln( 'Control character' )
else
   if (Ch = 'A') or (Ch = 'E') or (Ch = 'I')
               or (Ch = 'O') or (Ch = 'U') then
      Writeln( 'Vowel' )
   else
      if (Ch >= '0') and (Ch <= '9') then
         Writeln( 'Digit' )
```

```
    else
      if (Ch >= ' ') and (Ch <= '/') or (Ch >= ':') and (Ch <= '@')
              or (Ch >= '[') and (Ch <= '`') or (Ch >= '{') then
        Writeln( 'Special Character' )
      else
        Writeln( 'Consonant' );
```

In general, the **case** statement looks as follows:

case *case selector* **of**
  constant list1 : statement1;
  constant list2 : statement2;
  constant list3 : statement3;
  ...
else
  statement
end;

The case selector may be of any byte- or word-sized ordinal type. *Constant list* may be a single constant, a range, or a list. The constants in the lists must be of an ordinal type compatible with the selector type. The statement corresponding to the constant list in which the selector falls is executed. If no match is found, the statement in the **else** part is executed. The **else** part is optional.

The selection of grades in the final mark program of the previous section can also be programmed with a **case** statement, if the mark is first converted to an integer variable **Mark**:

```
Mark:= Trunc( Fin );
case Mark of
  75..100  : begin
               Firsts:= Firsts + 1;
               Writeln( ' 1' )
             end;
  70..74   : begin
               UpSeconds:= UpSeconds + 1;
               Writeln( ' 2+' )
             end;
  60..69   : begin
               LowSeconds:= LowSeconds + 1;
               Writeln( ' 2-' )
             end;
  50..59   : begin
               Thirds:= Thirds + 1;
               Writeln( ' 3' )
             end;
else
             begin
               Fails:= Fails + 1;
               Writeln( ' F' )
             end;
end;
```

The **case** statement is useful for menu selection programs. The user is presented with a number of choices, which are usually indicated by single letters. A **case** statement can be used to choose the appropriate action, for example:

```
...
uses Crt;
var
  Ch : char;
begin
  Ch:= ReadKey;
```

```
      case UpCase( Ch ) of
        'L': Load;
        'R': Run;
        'X': Exit;
        ...
      else
        Writeln( 'Try again!' )
      end;
...
```

Note that **ReadKey** (**Crt** unit) can be used to read a character from the keyboard without it being echoed (displayed) on the screen.

Summary

- Boolean expressions can only have one of two values: true or false.
- Boolean expressions are formed from arithmetic expressions with relational operators (<, <=, =, <>, >, >=).
- The Boolean operators (**not**, **and**, **or**, **xor**) may be used to form more complex Boolean expressions from other Boolean expressions.
- The Boolean operators together with **shl** and **shr** are called bitwise operators when they operate on the bit representation of integers.
- The **if-then-else** and **case** conditional statements may be used to choose between alternative actions.

EXERCISES

5.1 Write a program which reads two numbers (which may be equal) and writes out the larger one with a suitable message, or if they are equal, writes out a message to that effect.

5.2 Write a structure plan and program for the following problem: read 10 integers and write out how many of them are positive, negative or zero. Write the program with an **if** statement, and then rewrite it using a **case** statement.

5.3 Design an algorithm (draw the flowchart or structure plan) for a machine which must give the correct amount of change from a \$10 note for any purchase costing less than \$10. The plan must specify the number and type of all notes and coins in the change, and should in all cases give as few notes and coins as possible.

5.4 Write a program for the general solution of the quadratic equation

$$ax^2 + bx + c = 0.$$

Use the structure plan developed in Chapter 3. Your program should be able to handle all possible values of the data a, b, and c. Try it out on the following values of a, b and c:

(a) 1 1 1 (imaginary roots);
(b) 2 4 2 (equal roots of −1.0);
(c) 2 2 −12 (roots of 2.0 and −3.0).

5.5 Develop a structure plan for the solution of two simultaneous linear equations (ie two straight lines). Your algorithm must be able to handle all possible situations, viz lines which are intersecting, parallel, or co-incident. Write a program to implement your algorithm, and test it on some equations for which you know the solutions, for example

$$x + y = 3$$
$$2x - y = 3$$

($x = 2, y = 1$). Hint: begin by deriving an algebraic formula for the solution of the system

$$ax + by = c$$
$$dx + ey = f.$$

The program should read the coefficients a, b, c, d, e and f.

6 Loops

We have already seen some examples of the powerful **for** construct, which is used to execute a block of statements repeatedly. This type of structure, where the number of repetitions must be determined in advance, is sometimes called **deterministic repetition.** However, it often happens that the condition to end a repeat structure **(loop)** is only satisfied during the execution of the loop itself. This type of repeat structure is called **non-deterministic.** This chapter is really about non-deterministic loops, but to make the transition we will first look at some more examples of **for** loops.

6.1 DETERMINISTIC REPETITION

Factorials!

The control variable in a **for** loop may be used in any expression inside the loop, as long as its value is not changed. The following program writes a table of n and $n!$ (spoken as n factorial, or n shriek), where

$$n! = 1\times 2\times 3\times \ldots \times (n-1)\times n .$$

```
program Factor;
{$N+}
const
  Fact : comp = 1;
var
  N : integer;

begin
  for N:= 1 to 20 do
  begin
    Fact:= N * Fact;
    Writeln( N:3, Fact:30:0 )
  end;
...
```

Since factorials can get rather large, comp type is used. This requires the **{$N+}** compiler directive to switch to 8087 mode (see Appendix E).

The Binomial coefficient

This is widely used in statistics. The number of ways of choosing r objects out of n without regard to order is given by:

$$\binom{n}{r} = \frac{n!}{r!(n-r)!} = \frac{n(n-1)(n-2)\ldots(n-r+1)}{r!},$$

e.g. $$\binom{10}{3} = \frac{10!}{3!\times 7!} = \frac{10\times 9\times 8}{1\times 2\times 3}.$$

If the first form is used, the numbers involved can get very big, and there could be an overflow. But using the form on the right is much more efficient:

```
program Binom;
const
  Bin : longint = 1;
var
  K, N, R : word;
begin
  Write( 'N and R? ' );
  Readln( N, R );

  for K:= 1 to R do
    Bin:= Bin * (N - K + 1) div K;
  Writeln( 'NcR:', Bin:10 );
...
```

Computing the limit of a sequence

for loops are ideal for computing successive members of a sequence. This example also highlights a problem that sometimes occurs when computing a limit. Consider the sequence

$$x_n = a^n/n!,\ n = 1, 2, 3, \ldots$$

where a is any constant, and $n!$ is the factorial function defined above. The question is: what is the limit of this sequence as n gets indefinitely large? Let's take the case $a = 10$. If we try to compute x_n directly we could get into trouble, because $n!$ gets large very rapidly as n increases, and a machine overflow could occur. However, the situation is neatly transformed if we spot that x_n is related to x_{n-1} as follows:

$$x_n = ax_{n-1}/n\ .$$

There are no overflow problems now. The following program computes x_n for $a = 10$, and increasing values of n, and writes it for every tenth value of n:

```
program Limit;
const
  X : real = 1;
var
  A : real;
  N : word;
begin
  A:= 10;

  for N:= 1 to 100 do
  begin
    X:= A * X / N;
    if N mod 10 = 0 then
      Writeln( N:3, '      ', X:12 )
  end;
...
```

The output is as follows:

```
 10   2.75573E+03
 20   4.11032E+01
 30   3.76999E-03
 40   1.22562E-08
 50   3.28795E-15
 60   1.20178E-22
 70   8.34824E-31
 80   0.00000E+00
 90   0.00000E+00
100   0.00000E+00
```

From these results it appears that the limit is zero, and this may be proved mathematically.

Nested for loops: the telephone

for loops may be **nested** inside each other. The control variable of the innermost loop moves fastest. It is best to label **begin-end** pairs in the loops according to the loop's control variable. This example imitates the ringing of a certain type of telephone (don't leave out the **NoSound** statements!):

```
program Phone;
uses Crt;
var
  Ring, I: word;
begin

  for Ring:= 1 to 8 do            { ring 8 times }
  begin { Ring }

    for I:= 1 to 30 do            { each ring = 30 alternations }
    begin { I }
      Sound( 600 );               { 600 Hz for 0.03 sec }
      Delay( 30 );
      NoSound;
      Sound( 1500 );              { 1500 Hz for 0.03 sec }
      Delay( 30 );
      NoSound
    end; { I }

    Delay( 2000 )
  end { Ring }

end.
```

The for statement in general

In general, the **for** statement has two forms:

for *I*:= *Expr1* to *Expr2* **do**
  Body;

or

for *I*:= *Expr1* **downto** *Expr2* **do**
  Body;

The **control variable** *I* must be of ordinal type. The initial and final values of *I* are determined from *Expr1* and *Expr2* (which must be assignment-compatible with *I*) once and for all when the **for** is entered. The statements in the compound statement *Body* are executed each time as *I* is incremented (with **to**) or decremented (with **downto**) by one, while moving from its initial to final value. In the case of **to,** if the initial value of *I* is greater than its final value, or in the case of **downto,** if the initial value is less than the final value, *Body* is not executed at all.

Note that the value of the control variable *I* should not be changed by a statement in *Body*. Because the control variable can be of any ordinal type, the incrementation in a **for** loop is through the ordinal values of the control variable. So the following piece of code, where **Ch** is of type char, writes the alphabet:

```
for Ch:= 'a' to 'z' do Write( Ch );
```

6.2 NON-DETERMINISTIC REPETITION

The number of loops executed by a **for** statement is determined in advance of its first execution by Turbo Pascal, and therefore must be known in principle by the programmer. This is sometimes a little tricky to work out – most bugs are caused by loops that repeat one time too few or one time too many.

Vertical motion again

Recall the vertical motion problem in section 2.6. Suppose we want to write the stone's displacement at regular half-second intervals for a period of 10 seconds. If we want output at the start as well, this means we need precisely 21 repeats ($1 + 2 \times 10$). So the problem could be coded with a **for** statement as follows:

```
program Vertical;
const
  G = 9.8;
  T : real = 0;                  { initial value }
  U : real = 60;                 {       "          }
var
  I : word;
  S : real;
begin
  Writeln( ' Time          Displacement' );
  Writeln;

  for I:= 1 to 21 do
  begin
    S:= U * T - G / 2 * Sqr( T );
    Writeln( T:5:2, S:10:2 );
    T:= T + 0.5
  end

end.
```

If you run this example, you will see that the stone goes up and comes down during this period. Use trial-and-error to find out more precisely when the stone reaches the ground again.

Now, as an experiment, make *one* change to this program. Replace the line

```
for I:= 1 to 21 do
```

with

```
while T <= 10 do
```

and run it. You should get the same results. Now suppose you wanted to vary the output interval (0.5 seconds at the moment). Replace

```
T:= T + 0.5
```

with

```
T:= T + Dt
```

where **Dt** represents the output interval. Remember to declare **Dt** real. Give it a value of 0.25 and run the program again. The point about introducing the new **while** statement is that you no longer have to hassle over precisely how many repeats you want. In plain English, you want the calculation of **S** repeated as long as (while) **T <= 10 seconds**. As far as Turbo Pascal is concerned, the loop is now non-deterministic: it does *not* know in advance of the **while** how many repeats to make (you may have a shrewd idea, but that's beside the point).

The general form of the while-do statement

In general the **while** statement looks like this:

while *condition* **do**
  Body;

The **while** construct repeats the (compound) statement *Body* ***while*** its (Boolean) *condition* ***remains*** true. The condition therefore is the condition to repeat ***again***. The condition is tested each time before *Body* is repeated. Since the condition is at the head of the loop, it is therefore possible to arrange for *Body* not be executed at all under certain circumstances.

Simulating for with non-unit increments

The control variable in a **for** loop may only be increased or decreased by one at each repeat. Increments other than unity may be simulated with **while.** The following program shows how this may be done with four examples:

1) **I** from 2 to 7 in steps of 2;
2) **I** from 5 to 4 in steps of 1;
3) **I** from 5 to 1 in steps of -1;
4) **I** from 6 to 2 in steps of -2.

```
var
  I, Step : integer;
begin
  Step:= 2;
  I:= 2;
while I <= 7 do                    { 2 to 7 in steps of 2 }
  begin
    Write( I:3 );
    I:= I + Step
  end;
  Writeln;

  Step:= 1;
  I:= 5;
  while I <= 4 do                  { 5 to 4 in steps of 1 }
  begin
    Write( I:3 );
    I:= I + Step
  end;
  Writeln;

  Step:= -1;
  I:= 5;
  while I >= 1 do                  { 5 to 1 in steps of -1 }
  begin
    Write( I:3 );
    I:= I + Step
  end;
  Writeln;
  Step:= -2;
  I:= 6;
  while I >= 1 do                  { 6 to 1 in steps of -2 }
  begin
    Write( I:3 );
    I:= I + Step
  end;
  Writeln;
```

Output:

```
2   4   6

5   4   3   2   1
6   4   2
```

The variable *I* is no longer strictly a control variable. It is better to call it a **counter.**

In general (positive steps):

```
I:= First;
while I <= Last do
begin
  Body;
  I:= I + Step
end
```

```
or (negative steps
I:= First;
while I >= Last do
begin
  Body;
  I:= I + Step
end
```

Nested while loops: loan repayments

The regular fixed payment *P*, made *n* times a year, to repay a loan of amount *A* over a period of *k* years, where the nominal annual interest rate is *r*, is given by

$$P = (r/n)A(1 + r/n)^{nk}/[(1 + r/n)^{nk} - 1].$$

The next program uses nested **while** loops to write a table of the repayments on a loan of $1000 over 15, 20 or 25 years, at interest rates that vary from 10% to 20% per annum. Since the formula is linear in the amount of the loan, the repayments on a loan of any amount may be found from the table generated by the program, by simple proportion. The program needs the exponentiation function **Power** developed in section 4.5. This may either be copied into the program after the **uses** statement, or the **{$I}** compiler directive may be used. The effect of this is to copy the contents of the named file (POWER – extension .PAS is assumed) from the logged disk drive during compilation.

```
program Bond;
uses Crt;
{$I POWER}
const
  A : real = 1000;              { principal }
  N : byte = 12;                { number of payments per year }
var
  K, P, Rate, X : real;
begin
  ClrScr;
  Writeln( 'Rate      15 yrs      20 yrs      25 yrs' );
  Writeln;
  Rate:= 0.1;
  while Rate <= 0.2 do          { loop on interest rate }
  begin { Rate }
    Write( 100 * Rate:3:0, '%' );
    K:= 15;
    while K <= 25 do            { loop on period of repayment }
    begin { K }
      X:= Power( 1 + Rate / N, N * K );
      P:= Rate / N * A * X / (X - 1);
      Write( P:9:2 );
      K:= K + 5
    end { K };
    Writeln;
    Rate:= Rate + 0.01
  end { Rate }
end.
```

The output is:

```
Rate     15 yrs     20 yrs     25 yrs
10%      10.75      9.65       9.09
11%      11.37      10.32      9.80
...
19%      16.83      16.21      15.98
20%      17.56      16.99      16.78
```

A guessing game

The examples of **while** loops so far have not really been non-deterministic. We could in principle have worked out how many repeats to make, and we could with some ingenuity have programmed all the situations with **for.** But in the next problem, there is no way *in principle* of knowing how many repeats are required, so **for** *cannot* be used.

The problem is easy to state. Turbo Pascal thinks of an integer between 1 and 10 (ie generates one at random). You have to guess it. If your guess is too high or too low, the program must say so. If your guess is correct, a message of congratulations must be displayed.
A little more thought is required here, so a structure plan might be helpful:

1. Generate random integer
2. Ask user (assumed male) for guess
3. While guess is wrong repeat:
   3.1. If guess is too low then
   3.1.1. Tell him it is too low
   Otherwise
   3.1.2. Tell him it is too high
   3.2. Ask him for another guess
4. Polite congratulations
5. Stop.

Before we look at the whole program let's see how the random integer is generated by the statement

```
TPNum:= Trunc( 10 * Random + 1 );
```

Since **Random** is a decimal number in the range [0; 1), **(10 * Random)** will be in the range [0; 10), and **(10 * Random** + 1) will be in the range [1; 11), ie between 1.000000 and 10.999999 inclusive. Using **Trunc** on this will then give an integer in the range 1 to 10, as required.

```
program Guess;
var
  TPNum, MyGuess: word;
begin
  Randomize;
  TPNum:= Trunc( 10 * Random + 1 );
  Write( 'Your guess? ' );
  Readln( MyGuess );

  while MyGuess <> TPNum do
  begin
    if MyGuess < TPNum then
      Write( 'Too low. Try again. ' )
    else
      Write( 'Too high. Try again. ' );
    Writeln( 'Your guess? ' );
    Readln( MyGuess )
  end;

  Writeln( 'BINGO! Well done!' )
end.
```

Try it out a few times. Note that the **while** loop repeats as long as **MyGuess** is not equal to **TPNum.** There is no way of knowing in principle how many loops will be needed before they are equal, and so the **while** construct is essential here. The problem is truly non-deterministic.

On reflection, you might feel the coding is a little wasteful. The section

```
Write( 'Your guess? ' );
Readln( MyGuess );
```

has to appear twice. Once, to start the loop going (or **MyGuess** would not have a meaningful value), and a second time in the loop itself. Change the program as indicated below and try running it (the main changes are highlighted)

```
...
TPNum:= Trunc( 10 * Random + 1 );
repeat
  Writeln( 'Your guess? ' );
  Readln( MyGuess );
  if MyGuess < TPNum then
    Write( 'Too low. Try again. ' )
  else
    if MyGuess > TPNum then
      Write( 'Too high. Try again. ' )
    else
      Writeln( 'BINGO! Well done!' )
until MyGuess = TPNum;
```

The new **repeat-until** statement introduced here is similar in concept to **while-do.** The essential difference is that the statements in the **repeat** loop *must* be executed at least once, whereas in a **while** loop they may never be executed. In this example, since the user must guess at least once, it is more natural to use **repeat-until.**

The equivalent structure plan for this problem is:

1. Generate random integer
2. Repeat:
   2.1. Ask user for guess
   2.2. If guess is too low then
        2.2.1. Tell him it is too low
        Otherwise
        2.2.2. If guess is too high then
               2.2.2.1. Tell him it is too high
               Otherwise
               2.2.2.2. Guess is correct
   Until guess is correct
3. Stop.

The essential difference is that the **repeat** construct loops ***until*** a condition ***becomes*** true, whereas the **while** construct loops ***while*** a condition ***remains*** true.

The general form of the repeat-until statement

In general the **repeat** statement looks like this:

```
repeat
  Body
until condition;
```

The **repeat-until** construct repeats ***until*** its condition ***becomes*** true. The condition is therefore the condition to ***stop*** repeating. The condition is tested after each repeat before making another repeat. Since the condition is at the *end* of the loop, the body of the loop will always be executed *at least once*. **repeat-until** is useful for programming menu selection, where the menu is always presented at least once.

Note that *Body* does not need to be enclosed with **begin-end.**

repeat *versus* while

A problem coded with **while** can logically always be rewritten with **repeat,** and vice versa. The question then arises, when should we use **while,** and when should we use **repeat**? This is largely a matter of taste. There is a large body of opinion among programmers which maintains that it is good programming style for conditions under which loops are repeated to be stated at the *beginning* of the loop. This favours the **while** construct, since its condition is stated at the beginning. However, in situations where at least one repeat must be made, it often seems more natural to use the **repeat** construct.

Doubling time of an investment

Suppose we have invested some money which draws 10% interest per year, compounded. We would like to know how long it takes for the investment to double. More specifically, we want a statement of the account each year, *until* the balance has doubled. The English statement of the problem hints heavily that we should use **repeat-until.** The structure plan and program for the problem are:

1. Start
2. Initialise balance, year, rate, interest
3. Write headings
4. Repeat
   4.1. Update balance according to interest rate
   4.2. Write year, interest, balance
   Until balance exceeds twice original balance
5. Stop.

```
program Double;
var
  Year : integer;
  Interest, Old, New, Rate: real;
begin
  Write( 'Original balance: ' );
  Readln( Old );
  Rate:= 0.1;
  New:= Old;                    { keep a copy of the original balance }
  Year:= 0;
  Writeln( 'Year      Interest      Balance' );
  Writeln;

  repeat
    Interest:= Rate * New;
    New:= New + Interest;
    Year:= Year + 1;
    Writeln( Year:3, Interest:10:2, New:12:2 )
  until New > 2 * Old
end.
```

The condition **New > 2 * Old** is checked each time before the body of the loop is repeated. Repetition occurs only if the condition is true. The body of the loop must be executed at least once, since you must invest your money for at least a year for anything to happen. The output looks like this (for an opening balance of $1000):

Year	Interest	Balance
1	100.00	1100.00
2	110.00	1210.00
3	121.00	1331.00
4	133.10	1464.10
5	146.41	161
6	161.05	1771.56
7	177.16	1948.72
8	194.87	2143.59

Note that when the last loop finishes, the condition is true for the first time, since the new balance ($2143.59) is more than $2000. Note also that a **for** loop *cannot* be used here because we don't know how many repeats are going to be needed (eight in this case) until after the program has run.

If you want to write the new balance only while it is less than $2000, all that has to be done is that the statement

```
Writeln( Year:3, Interest:10:2, New:12:2 )
```

must be moved until it is the first statement in the **repeat** loop (try it). Note that the starting balance of zero is written now.

The original **repeat-until** can be replaced by a **while-do** as follows:

```
while New < 2 * Old do
  begin
  Interest:= Rate * New;
  New:= New + Interest;
  Year:= Year + 1;
  Writeln( Year:3, Interest:10:2, New:12:2 )
end;
```

Try this also. Either form is acceptable, although as mentioned above, the purists might prefer the **while-do** version, since this states the condition for repeating clearly at the beginning of the loop. This condition is immediately apparent to anyone reading the program: you do not have to search for the end of the loop to find the condition to stop repeating.

Prime numbers

Many people are obsessed with prime numbers, and most books on programming have to include a program to test if a given number is prime. So here's mine. A number is prime if it is not an exact multiple of any other number except itself and unity, ie if it has no factors except itself and unity. The easiest plan of attack then is as follows. Suppose P is the number to be tested. See if any numbers N can be found that divide into P without remainder. If there are none, P is prime. Which numbers N should we try? Well, we can speed things up by restricting P to odd numbers, so we only have to try odd divisors N. When do we stop testing? When $N = P$? No – we can stop a lot sooner. In fact, we can stop once N reaches $\sqrt{P}$, since if there is a factor greater than $\sqrt{P}$ there must be a corresponding one less than $\sqrt{P}$, which we would have found. And where do we start? Well, since $N = 1$ will be a factor of any P, we should start at $N = 3$. The structure plan is as follows:

1. Read P
2. Initialise N to 3
3. Find remainder *Rem* when P is divided by N
4. While *Rem* <> 0 and $N < \sqrt{P}$ repeat
   4.1. Increase N by 2
   4.2. Find *Rem* when P is divided by N
5. If *Rem* <> 0 then
   5.1. P is prime
   Else
   5.2. P is not prime
6. Stop.

Note that a **while** loop is going to be used because there might be no repeats – *Rem* might be zero the first time. Note also that there are *two* conditions under which the loop will stop. An **if** is required after completion of the loop to determine which condition stopped it.

Here's the program:

```
program Prime;
{ tests if an odd integer is prime }
const
  N        : word = 3;
var
  P, Rem   : longint;
  SqrtP    : real;
begin
  Write( 'Gimme an odd integer: ' );
  Readln( P );
  Rem:= P mod N;
  SqrtP:= Sqrt( P );

  while (Rem <> 0) and (N < Trunc( SqrtP )) do
  begin
    N:= N + 2;
```

```
      Rem:= P mod N
    end;

    if Rem <> 0 then
      Writeln( P, ' is prime' )
    else
      Writeln( P, ' is not prime' )
  end.
```

Try it out on the following: 4058879 (not prime), 193707721 (prime) and 2147483647 (**MaxLongint** – prime). If such things interest you, the largest prime number I am aware of is $2^{132049}-1$. It has 39233 digits and takes about five pages to print. You can have a copy of it if you send me an addressed envelope (my address is in the last program of section 16.6). Obviously this program cannot test such a large number, since it's greater than **MaxLongint.** Ways of testing such huge numbers for primality are described in Knuth (1981).

Testing for more data

The next program reads an unknown number of experimental observations from a disk file B:EXP and computes their mean:

```
...
const
  Num     : word = 0;
  Sum     : real = 0;
var
  Mean    : real;
  X       : real;
  F       : text;
begin
  Assign( F, 'B:EXP.' );
  Reset( F );
  while not Eof( F ) do
  begin
    Read( F, X );
    Sum:= Sum + X;
    Num:= Num + 1
  end;
  if Num > 0 then
  begin
    Mean:= Sum / Num;
    Writeln( 'Mean value of ', Num, ' readings: ', Mean:6:2 )
  end
  else
    Writeln( 'No readings, no mean!' );
  close( F );
...
```

The Boolean function **Eof(F)** is only true when the last item in the file **F** has been read (**E**nd **O**f **F**ile). There is a special **end-of-file marker (Ctrl-Z)** at the end of text files (including the standard file **Input** from the keyboard). So to adjust the program to read from the keyboard, delete the references to the file **F**, and type **Ctrl-Z** followed by **Enter** when you have finished entering data:

```
while not Eof do
begin
  Read( X );
  Sum:= Sum + X;
  Num:= Num + 1
end;
```

Taylor series for sine

You may have wondered how a computer calculates functions such as sine and cosine. Really ancient computers actually used to look up tables entered in memory, but young and upwardly mobile ones are more cunning. Mathematically, it can be shown that sin(x), for example, is the sum of an infinite series (called a Taylor series), as follows:

$$\sin(x) = x - x^3/3! + x^5/5! - x^7/7! + \ldots$$

We obviously can't compute the sum of an infinite series (why not?), but we can at least arrange to stop after the terms in the series are all less than some prescribed value, say 1E−6. It can be shown that we can always get a term less than some arbitrarily small number by going far enough in the Taylor series. As an exercise you should try to draw a flowchart or structure plan before studying the program below. The main idea here is to construct each term in the series from the previous one, as described in the limit example above. In constructing the denominator each time, use has been made of the fact that if k is any integer, $2k$ is even and $2k+1$ is odd. So if $k = 0$ labels the first term (x), the second term (labelled by $k = 1$) can be obtained from the first term by multiplying it by:

$$\frac{-x^2}{2k(2k+1)}$$

Work out the first few terms by hand as a check. The program is as follows:

```
program Taylor;
{ computes sine(x) with Taylor series }
const
  Err        : real = 1E-6;        { max error allowed }
  K          : word = 1;           { term counter }
  MaxTerms   = 10;                 { max number of terms }

var
  Sine       : real;               { sum of series }
  Term       : real;               { general term in series }
  X          : real;               { angle in radians }
begin
  Write( 'Angle in degrees: ' );
  Readln( X );
  X:= X * Pi / 180;                { convert to radians }
  Term:= X;                      { first term in series }
  Sine:= Term;

  while (Abs( Term ) > Err) and (K <= MaxTerms) do
  begin
    Term:= - Term * Sqr( X ) / (2 * K * (2 * K + 1) );
    K:= K + 1;
    Sine:= Sine + Term
  end;

  if Abs( Term ) > Err then
    Writeln( 'Series did not converge' );
  Writeln( 'After ', K, ' terms Taylor series gives', Sine:12:8 );
  Writeln( 'Turbo Pascal standard function gives', Sin( X ):12:8)
end.
```

A **while** loop is appropriate because the initial term might be small enough (in which case k will still be 1, not having been updated in the loop). Algorithms such as this can be used to compute other standard functions on calculators and computers.

At this stage it should be pointed out that some programmers (definitely the minority!) might use a **for** loop with a **goto** statement to escape from it when **Term** is small enough:

```
program Taylor;
{ computes sine(x) with Taylor series }
label
  99;
...
  Term:= X;                        { first term in series }
```

```
      Sine:= Term;

      for K:= 1 to MaxTerms do
      begin
        if Abs( Term ) <= Err then
          goto 99;
        Term:= - Term * Sqr( X ) / (2 * K * (2 * K + 1) );
        Sine:= Sine + Term
      end;

      if Abs( Term ) > Err then
        Writeln( 'Series did not converge' );
  99: Writeln( 'After ', K, ' terms Taylor series gives', Sine:12:8 );
  ...
```

As soon as the condition **Abs(Term) <= Err** is true, **goto 99** is executed, so control jumps to the **Writeln** statement labelled 99. This practice is ***not recommended***! The reason that it is frowned upon is that the second condition for terminating the loop is hidden inside the loop, and not apparent as you read the code from the top down.

The notorious goto statement

The statement

goto *there*;

transfers control immediately to the statement labelled *there*:

there: *statement*;

The label must be declared in the **label** part of the declarations at the beginning of the program:

label
  there;

It must be the first non-comment line in the program, unless there is a **uses** statement, in which case it must be the first non-comment line after **uses.** A label must be an unsigned number or an identifier.

The **goto** statement should be ***avoided at almost any cost!*** It is mentioned here only for completeness and historical interest. Ironically, the presence of **goto** in unstructured languages such as FORTRAN and Street (or gutter) BASIC was one of the motivating factors in the development of Pascal, which is a highly structured language. So don't use it!

Drawing a sine graph

It has been said that a picture is worth a thousand words. If you have a scientific or engineering interest in programming, you will be keen to draw some graphs. Turbo Pascal graphics is discussed in detail in Chapter 13, but it seems a pity to wait until then because we have at this stage covered enough Turbo Pascal to draw some quite impressive graphs, apart from the graphics statements themselves. The rest of this section will present some interesting graphics programs, without much explanation of the graphics statements – at this stage the emphasis will be on the algorithms that produce the graphs.

Before you can use any Turbo graphics you must have on your working Turbo Pascal disk the special **Graph** unit GRAPH.TPU, and the **graphics drivers,** which are files with the extension .BGI. These should have been copied over when you installed Turbo Pascal.

The first graphics example is to draw two complete cycles of a sine curve on the screen, ie we want to draw the graph of

$$y = \sin(x)$$

for $0 \leq x \leq 4\pi$. The x-axis will run horizontally from 0 to 4π, and the y-axis vertically from -2 to 2, so that the graph covers only half the vertical distance. Now here we have a slight problem, because the graphics screen is defined in terms of **pixels,** the smallest area which can be lit up. A screen typically has 200 pixels vertically and 640 horizontally (depending on the graphics card in the computer). So a conversion program needs to be written to convert our required horizontal range of 0 to 4π into 640 pixels.

Let's suppose we want the x co-ordinates in our problem to range between **Left** and **Right,** and the y co-ordinates to range between **Bottom** and **Top.** We will call these **world** co-ordinates. The following two functions, **ScaleH** and **ScaleV**, will scale the x (**H**orizontal) and y (**V**ertical) world co-ordinates into the correct pixel co-ordinates for your screen. How these functions actually work will be fully discussed in Chapter 13. The procedure **SetGraphics** initialises the graphics screen on your computer.

```
function ScaleH( X: real): integer;
{ scales X coordinate }
var
  TempX : real;
begin
  TempX:= GetMaxX * (X - Left) / (Right - Left);
  ScaleH:= Round( TempX )
end; { ScaleH }

function ScaleV( Y: real): integer;
{ scales Y coordinate }
var
  TempY : real;
begin
  TempY:= GetMaxY * (Y - Top) / (Bottom - Top);
  ScaleV:= Round( TempY )
end; { ScaleV }

procedure SetGraphics;
{ Initialises Graphics }
var
  GrDriver, GrMode, MaxX, MaxY: integer;
begin
  GrDriver:= Detect;
  InitGraph( GrDriver, GrMode, 'B:\GR' );
end; { SetGraphics }
```

The statement

InitGraph(GrDriver, GrMode, 'B:\GR');

in **SetGraphics** is very important. The string parameter of **InitGraph** must be the name of the drive (and directory) where the .BGI graphics drivers may be found. In this example, I am assuming that they are in the directory \GR on the disk in drive B. If they are in the logged (default) drive, the null string '' may be given. Otherwise an error will occur. **ScaleH**, **ScaleV** and **SetGraphics** should all be saved together in a disk file for use in the following graphics programs. Let's suppose they are saved under the name B:GRSCALE.PAS.

The following program uses these functions and procedure to draw the sine graph over the required range. Try it out.

```
program SineGraph;
uses Graph;
var
  X, Y, Left, Right, Bottom, Top : real;

{$I B:GRSCALE}

begin
  SetGraphics;
  Left:= 0;
  Right:= 4 * Pi;
  Bottom:= -2;
```

```
Top:= 2;
X:= 0;
Y:= 0;
MoveTo( ScaleH( X ), ScaleV( Y ) );

while X <= 4 * Pi do
begin
  Y:= Sin( X );
  LineTo( ScaleH( X ), ScaleV( Y ) );
  X:= X + Pi / 40
end;
   Readln;
   CloseGraph
   end.
```

Note that the program uses the **Graph** unit, and that the world co-ordinate ranges **Left, Right, Bottom** and **Top** *must* be declared real. The compiler directive

```
{$I B:GRSCALE}
```

ensures that the code for **ScaleH, ScaleV** and **SetGraphics** is included during compilation. The declaration of **Left, Right, Bottom** and **Top** *must come before* this directive, since they are used in the functions **ScaleH** and **ScaleV.**

The program must start by activating the **SetGraphics** procedure. You can then assign whatever values you like to **Left, Right, Bottom** and **Top.** For example, try enlarging the picture by changing **Bottom** to -1 and **Top** to 1.

The procedure

```
MoveTo( ScaleH( X ), ScaleV( Y ) );
```

moves the current pointer to the initial position (x, y) in world co-ordinates (without drawing a line, and without lighting up the pixel). The procedure

```
LineTo( ScaleH( X ), ScaleV( Y ) );
```

moves the current pointer to the position (x, y) drawing a line as it does. Points are plotted a distance $\pi/40$ apart.

The procedure **CloseGraph** (in the **Graph** unit) must be called before the end of the program to return Turbo Pascal to normal text mode, otherwise dire things can happen.

Play around with the program a bit, especially with the co-ordinate ranges. Incidentally, it doesn't matter if a point is plotted off the screen – it simply isn't seen. Try drawing other functions, like **Cos(X)** and **Exp(X).**

Projectile trajectory

The x and y co-ordinates of a projectile a time t after launch are given by

$$x = u \cos(a)t,$$
$$y = u \sin(a)t - 0.5gt^2,$$

where a is the angle of launch, g is the acceleration due to gravity and u is the launch velocity. We want to plot its trajectory on the screen during flight. Fortunately, there are convenient formulae for its maximum height and range, and time of flight. Using these we can be sure to fit the trajectory onto the graphics screen. The maximum height is:

$$u^2 \sin(a)^2 / (2g),$$

the maximum range is

$$u^2 \sin(2a)/g,$$

and the time of flight is

$$2u\sin(a)/g.$$

The program below allows the trajectory of a projectile launched at 60 m/s at an angle of 45° to cover the width of the screen but only half its height. The user is invited to input any *a* and *u*.

```
program Traj;
uses Graph;
const
  G   = 9.8;
  T   : real = 0;                { initial time }
  X   : real = 0;                { initial position }
  Y   : real = 0;
var
  Left, Right, Top, Bottom                 : real;
  Ang, MaxHt, MaxRange, MaxTime, U         : real;

{$I GrScale}

begin
  Ang:= Pi / 4;                  { angle for max range in radians }
  U:= 60;

  MaxHt:= Sqr( U ) * Sqr( Sin( Ang ) ) / (2 * G);
  Maxrange:= Sqr( U ) * Sin( 2 * Ang ) / G;

  Left:= 0;
  Right:= MaxRange;
  Bottom:= 0;
  Top:= 2 * MaxHt;
  Write( 'Give any positive angle in degrees, and a velocity less than
       60: ' );
  Readln( Ang, U );
  Ang:= Ang * Pi / 180;
  MaxTime:= 2 * U * Sin( Ang ) / G;

  SetGraphics;
  MoveTo( ScaleH( X ), ScaleV( Y ) );

  while T <= MaxTime do
  begin
    LineTo( ScaleH( X ), ScaleV( Y ) );
    T:= T + MaxTime / 40;
    X:= U * Cos( Ang ) * T;
    Y:= U * Sin( Ang ) * T - 0.5 * G * Sqr( T )
  end;

  Readln;
  CloseGraph
end.
```

There is a subtle feature in the **while** loop. The **LineTo** call is at the beginning of the loop to prevent any points being plotted *below* the ground.

6.3 TAKING STOCK

Once repetition and the basics of graphics have been mastered, a great vista of interesting and solvable problems begins to unfold. Three such problems are presented in this section.

Damped oscillations

The current *i* flowing in a electric circuit consisting of a resistance, inductance and initially charged condenser, connected in series is given by:

$$i = Ae^{-Rt/2L}\sin(2\pi f_1 t)$$

where

$$A = 2\pi f_0^2 Q/f_1,$$
$$f_0 = \sqrt{[1/(LC)]}/(2\pi),$$
$$f_1 = \sqrt{[1/(LC) - R^2/(4L^2)]}/(2\pi),$$

and the symbols have the meanings:

i: current (amperes) at time t;
A: maximum current;
t: time (seconds elapsed since circuit connected);
R: resistance (ohms);
L: inductance (henrys);
f_0: frequency (cycles/sec) of undamped ($R = 0$) circuit;
f_1: frequency of damped circuit;
C: capacitance (farads) of the condenser;
Q: initial charge (coulombs) on the condenser.

We want to compute the current over a period of **Cycles** complete cycles, where **PerCy** evaluations per cycle are made. The current must therefore be computed **Cycles * PerCy** times altogether. The time **Dt** between successive evaluations will be given by the statement

Dt:= 1 / (PerCy * F1)

since the period of the oscillations is $1/f_1$ seconds.

Note that the dependent (vertical) variable is i instead of y, and the independent (horizontal) variable is t instead of x. The program is as follows:

```
program Damp;
uses Graph;
const
  Pi          = 3.1415927;
  TwoPi       = 2 * Pi;
  Cycles      : real = 3;
  I           : real = 0;
  PerCy       : real = 40;
  T           : real = 0;
  Left        : real = 0;
  Right       : real = 0.3E-2;
  Bottom      : real = -0.8E-1;
  Top         : real = 0.8E-1;
var
  A, C, Dt, F0, F1, L, Q, R: real;
  K : integer;
{$I GrScale}
begin
  Write( 'Q, R, C, L: ' );
  Readln( Q, R, C, L );
  F0:= Sqrt( 1 / (L * C) ) / TwoPi;
  F1:= Sqrt( 1 / (L * C) - Sqr( R ) / (4 * Sqr( L )) ) / TwoPi;
  A:= TwoPi * Sqr( F0 ) * Q / F1;
  Dt:= 1 / (PerCy * F1);
  SetGraphics;
  MoveTo( ScaleH( T ), ScaleV( I ) );      { initial position }
  for K:= 1 to Round( Cycles * PerCy + 1 ) do
  begin
    T:= T + Dt;
    I:= A * Exp( - R * T / (2 * L) ) * Sin( TwoPi * F1 * T);
    LineTo( ScaleH( T ), ScaleV( I ) )
  end;

  MoveTo( ScaleH( 0 ), ScaleV( 0 ) );
  LineTo( ScaleH( T ), ScaleV( 0 ) );        { draw T-axis }
 Readln;
 CloseGraph
end.
```

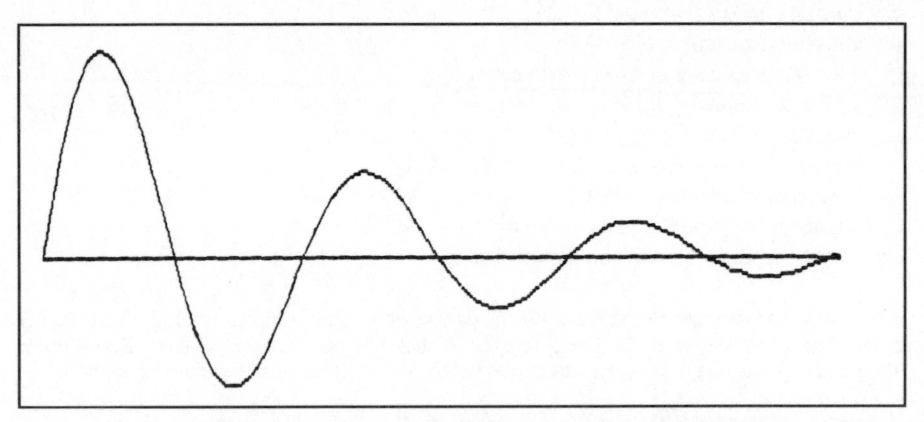

Figure 6.1 Damped Oscillations in a RLC Circuit.

This is an example of a **model:** the program behaves like the real thing. You can tune the apparatus by fiddling with the values of *Q*, *R*, *C* and *L*. For example, changing *R* will change the amount of damping, but it will also change the frequency f_1, whereas changing *C* will only affect the frequency. Do a few experiments with your model. Some sample data are: $Q = 1e{-5}$, $R = 4$, $C = 1e{-5}$ and $L = 2e{-3}$.

Chaos

A sequence $\{x_k\}$ with very interesting properties is defined by

$$x_{t+1} = rx_t(1 - x_t).$$

The notation x_t means that x is defined only at certain discrete values of t, instead of continuously, as the notation $x(t)$ would imply. Given x_0 and r, successive members of this sequence may be computed very easily, eg if $x_0 = 0.2$ and $r = 1$, then $x_1 = 0.16$, $x_2 = 0.1334$, and so on. This iterative formula is often used to model population growth in cases where the growth is not unlimited, but is restricted by shortage of food, living area, etc. The sequence has fascinating behaviour, described as **mathematical chaos,** for values of r between 3 and 4 (independent of x_0). The following program plots x_t against t, one point per pixel across the screen. Values of r that give particularly beautiful graphs are 3.3, 3.5, 3.5668, 3.575, 3.5766, 3.738, 3.8283, 3.8287, and many more that may be found by patient exploration.

```
program Chaos;
uses Graph;
var
  R, X, Left, Right, Bottom, Top : real;
  T : integer;
{$I GrScale}
begin
  Readln( R );
  SetGraphics;
  Left:= 0;
  Right:= GetMaxX;
  Bottom:= 0;
  Top:= 1;
  T:= 0;
  X:= 0.1;
  PutPixel( ScaleH( T ), ScaleV( X ), 1 );

  for T:= 1 to Round( Right ) do
  begin
    X:= R * X * (1 - X);
      PutPixel( ScaleH( T ), ScaleV( X ), 1 )
  end;
```

```
readln;
  CloseGraph
end.
```

A related and even more fascinating phenomenon is the Mandelbrot set, which is drawn in section 13.3. The **Graph** unit procedure **PutPixel** lights up the pixel at the given position with the specified colour (1 in this case).

Modelling a population of gnus

The wildebeest (gnu) population in the Kruger National Park, South Africa, declined from about 14000 in 1969 to 6700 in 1975, giving rise to considerable concern (see Table 6.1). Mathematical modelling techniques were applied to this problem, as described in Starfield and Bleloch (1986).

The population in year k may be divided into four biologically distinct age groups:

c_k : the number of new-born calves;
y_k : the number of yearlings;
t_k : the number of two-year-olds;
w_k : the number of adults (older than two years).

We can think of the population as a vector with four components, each measured annually (in January, when the females calve). The essence of the problem is to predict the next year's vector, given an initial population at some time. At this stage we turn to the game rangers, who tell us that yearlings do not produce young – this is the prerogative of the two-year-olds and adults. We thus have the equation modelling the dynamics of calves:

$$c_{k+1} = aw_{k+1} + a' t_{k+1} , \qquad (1)$$

where a and a' are the birth-rates (number of expected offspring per individual per year) for adults and two-year-olds respectively. It turns out that the best way to model yearling population dynamics is simply

$$y_{k+1} = bc_k , \qquad (2)$$

where b is the overall survival-rate for calves. Obviously (?) this year's yearlings can only come from last year's calves, so $b < 1$.

For the other two age groups life is fairly uncomplicated. Their members die of practically only one cause – lion attack. This is modelled as follows. It seems that lion are indiscriminate in their attacks on all groups except the calves. Therefore the number of yearlings taken by lion is in direct proportion to the fraction of yearlings in the total non-calf population, and so on. Of course the number taken in year k is also in proportion to the number of hunting lion in year k – call this number l_k. So we can model the number of two-year-olds and adults with

$$t_{k+1} = y_k - gl_k y_k / (y_k + t_k + w_k) \qquad (3)$$

and

$$w_{k+1} = w_k + t_k - gl_k(t_k + w_k) / (y_k + t_k + w_k) \qquad (4)$$

where g is the lion kill-rate (number of gnu taken per lion per year).

(The order in which these equations are computed is important. w_{k+1} and t_{k+1} must be computed before c_{k+1}.)

After consultation with game rangers, a is estimated as 0.45, and a' as 0.15 (Starfied and Bleloch, 1986). The lion kill-rate is between 2.5 and 4 (lion have other choices on their menu), and calf survival b is between 0.5 and 0.7.

More precise values of g and b for each year were found experimentally by seeing which values gave a total population that agreed more or less with the annual census figures. Fitting the model to the census data was further complicated by the culling (killing by rangers) of wildebeest between

1969 and 1972. However, since culling is indiscriminate among the non-calf population it is easy to argue that the term gl_k in eqns (3) and (4) must be replaced by $(gl_k + d_k)$, where d_k is the total number culled in year k. This number of course is accurately known.

The model run starts in 1969 ($k = 1$), with $c_1 = 3660, y_1 = 2240, t_1 = 1680$ and $w_1 = 6440$. These figures are from the census. Table 6.1 shows the total population predicted by the model compared with the census data. The column headed *Model 1* shows projections taking the annual culling into account, whereas *Model 2* assumes *no* culling (by setting $d_k = 0$ when running the model). Note also that a particular projection is based on the input in the previous row, for example if $l_1 = 500$, $d_1 = 572$, $b = 0.5$ and $g = 4$, the model predicts $c_2 + y_2 + t_2 + w_2 = 12617$.

Year	l_k	d_k	b	g	*Census*	*Model 1*	*Model 2*
1969	500	572	0.5	4	14020		
1970	520	550	0.5	4	11800	12617	13140
1971	530	302	0.5	4	10600	11233	12932
1972	540	78	0.5	4	8000	9847	12248
1973	550	0	0.7	3.5	7700	8457	11369
1974	540	0	0.7	3.5	?	7679	11239
1975					6700	6779	11120

Table 6.1 Wildebeest Model Data and Output.

The parameters g and b are realistic. 1970-1972 were dry years in the Park, when lion killed regularly at waterholes. This justifies the higher g and lower b values. In subsequent years the lion did not kill so freely, since the improved vegetation and declining wildebeest population made the prey more difficult to find. The same factors lead to a higher calf survival.

The program below implements this model. Note that two sets of variables are used to represent the age groups. **C, Y, T** and **W** represent values in year k, while **NC, NY, NT** and **NW** represent values in year $k+1$. One might have been tempted to code the update equations as follows:

```
Y:= B * C;                              { Eqn 2 }
T:= Y - (G * L + D) * Y/ (Y + T + W);   { Eqn 3 }
...
```

This, however, would mean that we would be using *next* year's **Y**, obtained from eqn (2), on the righthand side of eqn (3), instead of *this* year's. Using two sets of variables means that the set representing the current year's values must be updated at the end of each year in readiness for next year's update. The program also makes use of the **GoToXY** cursor control procedure to produce output in the same format as Table 6.1. Try the program out with different parameter values, to see what happens. Also try running it for longer.

```
Program Gnus;
uses Crt;
const
  Line  : integer = 5;     { Line on output screen }
  A     : real    = 0.45;  { adult birth-rate }
  Ad    : real    = 0.15;  { a-dash: two-year-old birth-rate }
  C     : real    = 3660;  { calves }
  Y     : real    = 2240;  { yearlings }
  T     : real    = 1680;  { two-year-olds }
  W     : real    = 6440;  { adults }
var
  Yr : integer;
  NC, NY, NT, NW  : real;    { next year's population }
  L, D, B, G      : real;    { model parameters }
  Tot             : real;    { total population }
```

```
begin
  ClrScr;
  HighVideo;
  Writeln( 'Starfield''s Wildebeest Model (Ctrl-Break twice to stop)');
  NormVideo;
  Writeln;
  Writeln( 'Year      l      d      b      g      Model' );
  Writeln;

  for Yr:= 1969 to 1974 do
  begin
    if Yr = 1969 then
      Write( Yr, '        ' );
    Readln( l, d, b, g );
    NY:= B * C;                                          { Eqn 2 }
    NT:= Y - (G * L + D) * Y/ (Y + T + W);               { Eqn 3 }
    NW:= W + T - (G * L + D) * (T + W) / (Y + T + W);
                                                         { Eqn 4 }
    NC:= A * NW + Ad * NT;                               { Eqn 1 }
    C:= NC;
    Y:= NY;
    T:= NT;
    W:= NW;
    Tot:= C + Y + T + W;
    Writeln( Yr + 1, ' ':21, Round( Tot ):7 );
    Line:= Line + 1;
    GoToXY( 8, Line)
  end

end.
```

SUMMARY

- A **for** loop should be used to program a deterministic repeat structure, where the number of repeats is known to the program (ie in principle to the programmer) ***before*** the loop is encountered, and where the loop counter *N* is incremented or decremented by one each time. This situation is characterised by the general structure plan

  1. Repeat *N* times:
     1.1 Statements to be repeated

where *N* is known or computed ***before*** step 1 is encountered, and is ***not*** changed by step 1.1. The general syntax for **for** is

> **for** *ident*:= *first* **to** *last* **do**
> *Body*;

or

> **for** *ident*:= *first* **downto** *last* **do**
> *Body*;

where *ident* is a variable of ordinal type.

- A **while-do** loop or a **repeat-until** loop should be used to program a non-deterministic repeat structure, where the exact number of repeats is ***not*** known in advance. Another way of saying this is that **while-do** or **repeat-until** should be used to repeat whenever the truth value of the ***condition*** for repeating is ***changed*** in the body of the loop. This situation is characterised by the following two structure plans:

  1. While *condition* is **true** repeat:
     1.1. Statements to be repeated (which should reset the truth value of *condition*)

  or

1. Repeat:
   1.1. Statements to be repeated (which should reset the truth value of *condition*)

   Until *condition* is **true**

The syntax of these two forms is:

while *condition* **do**
  Body;

or

repeat
  Body
until *condition*;

- **while-do** should also be used to code a deterministic repeat where the loop counter is changed by steps greater than one. In general:

```
ident:= first;
while ident <= last do                    { positive step }
begin
  Body;
  ident:= ident + step;
end;

ident:= first;
while ident >= last do                    { negative step }
begin
  Body;
ident:= ident + step;
end;
```

- The body of a **repeat-until** structure may sometimes never be executed.
- The body of a **while-do** structure is always executed at least once.
- Loops may be nested inside each other.
- **Eof(F)** is only true when there are no more data to be read from the text file **F**. The equivalent form for keyboard input is **Eof.**

EXERCISES

6.1 Write a program to find the sum of the successive even integers 2, 4, ..., 200, using while-do. (Answer: 10100)

6.2 Write a program which produces a table of sin(*x*) and cos(*x*) for angles *x* from 0° to 90° in steps of 15°.

6.3 A person deposits $1000 in a bank. Interest is compounded monthly at the rate of 1% per month. Write a program which will compute the monthly balance, but write it only *annually* for 10 years (use nested for loops, with the outer loop for 10 years, and the inner loop for 12 months). Note that after 10 years, the balance is $3300.39, whereas if interest had been compounded annually, at the rate of 12% per year, the balance would only have been $3105.85.

6.4 There are many formulae for computing π (the ratio of a circle's circumference to its diameter). The simplest is

$$\pi/4 = 1 - 1/3 + 1/5 - 1/7 + 1/9 - \ldots \qquad (1)$$

which comes from the series

$$\arctan(x) = x - x^3/3 + x^5/5 - x^7/7 + x^9/9 - \ldots \qquad (*)$$

by letting $x = 1$.

(a) Write a program to compute π using series (1). Use as many terms in the series as your computer will reasonably allow (start modestly, with 100 terms, say, and re-run your program with more and more each time). You should find that the series converges very slowly, ie it takes a lot of terms to get fairly close to π.

(b) Rearranging the series speeds up the convergence:

$$\pi/8 = 1/(1\times3) + 1/(5\times7) + 1/(9\times11) \ldots \qquad (2)$$

Write a program to compute π using series (2) instead. You should find that you need fewer terms to reach the same level of accuracy that you got in (a).

(c) One of the fastest series for π is

$$\pi/4 = 6 \arctan(1/8) + 2 \arctan(1/57) + \arctan(1/239) \qquad (3)$$

Use this formula to compute π. Don't use the standard function **ArcTan** to compute the arctangents, since that would be cheating. Rather use the series (*) above.

6.5 The following method of computing π is due to Archimedes:

1. Let $A = 1$ and $N = 6$
2. Repeat 10 times, say:
   2.1. Replace N by $2N$
   2.2 Replace A by $\sqrt{[2 - \sqrt{(4 - A^2)}]}$
   2.3. Let $L = NA/2$
   2.4. Let $U = L/\sqrt{(1 - A^2/2)}$
   2.5. Let $P = (U + L)/2$ (estimate of π)
   2.6. Let $E = (U - L)/2$ (estimate of error)
   2.7. Write N, P, E
3. Stop.

Write a program to implement the algorithm.

6.6 Write a program to compute a table of the function

$$f(x) = x \sin[\pi (1 + 20x)/2]$$

over the interval [–1; 1] using increments in x of (a) 0.2 (b) 0.1 and (c) 0.01. Use your tables to plot a graph of $f(x)$ for the three cases, and observe that the tables for (a) and (b) give totally the wrong picture of $f(x)$. When you have learnt some graphics get your program to draw the graph of $f(x)$ for the three cases superimposed (see the solution to Exercise 13.1).

6.7 The statements

```
PutPixel( Random, Random, 1 );
Delay( 100 );   { Crt unit }
```

will plot random points on the graphics screen, with a delay of 0.1 seconds between each point. Set up the graphics screen with a range of 0 to 1 horizontally and vertically, and write a program to plot about 100 such points.

Then use **LineTo** to plot lines instead of points.

6.8 The transcendental number e (2.718281828 ...) can be shown to be the limit of

$$1 / (1 - x)^{(1/x)}$$

as x tends to zero (from above). Write a program which shows how this expression converges to e as x gets closer and closer to zero (use {$N+} and double type for best results).

6.9 A square wave of period T may be defined by the function

$$f(t) = 1 \quad (0 < t < T),$$
$$= -1 \quad (-T < t < 0).$$

The Fourier series for $f(t)$ is given by

$$\frac{4}{\pi} \sum_{k=0}^{\infty} \frac{1}{2k+1} \sin\left[\frac{(2k+1)\pi t}{T}\right]$$

It is of interest to know how many terms are needed for a good approximation to this infinite sum. Taking $T = 1$, write a program to compute n terms of the series for t from 0 to 1 in steps of 0.1, say. Run the program for different values of n, for example 1, 3, 6, etc. (See Chapter 13 for the graphics version.)

6.10 If an amount of money A is invested for k years at a nominal annual interest rate r (expressed as a decimal fraction), the value V of the investment after k years is given by

$$V = A(1 + r/n)^{nk}$$

where n is the number of compounding periods per year. Write a program to compute V as n gets larger and larger, ie as the compounding periods become more and more frequent, like monthly, daily, hourly, and ultimately instantaneously (?). Take $A = 1000$, $r = 4\%$ and $k = 10$ years. You should observe that your output gradually approaches a limit. Hint: use a for loop which doubles n each time, starting with $n = 1$.

Also compute the value of the formula

$$Ae^{rk}$$

for the same values of A, r and k (use the standard function **Exp**), and compare this value with the values of V computed above. What do you conclude?

6.11 Write a program to compute the sum of the series 1 + 2 + 3... such that the sum is as large as possible without exceeding 100. The program should write out how many terms are used in the sum.

6.12 The compound interest program earlier in the chapter shows that an amount of $1000 will double in about seven years with an interest rate of 10%. Using the same interest rate, run the program with initial balances of $500, $2000 and $10000 (say) to see how long they all take to double. The results may surprise you.

6.13 Write a program to implement the structure plan of Exercise 3.2.

6.14 Use the Taylor series

$$\cos(x) = 1 - x^2/2! + x^4/4! - x^6/6! + \ldots$$

to write a program to compute cos(x) correct to four decimal places (x is in radians). See how many terms are needed to get four-figure agreement with the standard function Cos.

6.15 A man borrows $10000 to buy a used car. Interest on his loan is compounded at the rate of 2% per month while the outstanding balance of the loan is more than $5000, and at 1% per month otherwise. He pays back $300 every month, except for the last month, when the repayment must be less than $300. He pays at the end of the month, *after* the interest on the balance has been compounded. The first repayment is made one month after the loan is paid out to him. Write a program which writes out a monthly statement of the balance (after the monthly payment has been made), the final payment, and the month of the final payment.

6.16 A projectile, the equations of motion of which are given in Chapter 4, is launched from the point O with an initial velocity of 60 m/s at an angle of 50° to the horizontal. Write a program which computes and writes out the time in the air, and horizontal and vertical displacement from the point *O* every 0.5 seconds, as long as the projectile remains above a horizontal plane through *O*.

6.17 When a resistor (*R*), capacitor (*C*) and battery (*V*) are connected in series, a charge *Q* builds up on the capacitor according to the formula

$$Q(t) = CV(1 - e^{-t/RC})$$

if there is no charge on the capacitor at time $t = 0$. The problem is to monitor the charge on the capacitor every 0.1 seconds in order to detect when it reaches a level of 8 units of charge, given that $V = 9$, $R = 4$ and $C = 1$. Write a program which writes the time and charge every 0.1 seconds until the charge first exceeds 8 units (ie the last charge written must exceed 8). Once you have done this, rewrite the program to output the charge only while it is strictly less than 8 units.

6.18 If a population grows according to the logistic model, its size *X*(t) at time t is given by the formula

$$X(t) = KX_0 / [(K - X_0)e^{-rt} + X_0],$$

where X_0 is the initial size at time $t = 0$, *r* is the growth-rate, and *K* is the **carrying capacity** of the environment. Write a program which will plot a graph of *X*(*t*) against *t* over a period of 200 years. Take $X_0 = 2$, $r = 0.1$ and $K = 1000$. Choose a suitable scale for the graph. Experiment with different values of *K*, and see if you can interpret *K* biologically.

6.19 Write a program which uses a **for** loop to sound a note of duration 0.01 seconds rising in frequency from, say, 400 to 600 Hertz. Then use another **for** loop to make the note drop back from 600 to 400 Hertz. Finally, enclose both loops in an outer **for** which repeats the whole process a number of times. (Make sure to use a different control variable in the outer loop.) If the noise becomes unbearable, remember that **Ctrl-Break** will stop the program.

6.20 Adapt the prime number program in section 6.2 to find all the prime factors of a given number (even or odd).

6.21 The chaos graphics program in section 6.3, which plots

$$x_{t+1} = rx_t(1 - x_t),$$

may be adapted to draw the famous pitchfork or "roads to chaos" picture. The basic idea involves a re-arrangement of what is plotted. Instead of drawing *x* against *t*, we draw *x* against *r*, as follows:

Set the graphics scales so that *x* varies from 0 to 1 horizontally, and *r* varies from 4 to 2.95 up the screen (ie **Top** = 2.95 and **Bottom** = 4 – the effect of this is to draw the picture upside down). Use a **while** loop to change *r* from 2.95 to 4 in steps of 0.005. For each *r* set *x* to 0.1 and generate the next 300 values of *x* from the formula above in a **for** loop (without plotting anything). Then, still for the same *r*, use another **for** loop to generate a further 100 values of *x*, this time plotting each *x* against *r* with **PutPixel** (*x* horizontally, and *r* vertically). You should get an interesting picture, which will improve if *r* increases by yet smaller steps.

7 Errors

Even experienced programmers seldom get programs to run correctly the first time! In computer jargon, an error in a program is called a **bug**, and the process of detecting and correcting such errors is called **debugging.** There are three main types of errors: **compilation** errors, a number of different kinds of **run-time** errors, and errors of **logic**. There is also a more subtle error – **rounding error** – which creeps in sometimes because of finite machine precision. In this chapter we deal with the sort of errors that can arise with the programming we have done so far. Other possible sources of error will be pointed out in later chapters in the appropriate places.

7.1. COMPILATION ERRORS

These are errors of syntax and construction, like spelling mistakes, that are picked up by the compiler during compilation, the process whereby your program is translated into machine code. They are the most frequent type of error, and in Turbo Pascal they are fatal, ie the program will not execute until the error has been corrected. Turbo Pascal generates compiler messages that are usually quite helpful. The cursor stops in the Edit window at the place where the error was spotted, and an error message appears at the top of the screen. **Ctrl-QW** finds the position of the last error, and displays the error message.

There are a large number of compiler error messages, listed in an appendix of the *Turbo Pascal Reference Guide*, with some indications of the most likely cause of the errors. These should be consulted if you are unable to correct the error yourself. Since the compiler is not as intelligent as you are, the error message can sometimes be rather unhelpful, or even misleading. Some examples are given below.

10 Unexpected end of file.

This message is generated by the following code:

```
begin
  if 4 > 5 then { comment )
  begin
  end
end.
```

The error position is the final period. The problem is that the comment is not correctly closed –) is used instead of }. This error can also occur when **begin**s and **end**s are not balanced.

36 BEGIN expected.

This error is generated by the uses clause in this code:

```
program Test;
const
  C = 10;
uses Graph;
```

uses is in the wrong place – it should be the first non-comment line in the program.

85 ";" expected.

This occurs with the following:

```
begin
  if 4 > 5 then
```

```
  begin
end.
```

The period is flagged as the error position. The problem is that the second **begin** has not been paired with an **end**. This is a common error. It helps to label each **begin-end** with comments, for example:

```
begin {1}
  ...
  begin {2}
    ...
  end {2}
end {1}
```

189 ")" expected.

This error comes up often, for example in

```
procedure Junk( X: string[20] );
```

The cursor stops under the [because the compiler expects a type identifier here. The solution is to declare a type **String20** and to change the procedure header to

```
procedure Junk( X: String20 );
```

This error also occurs, for example, at the second colon in

```
Writeln( I:4:2 )
```

if **I** is an integer type, because this format is invalid for an integer.

94 "." expected.

This occurs with

```
program Pi;
begin
  Writeln( 'π = ', Pi );
  readln
end.
```

The) at the end of **Writeln** is flagged as the error position. This one seems quite inexplicable! The actual problem is that **Pi** is the name of a standard function, which is its intended usage. Although the names of standard functions and procedures may be used as identifiers for other purposes (in this case as the program name), they may not also be used with their original meaning in the same program.

However, if you declared a variable **My** in the program, you could then refer to **Pi.My** with no error. It is this period the compiler was looking for. This is therefore a good time to confess that an identifier may be preceded by a **qualifier**, which must be the name of the program or unit containing that identifier. The combined identifier is then called a **qualified identifier**. This explains the curious error message. Since the first encounter with **Pi** was as the program name, the compiler would not accept the second occurrence as the standard function, but interpreted it as a qualifier, which should have been followed by a period and identifier.

113 Error in statement.

This occurs, for example, at the **else** below:

```
if X > 2 then
  Y:= 1;
else
  Y:= 2;
```

The mistake is the semi-colon *before* the **else**, which closes the **if. else** cannot start a statement of its own.

7.2 RUN-TIME ERRORS

If a program is successfully compiled, it runs. Errors occurring at this stage in the proceedings are called run-time errors, and are usually fatal, causing the program to crash. An error message, such as

200 Division by zero

or

207 Invalid floating point operation

is generated. The latter (no. 207) is quite common. It occurs when the argument passed to **Ln** or **Sqrt** is negative (or zero in the case of **Ln**). It also occurs when the real argument of **Trunc** or **Round** cannot be converted to an integer in the longint range. It could also mean an 8087 stack overflow.

All the run-time error messages are listed in the *Turbo Pascal Reference Guide* in order of error number.

The integrated debugger

Turbo Pascal has a facility called the *Debugger* which runs quietly behind the scenes. It is one of the most outstanding features of versions 5.0 and above, and its usefulness cannot be emphasised enough. To sample it, put a small program into the Edit window, for example,

```
program Bug;
var
  I: integer;
  Sum: real;
begin
  Sum:= 0;
  for I:= 1 to 100 do
    Sum:= Sum + I;
  Writeln( Sum );
  Readln;
end.
```

Select the **B**reak/watch menu, and then the **A**dd watch command (hot key **Ctrl-F7**). A dialogue box appears on the screen. Enter the variable **Sum**. If you display the Watch window (with **F5**) you will see this variable in the window. Add **I** to the Watch window in the same way. Now press **F7**. The first executable line in the program is highlighted. This means that it is the next statement to be executed. As you continue to press **F7**, the statements are executed one at a time, and the variables in the Watch window are updated accordingly. In this way you can work through the program to see if the variables take the values you anticipated.

You can add variables to the Watch window *after* a program has finished executing. You can then see their values at the moment the program stopped running.

The Debugger is described in detail in the *Turbo Pascal User's Guide*. Some of the highlights are mentioned here briefly.

F4 (**R**un/**G**o to Cursor) runs a program stopping when and if the line on the cursor is executed.

F7 (**R**un/**T**race Into) executes the current line, tracing into all procedures and functions if possible.

F8 (**R**un/**S**tep Over) executes the current line, but does not trace into procedures or functions.

Break/**T**oggle Breakpoint (**Ctrl-F8**) sets or clears a breakpoint on the current line in the Edit window.

Run/**R**un (**Ctrl-F9**) runs a program to a breakpoint, and stops there.

Run/**P**rogram Reset (**Ctrl-F2**) ends a debugging session, and tidies up in preparation for starting a new session.

Debug/**E**valuate (**Ctrl-F4**) brings up the Evaluate box. This allows you to evaluate variables and expressions, and to change variables. You can also use the Evaluate box as a simple calculator, for example to convert hexadecimal numbers to decimal.

If you are serious about programming, you should spend some time mastering the Debugger.

Intercepting errors: input/output checking

Sometimes it is very inconvenient (to say the least!) when a large program crashes leaving everything hanging. Turbo Pascal enables you to write error handling code for intercepting otherwise fatal run-time errors.

A program might require you to enter a lot of data from the keyboard. If you make a single mistake when entering the data (for example typing ! instead of 1 for numeric data) the program crashes, and all your data is lost. There is no alternative to starting all over again.

The following program requires two numbers to be entered. Run it, and type some deliberate mistakes, for example separate the numbers with a comma, or type a letter instead of a number:

```
program IOBug;
var
  A, B : real;
  IOCheck : integer;
begin
  repeat
    Write( 'Two numbers please: ' );
    {$I-}                          { I/O checking off }
    Readln( A, B );
    {$I+}                          { I/O checking on again }
    IOCheck:= IOResult;
    if IOCheck <> 0 then
      Writeln( #7#7#7, 'Try again, dum-dum!' )
  until IOCheck = 0;
  Writeln( 'Thank you!' )
end.
```

The **{$I–}** compiler directive switches off Turbo Pascal's input/output error checking. So no crash occurs at the **Readln** if a mistake is made. **IOResult** is a standard function which is only zero if the last **Read** was successful. As soon as it is called, it is reset to zero, which is why its value must be assigned to a variable **(IOCheck)** – its value must be used again in the **until** clause. The **{$I+}** switches I/O error checking on again for subsequent **Read**s (this is the default state).

Error interception is very useful in file handling programs, where one might accidentally attempt to read from files that aren't there, or write to files that already are there. Examples of usage are given in Chapter 11.

Range checking

Turbo Pascal normally does not check for values out of range during execution, in order to save code and time. You can switch range checking on with **{$R+}**. This results in slightly bigger and slower code, but can be worth it if it prevents disaster. Range checking is switched off with **{$R–}** (the default state).

7.3 ERRORS IN LOGIC

These are errors in the actual algorithm you are using to solve a problem, and are the most difficult to find: the program runs, but gives the wrong answers! It's even worse if you don't realise the answers are wrong. The following tips might help you to check out the logic.

- Try to run the program for some special cases where you know the answers.
- If you don't know any exact answers, try to use your insight into the problem to check whether the answers seem to be of the right order of magnitude.
- When debugging remember that the variables remain active after the program has run. You can use the Debugger to display them in the Watch window.
- Try working through the program by hand (or use the Debugger) to see if you can spot where things start going wrong.

7.4 ROUNDING ERROR

At times a program will give numerical answers to a problem which appear inexplicably different from what we know to be the correct mathematical solution. This can be due to rounding error, which results from the finite precision available on the computer, for example two or four bytes per variable, instead of an infinite number.

Run the following program extract:

```
var
  X : real;
begin
  X:= 0.1;
```

```
repeat
  X:= X + 0.001;
  Writeln( X );
until X = 0.2;
```

You will find that you need **Ctrl-Break** to stop the program. **X** never has the value 0.2 *exactly*, because of rounding error (the displayed value is also rounded). In fact, **X** misses the value of 0.2 by about 2.3e−12, as can be seen by displaying **(X − 0.2)** as well each time. It would be better to replace the **until** clause with

until X > 0.2

or

until Abs(X − 0.2) < 1e−6

Even in the {**$N+**} numeric coprocessor state, using double type, there is a difference of 9.4e−17 at the closest approach.

Consider also the following example:

```
var
  A, B: real;
begin
  A:= 3;
  B:= Sqr( Sqrt( A ) );
  if A = B then
    Writeln( 'Numbers equal' );
  Writeln( A - B );
```

The output is **−3.6379788071E−12**. Mathematically, **A** should be equal to **B**. But the test for equality fails because they have a non-zero difference, due to rounding error. The **if** statement should be replaced by something like

```
if Abs( A - B ) < 1e-10 then
  Writeln( 'Numbers are practically equal' );
```

It is always better to use a test like this to compare two expressions, rather than a straight test for equality, which can often fail because of rounding error.

In the {**$N+**} numeric co-processor mode, there is no rounding error in this case, and **A** and **B** are computed as equal. Rounding error may also be reduced by a mathematical re-arrangement of the problem. If the well-known quadratic equation is written in the less usual form

$$x^2 - 2ax + e = 0$$

the two solutions may be expressed as

$$x_1 = a + \sqrt{(a^2 - e)},$$
$$x_2 = a - \sqrt{(a^2 - e)}.$$

If e is very small compared with a, the second root is expressed as the difference between two nearly equal numbers, and considerable significance is lost. For example taking $a = 5e6$ and $e = 1$ gives $x_2 = 0$ in Turbo Pascal. However, the second root may also be expressed mathematically as

$$x_2 = e/[a + \sqrt{(a^2 - e)}]\ e/2a.$$

Using this form in Turbo Pascal gives x_2 = 1E−7, which is more accurate.

Rounding error is also discussed in section 16.3.

SUMMARY

- Compilation errors are mistakes in the syntax (coding).
- Execution (run-time) errors occur while the program is running,
- Input/output errors may be intercepted at run-time with the {**$I+**} switch and the standard function **IOResult**.
- The Debugger may be used to work through a program, statement by statement.
- The Watch window may be used to monitor the values of variables during and after execution.

- Logical errors are errors in the algorithm used to solve the problem.
- Rounding error occurs because the computer can store numbers only to a finite accuracy. It is reduced but not necessarily eliminated by running the program in the **{$N+}** numeric co-processor mode.

EXERCISES

7.1 The Newton quotient

$$[f(x + h) - f(x)]/h$$

may be used to compute the first derivative $f'(x)$ of a function $f(x)$, if h is small. Write a program to compute the Newton quotient for the function

$$f(x) = x^2$$

at the point $x = 2$ (the exact answer is 4) for values of h starting at 1, and decreasing by a factor of 10 each time. The effect of rounding error becomes apparent when h gets too small, ie less than about 1e−6. (See section 16.3 for the solution.)

7.2 The solution of the set of simultaneous equations

$$ax + by = c$$
$$dx + ey = f$$

quoted in Exercise 5.5 is given by

$$x = (ce - bf) / (ae - bd),$$
$$y = (af - cd) / (ae - bd).$$

If $(ae - bd)$ is small, rounding error may cause quite large inaccuracies in the solution. Consider the system

$$0.2038x + 0.1218y = 0.2014,$$
$$0.4071x + 0.2436y = 0.4038.$$

Show that with four-figure floating point arithmetic the solution obtained is $x = -1.714$, $y = 4.286$. This level of accuracy may be simulated in the solution of Exercise 5.5 with some statements like

```
AE = Round( A * E * 1e5 ) / 1e5;
```

and appropriate changes in the coding. The exact solution, however, which can be obtained with normal computer accuracy, is $x = -2$, $y = 5$. If the coefficients in the equations are themselves subject to experimental error, the solution of this system using limited accuracy is totally meaningless.

7.3 This problem, suggested by R.V. Andree, demonstrates another numerical problem called **ill-conditioning**, where a small change in the coefficients causes a large change in the solution. Show that the solution of the system

$$x + 5.000y = 17.0$$
$$1.5x + 7.501y = 25.503$$

is $x = 2$, $y = 3$, using the program in Exercise 5.5 with normal precision. Now change the constant term in the second equation to 25.501, a change of about one part in 12000, and observe that a totally different solution results. Also try changing this term to 25.502, 25.504, etc. If the co-efficients are subject to experimental errors, the solution is again meaningless. One way to anticipate this sort of error is to perform a **sensitivity analysis** on the coefficients: change them all in turn by the same percentage, and observe what effect this has on the solution.

8 User-defined Functions and Procedures

We pointed out in Chapter 3 that the logic of a non-trivial problem should be broken down into separate subprograms, each carrying out a particular, well-defined task. It often happens that such subprograms can be used by many different programs, and in fact by different users of the same computer system. Turbo Pascal enables you to implement these subprograms as **functions** and **procedures** which are independent of the **main program**. Examples are procedures to perform statistical operations, or to sort items, or to find the best straight line through a set of points, or to solve a system of differential equations. This facility also enables you to access collections of procedures, called **units**, such as the Turbo Pascal graphics unit.

8.1 FUNCTIONS

We have already seen how to use some of the standard functions supplied by Turbo Pascal, such as **Sin, Cos, Ln,** etc. You can declare your own functions (for example, the exponentiation function described in Chapter 4) to be used in the same way in a program. Before we discuss the rules in detail, we will look at some examples.

Newton's method in general

Newton's method (which is described in Chapter 16) may be used to solve a general equation

$$f(x) = 0$$

by repeating the assignment

$$x \text{ becomes } x - f(x)/f'(x),$$

where $f'(x)$ is the first derivative of $f(x)$, until $f(x)$ has come close enough to zero. (You can check the algorithm for finding the square root of a in section 2.11 by using $f(x) = x^2 - a$). But now suppose that

$$f(x) = x^2 + x - 3.$$

Then

$$f'(x) = 3x^2 + 1.$$

The program below uses Newton's method to solve this equation starting with $x = 2$, and stopping either when the absolute value of $f(x)$ is less than 1e−6, or after 20 iterations, say. It uses two functions: **F(X)** for $f(x)$ and **DF(X)** for $f'(x)$.

```
program Isaac;
{ Newton's method in general }

function F( X : real ): real;
{ Function to be solved }
begin
  F:= X * X * X + X - 3
end; { F }

function DF( X : real ): real;
{ First derivative }
begin
  DF:= 3 * X * X + 1
end;{ DF }
```

```
const
  Eps              : real = 1e-6;          { maximum error }
  Its              : integer = 0;          { iteration counter }
  Max              : integer = 20;         { maximum iterations }
  X                : real = 2;             { starting guess }
var
  Converged : boolean;                     { covergence flag }
begin
  Converged:= Abs( F(X) ) <= Eps;
  while (not Converged) and (Its < Max) do
  begin
    X:= X - F(X) / DF(X);
    Writeln( X:10:6, '     ', F(X):11 );
    Its:= Its + 1;
    Converged:= Abs( F(X) ) <= Eps
  end;
  Writeln;
  if Converged then
    Writeln( 'Newton converged' )
  else
    Writeln( 'Newton diverged' )
end.
```

The output is as follows:

```
 1.461538     1.5835E+00
 1.247788     1.9056E-01
 1.214185     4.1891E-03
 1.213412     2.1733E-06
 1.213412     0.0000E-13
Newton converged
```

Note that there are two conditions that will stop the **while** loop: either convergence, or the completion of 20 iterations. Otherwise the program could run indefinitely.

Rotation of co-ordinate axes

Functions are particularly useful when arithmetic expressions, which can become long and cumbersome, need to be evaluated repeatedly. A good example is the rotation of a Cartesian co-ordinate system. If such a system is rotated counter-clockwise through an angle of t radians, the new co-ordinates (x', y') of a point referred to the rotated axes are given by

$$x' = x\cos(t) + y\sin(t)$$
$$y' = -x\sin(t) + y\cos(t),$$

where (x, y) are its co-ordinates before rotation of the axes. The following functions could be used to define the new co-ordinates:

```
function Xnew( X, Y, T : real ): real;
begin
  Xnew:= X * Cos( T ) + Y * Sin( T )
end; { Xnew }

function Ynew( X, Y, T : real ): real;
begin
  Ynew:= - X * Sin( T ) + Y * Cos( T )
end;{ Xnew }
```

Bending of a beam

A uniform beam (such as exists only in textbooks and university examinations) is freely hinged at its ends $x = 0$ and $x = L$, so that the ends are at the same level. It carries a uniformly distributed load of W per unit length, and there is a tension T along the x-axis. The deflection y of the beam a distance x from one end is given by

$$y = \frac{WEI}{T^2}\left[\frac{\cosh[a(L/2 - x)]}{\cosh(aL/2)} - 1\right] + \frac{Wx(L - x)}{2T},$$

where $a^2 = T/EI$, E being the Young's modulus of the beam, and I the moment of inertia of a cross-section of the beam. The beam is 10 m long, the tension 1000 N, the load 100 N/m, and EI is 1e4. The following program computes the deflection of the beam from the horizontal every metre along the beam up to its midpoint, using a user-defined function for the hyperbolic cosine, cosh(x):

```
program Beam;

function Cosh( X: real ): real;
{ hyperbolic cosine }
begin
  Cosh:= (Exp( X ) + Exp( - X )) / 2
end; { Cosh }

const
  EI : real = 1e4;
  L : integer = 10;
  T : real = 1000;
  W : real = 100;
var
  A, X, Y : real;
begin
  A:= Sqrt( T / EI );
  X:= 0;

  while X <= L do
  begin
    Y:= W * EI / Sqr(T) * (Cosh(A * (L/2 - X)) / Cosh(A * L/2) - 1);
    Y:= Y + W * X * (L - X) / (2 * T);
    Writeln( X:10:1, Y:10:3 );
    X:= X + 1
  end
end.
```

Output:

```
        0.0       0.000
        1.0       0.205
        2.0       0.386
        3.0       0.526
        4.0       0.615
        5.0       0.645
        6.0       0.615
        7.0       0.526
        8.0       0.386
        9.0       0.205
       10.0       0.000
```

Parameters

Consider the declaration of the function cosh(x) in the above program, which begins with the line:

```
function Cosh( X: real ): real;
```

X is called a **formal parameter**. It has ***no connection*** with a variable of the same name in the main program. The function is **activated,** or **called** in the program, by using its name in any statement, for example

```
Y:= W * EI / Sqr(T) * (Cosh(A * (L / 2 - X)) / Cosh(A * L / 2) - 1);
```

When the function is activated, its parameter, ie

A * (L / 2 – X)

in the first instance, is called an **actual parameter.** The actual parameter (which may be an expression, but which must be assignment compatible with the corresponding formal parameter) is evaluated, and the ***value*** is ***copied*** into the formal parameter **X** in the function declaration. This value is then used to evaluate the function according to the definition. In the second instance, the actual parameter is **A * L / 2.** The value of this expression is passed to the formal parameter **X** in the function declaration.

As another example, consider the following program segment, which uses a function to compute the discriminant in solving the well-known quadratic equation:

```
function Disc( A, B, C: real ): real;
begin
  B * B – 4 * A * C
end; { Disc }
...
Readln( P, Q, R );
...
if Disc( P, Q, R ) > 0 then
  X1 = ( – Q + Sqrt( Disc( P, Q, R ) )/ 2 / P;
  ...
```

The formal parameters **A, B** and **C** in the function declaration inform the Turbo Pascal compiler that three real values are to be used to compute a value of **Disc** according to the rule in the function definiton. These formal parameters are not seen by the main program. Variables with the names **A, B** and **C** can therefore be used elsewhere in the program, and will have no connection with the formal parameters. ***Any*** three identifiers could have been used, for example **X, Y** and **Z.**

When the function **Disc** is activated later in the program, the values of its *actual* parameters **P, Q** and **R** are copied into the formal parameters **A, B** and **C** respectively, and used to compute the value of **Disc.** The function may be used repeatedly, with different actual parameters each time. On each call, the actual parameter values are copied into the formal parameters for use in the function definition.

In all the above examples, the formal parameters are **value parameters**, which means that changes to the formal parameter in the function definition are *not* passed back to the corresponding actual parameter on return. Technically, the parameters are passed **by value.**

If, however, a formal parameter is preceded by the reserved word **var**, it is called a **variable parameter**, which means that a change in the formal parameter value is reflected in the actual parameter. Technically, such parameters are passed **by reference** (or **name**). Stylistically, a function should only use value parameters. If parameters are to be changed on return, the function should be rewritten as a procedure (see section 8.2).

Local and global variables

The following program uses a function **Fact** to compute *N*!:

```
program Factorial;
type
vaPosLongint = 1..MaxLongint;
  I : word;

function Fact( N: word ): PosLongint;
{ calculates N! }
var
  I      : word;
  Temp   : longint;
begin
  Temp:= 1;
  for I:= 2 to N do
```

```
    Temp:= I * Temp;
    Fact:= Temp
end; { Fact }

begin
  for I:= 1 to 12 do
  Writeln( I:3, Fact( I ):12 )
end.
```

Output:

```
  1          1
  2          2
  3          6
  4         24
  5        120
  6        720
  7       5040
  8      40320
  9     362880
 10    3628800
 11   39916800
 12  479001600
```

If you use this program as it stands to compute the factorials above 12!, you will find some strange results, because longint type overflows and begins to cycle. If a **PosLongint** type is defined as above, and range-checking is switched on with {**$R+**}, the overflow will be trapped when **Temp** eventually becomes negative. Try it. Note that a type may not be defined in a function declaration. The following would cause an error:

```
function Fact( N: word ): 1..MaxLongint;
```

User-defined types must be declared before the function declaration. The same applies to the formal parameter list, so the following is not allowed:

```
function Fact( N: 1..MaxInt ) ...
```

The function name (**Fact**) must appear ***at least once***, without parameters, on the lefthand side of an assignment statement inside the function declaration. In this way the function is evaluated, and its value returned to the main (calling) program. If the function name is mentioned on the *righthand* side of an assignment statement in the function declaration, its parameters must be included, and the declaration becomes *recursive* (see below).

A concept fundamental to functions (and procedures) in Turbo Pascal is that of local and global variables. All variables declared inside a function are **local** to that function, and cannot be seen from the outside. So the two variables named **I** above are totally different – they are actually stored in different places.

By contrast, variables declared in the main program before any function declarations are **global**, and are known inside the functions (unless the same identifier is declared a variable inside a function, in which case it is local).

This is a crucial distinction, and can cause problems, as the following example illustrates. Remove the **var** declaration for **I** in the definition of **Fact**. Replace the lines

```
for I:= 2 to N do
  Temp:= I * Temp;
```

in Fact by

```
I:= 2;
while I <= N do
begin
  Temp:= I * Temp;
  I:= I + 1
end;
```

which is an equally acceptable way of coding the loop. However, the output is now

```
1           1
3           6
5         120
7        5040
9      362880
11   39916800
```

I is now a global variable, and represents the same thing inside and outside the function. **Fact** is first called when **I** = 1, which is the first value written. This value is passed to the function through its parameter **N**. The same **I** is now given the value 2 inside **Fact**, but since it is greater than **N**, the **while** loop is not executed. **I** therefore still has the value 2 when **Fact** returns to be written. However, **I** is now incremented to 3 in the **for** loop in the main program, which is the value it has when the second call to **Fact** takes place. In this way, **Fact** is never computed for an even value of **I**. All this is a consequence of the variable **I** being global (ie known both to main program and function).

Curiously, the same problem does not arise if the original **for** loop is retained in **Fact**, instead of the **while** loop being used, ie if the only change made is to remove **I**'s declaration from **Fact**. Can you figure out why?

This distinction between local and global variables is so important that it is worth looking at another example:

```
...
var I: word;
function Funny: real;
var I: word;
begin
  I:= I + 1;
  Funny:= 0;
end; { Funny }

begin
  I:= 1;
  Writeln (Funny, I:3 );
...
```

Since **I** is local to **Funny** increasing it by one in **Funny** has no effect on the **I** in the main program after **Funny** is activated. However, removing **I**'s declaration from **Funny** means that the statement **I:= I + 1** now applies to the **I** in the main program, so its value is 2 after **Funny** is activated.

Recursion

Many mathematical functions are defined **recursively**, ie in terms of simpler cases of themselves. For example $n!$ may be defined as follows:

$$n! = n(n-1)!$$

provided that 1! is defined as 1. Turbo Pascal allows functions and procedures to call themselves. This process is called **recursion**. The factorial function may be rewritten as a recursive function as follows:

```
...
type
  PosLongint = 1..MaxLongint;

function Fact( N: word ): PosLongint;
{ calculates N! recursively }
begin
  if N <= 1 then
    Fact:= 1
  else
    Fact:= N * Fact( N - 1 );
end; { Fact }
begin
  Writeln( Fact( 10 ) );
...
```

This is the way functions are generally computed recursively. An **if** statement traps the special case (**N** = 1 here) – for all other cases the recursive definition is used. Note that the function's parameters must be stated now when it appears on the righthand side of an assignment statement.

While recursion appears to be deceptively simple, it is an advanced topic which should be treated with care. This is demonstrated by the following experiment. Insert the statement

Write(N:3);

in the function declaration ***before*** the **if** statement. The effect is what you might expect: the integers 10 to 1 in descending order. Now move the **Write** statement to ***after*** the **if** statement, and see what happens. The result is the integers 1 to 10 in *ascending order*, which is rather surprising.

In the first case, the value of **N** is written every time the function is *called*, and the output is obvious enough. However, there is a big difference between a recursive function being *called*, and *executed*. In the second case, the **Write** statement can only be executed after the **if** has finished executing. And when exactly does that happen? Well, on the first call, **N** has the value 10, so the **else** part is evaluated. However, the value of **Fact(9)** is not known at this stage, so a *copy* is made of all the statements in the function which will need to be executed once the value of **Fact(9)** is known. The reference to **Fact(9)** makes **Fact** call itself with **N** = 9. Again, the **else** part of the **if** is evaluated, whereupon Turbo Pascal discovers that it doesn't know the value of **Fact(8)**. So another (different) copy is made of all the statements that will need to be executed once the value of **Fact(8)** is known. And so each time **Fact** is called, separate copies are made of all the statements *yet to be executed*. Finally, Turbo Pascal joyfully finds a value of **N** (1) for which it knows **Fact**, so it at last begins to execute the **Write** statements which have been stacked up inside the memory. And this it does in the order **N** = 1, 2, 3, etc., because this is the order in which it discovers the successive values of **Fact(N)**.

This discussion illustrates the point that recursion should be used carefully. While it is perfectly in order to use it in a case like this, it can chew up huge amounts of computer memory and time. This point is amply illustrated by Ackermann's function, one of the most notorious of all recursive functions, which is defined as follows:

$$A(0, N) = N + 1$$
$$A(M, 0) = A(M - 1, 1)$$
$$A(M, N) = A(M - 1, A(M, N - 1)).$$

The following program attempts to compute this function:

```
program Mindless;
var
  I, J : word;

function Ack( M, N: word ): word;
{ the notorious Ackermann function }
begin
  if M = 0 then
    Ack:= N + 1
  else
    if N = 0 then
      Ack:= Ack( M-1, 1 )
    else
      Ack:= Ack( M-1, Ack( M, N-1 ) )
end; { Ack }

begin
  for I:= 0 to 6 do
    for J:= 0 to 6 do
      Writeln( I:3, J:3, Ack( I, J ):4 )
end.
```

If you have the patience to wait long enough, you will find that the program runs out of memory long before it should stop executing.

There is an example of recursion in graphics in section 13.3.

8.2 PROCEDURES

Procedures are virtually the same as functions, with one very important difference: ***no value is attached to the name of a procedure.***

Swopping two variables

As an example, we consider a procedure **Swop** to exchange the values of two variables:

```
...
var
  X, Y : real;

procedure Swop( var A, B: real );
{ swops the contents of two real variables A and B }
var
  Temp : real;
begin
  Temp:= A;
  A:= B;
  B:= Temp
end; { Swop }
begin
  Readln( X, Y );
  Swop( X, Y );
  Writeln( X:10:2, Y:10:2);
...
```

The procedure is activated by a **procedure statement**, which mentions the procedure's name together with the actual parameters. Note that as no value is assigned to the procedure name, this name cannot appear on the lefthand side of an assignment statement, as in the case of a function.

Results are sent back from the procedure through its parameters, which must therefore be **variable parameters**, ie a list of formal parameters preceded by the keyword **var**. ***When a procedure with variable parameters is activated, the variable parameters in its list of formal parameters are allocated to the same memory locations as the corresponding actual parameters in its activating statement.*** It therefore follows that the variables **X** and **Y** in the procedure **Swop** occupy the *same memory locations* as the variables **A** and **B** in the main program. Consequently, any changes made to the values of **X** and **Y** in the procedure are obviously reflected in similar changes to **A** and **B** on return to the main program. This process is technically called **passing by reference**. The *names* of the actual parameters are passed to the procedure. These names are used for the actual memory locations of the respective parameters. All communication with a procedure therefore takes place through its parameters.

8.3 BLOCKS, LOCALITY AND SCOPE

The time is now ripe for some more definitions.

A **block** consists of declarations, which may generally be in any order, and statements. A program is therefore a block, in terms of this definition, and so are procedures, functions, and units (see below), since procedures, for example, contain declarations and statements.

All identifiers (and labels) declared in the declaration part of a block are **local** *to that block.*

The declaration part of a block may contain the following parts:

- label declarations;
- constant declarations;
- type declarations;
- variable declarations;
- procedure and function declarations;

It follows that an identifier declared in the main program before any procedure and function declarations is local to the whole program, ie global.

The **scope** of an identifier is the extent or domain of its validity, and stretches generally from its declaration ***to the end of the current block***. An exception to this scope rule occurs when an identifier is re-declared in an enclosed block, as we have seen. The inner block can in general only access its version of the identifier, while the outer block can only access its version. However, the inner block can access the outer version by using a qualified identifier, which must be the name of the outer block (ie the name of the program, procedure, function or unit). For example:

```
program Tweedledum;
var X: real;

procedure Tweedledee;
var X: real;
begin
  X:= 17;
  Writeln( Tweedledum.X )
end; { Tweedledee }

begin
  X:= 2;
  Tweedledee
end.
```

will give an output of 2. However, a reference to **Tweedledee.X** in **Tweedledum** will cause an error, since this is outside its scope.

8.4 GENERAL RULES FOR FUNCTIONS AND PROCEDURES

The basic syntax of a function header is

function *Ident(formal parameter list)*: *type*;

while that of a procedure is

procedure *Ident(formal parameter list*);

The type of the formal parameters must be stated in the case of value and variable parameters.

Value parameters are passed by value. The parameter list must not contain the keyword **var**. A value parameter must not be of file type or of any structured type that contains a file type.

Variable parameters are passed by reference. File types may be passed as variable parameters.

If a formal parameter is not given a type, it is **untyped**. The corresponding actual parameter may then be of any type.

Value, variable and untyped parameters may be mixed in the formal parameter list.

The control variable of a **for** loop in a block must either be global, or local to the block in which it is used. The following is not allowed, and causes error 97 (Invalid FOR control variable).

```
...
procedure Outer;
var I: byte;

  procedure Inner;
  begin
    for I:= 1 to 10 do
  end; { Inner }

begin
  Inner;
end; { Outer }

begin
  Outer;
...
```

I is not declared in the main program, nor is it declared in the block that uses it **(Inner)**.

Type identity

Type identity is required between actual and formal variable parameters in procedure and function calls (and nowhere else). The *Turbo Pascal Reference Guide* states that two types, *T1* and *T2*, are identical if either *T1* and *T2* are the same type identifier, or if *T1* is declared equivalent to a type identical to *T2*. This is best explained by an example. In

```
type
  T1 = integer;
  T2 = T1;
  T3 = integer;
  T4 = T2;
```

all four types are identical. However, in

```
type
  T5 = string[20];
  T6 = string[20];
```

T5 and *T6* are not identical types because **string[20]** is *not* a type identifier.

Type identity in respect of string parameters only is relaxed under the **{$V–}** compiler directive. The default setting is on (Var String Checking).

Forward declarations

It is helpful in a program with many functions and procedures to arrange them alphabetically. The following situation can then easily arise:

```
...
var
  A, B : real;

procedure Shakespeare;
begin
  Writeln( William( A, B ) )
end; { Shakespeare }

function William( X, Y: real ): real;
begin
  William:= X + Y;
end; { William }

begin
  A:= 1;
  B:= 2;
  Shakespeare;
...
```

An error occurs because **William** is referenced in **Shakespeare** without having first been declared. A **forward reference** to **William** may be made as follows:

```
...
var
  A, B : real;

function William( X, Y: real ): real; forward;

procedure Shakespeare;
begin
  Writeln( William( A, B ) )
end; { Shakespeare }

function William;
begin
  William:= X + Y;
end; { William }
...
```

Note that the function type declaration and formal parameter list are given in the forward reference. These are all omitted in the definition later. The forward reference warns the compiler that the full definition is coming up later.

Procedural type

Procedures and functions may themselves be passed as parameters which are of **procedural type**. This is useful in numerical analysis, where a function name may be passed to a numerical integration procedure, for example. Procedural type is discussed in section 16.2.

External and inline declarations

These enable you to link your Turbo Pascal program up with separately compiled functions and procedures written in assembly language. They are described in the *Turbo Pascal Reference Guide*.

Stubs

A large program will have many procedures and functions. To plan and code them all before compiling anything is asking for trouble. But because of Pascal's insistence on declaring everything before use, how can we avoid this? The answer is to use **stubs**, which declare the function and procedure names, but do nothing. So declare all the functions and procedures you will be using as stubs, and fill them in one at a time, compiling after each fill-in. That way it's much easier to catch the compilation errors:

```
program BigOne;

procedure First;
begin
end; { First }

procedure Last;
begin
end; { Last }

begin
  First;
  Last
end.
```

It may not do much at this stage, but at least it compiles!

8.5 UNITS

A **unit** is a collection of declarations (including functions and procedures) which have been precompiled, and which may be linked into your program. We have already seen how to use some of the standard units with a **uses** clause. Turbo Pascal allows you to write and precompile your own units. Large programs should generally be broken up into smaller units. This makes for cleaner, more structured programming, and also saves enormously on compilation time. It's also possible for your favourite units to be shared by many different programs. This section gives a brief introduction to units. You should consult the *Turbo Pascal User's Guide* and the *Turbo Pascal Reference Guide* for all the gory details.

An example

The functions **ScaleH** and **ScaleV** and the procedure **SetGraphics**, which we developed in Chapter 6 and saved for convenience under the name GRSCALE.PAS, are ideal candidates for amalgamation into a unit, since they can be used without alteration in many graphics programs.

They can be turned into a unit with very few changes. Edit GRSCALE as follows (highlighted lines indicate changes):

```
unit GrScale;
{ Initialises graphics and sets scale Right-Left and Bottom-Top }

interface
uses Graph;
var
  Left, Right, Top, Bottom: real;
```

```
  function ScaleH( X: real): integer;
  function ScaleV( Y: real): integer;
  procedure SetGraphics;

implementation
  function ScaleH;
  { scales X coordinate }
  var
    TempX : real;

    begin
      TempX:= GetMaxX * (X - Left) / (Right - Left);
      ScaleH:= Round( TempX )
    end; { ScaleH }

    function ScaleV;
    { scales Y coordinate }
    var
      TempY : real;
    begin
      TempY:= GetMaxY * (Y - Top) / (Bottom - Top);
      ScaleV:= Round( TempY )
    end; { ScaleV }

    procedure SetGraphics;
    { Initialises Graphics }
    var
      GrDriver, GrMode, MaxX, MaxY: integer;
    begin
      GrDriver:= Detect;
      InitGraph( GrDriver, GrMode, 'B:\GR' );
    end; { SetGraphics }

  end. { GrScale }
```

Save this under the filename GRSCALE.PAS. The filename must be the same as the unit name.

To compile the unit use the Compile Menu (**Alt-C**). Since you will be using this unit many times it makes sense to save it to disk. Select the **D**estination command. The destination will change to DISK (it toggles between DISK and MEMORY). Then select the **C**ompile command. If everything is OK, you should get the message SUCCESS flashing in the box on the screen. If you look in the current directory now (**F**ile/**D**irectory command) you should find the file GRSCALE.TPU. The .TPU extension means that the file contains a compiled **T**urbo **P**ascal **U**nit.

How do we use the unit? Easy! The following example is the solution to Exercise 6.18 (the logistic model). Try it out (but first use the **C**ompile Menu to change **D**estination back to MEMORY, or you will soon clutter up your disk with .EXE files!).

```
program Logistic;
uses Graph, GrScale;
var
  T : integer;
  X, X0, K, R, TMax : real;
begin
  X0:= 2;
  R:= 0.1;
  K:= 1000;
  Left:= 0;
  TMax:= 200;
  Right:= TMax;
  Bottom:= 0;
  Top:= 2 * K;
  SetGraphics;
  MoveTo( ScaleH( 0 ), ScaleV( X0 ) );
  for T:= 1 to Round( Tmax ) do
```

```
  begin
    X:= X0 * K / ((K - X0) * Exp( - R * T ) + X0);
    LineTo( ScaleH( T ), ScaleV( X ) )
  end;
  Readln;
  CloseGraph
end.
```

Note that the new unit **GrScale** must be mentioned in the **uses** clause. Also notice that you don't have to remember to declare the variables **Left, Right, Bottom** and **Top** any more, because they are declared in the unit **GrScale**, and those declarations, together with any functions and procedures in the unit, are available to any program (or unit) that references **GrScale** in a **uses** statement.

Unit construction

The general structure of a unit is as follows:

```
unit ident;
interface
uses list of units;     { Optional }
  { public declarations }
implementation
uses list of units;     { Optional }
  { private declarations }
  { definition (implementation) of procedures and functions }
begin
  { initialisation code }
end.
```

Note that the unit's name, like a program name, must be a legal identifier.

The section between the reserved words **interface** and **implementation** is called the **interface** section. This is the public part of the unit, and must contain the names (with formal parameter lists) of any functions and procedures in the unit which are to be accessible from the outside, ie from any program (or unit) using the unit. It may also contain constant, type, or variable declarations. The scope of such declarations extends to all programs using the unit. If any of these functions or procedures use other units, these units must be mentioned in a **uses** clause in the interface section. There may be only one **uses** clause in a unit. It may appear either immediately after the keyword **interface**, or immediately after the keyword **implementation**. Forward declarations are neither necessary nor allowed.

The **implementation** section starts at the reserved word **implementation**. This is the private part of the unit. Everything in the interface section is visible to the implementation section, but the implementation section may have declarations of its own, which will not be visible to any programs using the unit. If procedures or functions appear in the interface section, the short form of their names must be used in the implementation section (ie **procedure/function** *ident*;).

The **initialisation** section is enclosed between **begin-end.** after the implementation section. It looks just like the main body of a program. Any data structures made available by the unit are initialised here, for example files may be opened. When a program using a unit is executed, the unit's initialisation code is executed before the main body of the program is run. If a program uses a number of units, the initialisation code of the units is executed in the order in which the units appear in the **uses** clause – before the main body of the program is run.

General information and hints

There may be only one **uses** clause in a program or unit, and it must be the first non-comment line in the program or unit.

Only one unit may be saved in a disk file, the filename of which must be the same as the name of the unit.

The ordering of units in a **uses** clause is not important.

If *Unit1* uses *Unit2*, and a program only needs the declarations in *Unit1*, it is only necessary for *Unit1* to appear in a **uses** clause in the program.

If *Unit1* uses *Unit2* and they both declare the same identifier, *ident*, then *Unit2*'s ident is not normally available to *Unit1*. However, if the identifier is qualified with the unit name, it is. So *Unit1* can reference its own *ident* and *Unit2.ident*. Perhaps the next example will make this clear. Save the following unit:

```
unit Wisconsin;
interface
const
  Pi = 3.0;          { good enough? }
implementation
end. { Wisconsin }
```

Then use it in this program:

```
program Pie;
uses Wisconsin;
const
  Pi = 3.1415927;
begin
  Writeln( Wisconsin.Pi:10:1, Pi:10:6 );
...
```

Although a program or unit may not take up more than 64K of memory, the use of units enables you to write programs which use as much memory as your operating system will allow.

In large applications it is common to group procedures in units according to their function, and even to have one unit entirely devoted to global declarations, ie constants, types and variables that must be accessible to all units. For example:

```
program TheLastOne;
uses Globals, MyInput, MyOutput, MyPrinter, MyGraphics;
```

If you are using a number of large units repeatedly (for example during development of software) you may find that quite a lot of time is spent reading the units from the disk (even from a hard disk). In that case, it may be worthwhile configuring a virtual (RAM) disk drive (D) using software like MEMBRAIN, and copying your units to drive D before your heavy session. The access time during compilation is then more or less instantaneous. But remember that the RAM disk evaporates when you switch off!

If it's not convenient for a unit to be saved in the current directory, use the **O**ptions/**D**irectories/**U**nit Directories command (press **Enter** to get into the box) to specify any directories where your units may be found. If Turbo Pascal can't find a unit in the current directory, it searches the **U**nit Directories list. If you specify more than one search path, they must be separated by semi-colons *only* – no spaces! For example:

```
Unit Directories: C:\TP5;C:\UTIL;D:\FAST
```

The file TURBO.TPL on your Turbo Pascal disk contains a library of standard units: **Crt, Dos, Printer, Overlay** and **System**. The **System** unit contains all the standard functions and procedures of Turbo Pascal and is automatically linked to every program. The other units must be mentioned in a **uses** clause to be used. TURBO.TPL is loaded into memory every time you start up Turbo Pascal. The units in it are accessed immediately. You can move your own units into TURBO.TPL with TPUMOVER.EXE (see the *Turbo Pascal User's Guide*). This saves compilation time and disk wear and tear. You can also increase the memory available to your program by removing units that you may not need from TURBO.TPL.

When changes are made in the interface part of a unit, all other units using that unit must be recompiled. Turbo Pascal recognises this situation during compilation. Either an error will occur, or the unit will be recompiled under **C**ompile/**M**ake (see the *Turbo Pascal User's Guide*).

Overlays

Even the 640K of memory available on most PCs may not be enough for your program to end all programs. Turbo Pascal has a solution for this situation also: **overlays.** Basically, a group of units that are not required at the same time (for example, for input and output) can be shunted in and out of the same area of memory, so that the total memory required by the group is the memory required by the largest unit. This process is called an overlay. Turbo Pascal has a standard unit, **Overlay,** which manages overlays for you. Consult the *Turbo Pascal Reference Guide* for details.

8.6 MAKING .EXE FILES

A program can be compiled to disk with the **C**ompile/**D**estination set to **D**isk. It is then saved with the .EXE extension, and may be run directly from DOS in future simply by entering the filename (without the .EXE extension). In this way your programs can be run by someone who doesn't have a copy of Turbo Pascal. For example, if your program is saved under TEST.PAS, compiling it to disk will create the file TEST.EXE. To run it from DOS enter

TEST

after the DOS prompt.

Redirecting DOS input and output

A .EXE file run from DOS usually expects input from the keyboard and sends output to the monitor. Output can be redirected to a disk file with > *OutFile* after the filename, and input can be read from a disk file with < *InFile* (think of the > and < as arrows indicating the direction of data flow). For example:

TEST < DATA > RESULTS

The output file will be created by DOS if it doesn't already exist.

SUMMARY

- Good structured programming requires real problem-solving programs to be broken down into procedures and functions.
- A block consists of declarations and statements.
- Each block is part of a function declaration, a procedure declaration, a unit or a program.
- Identifiers declared in a block are local (accessible) to that block only. An exception is when the same identifier is declared in an enclosed block. The identifier in the outer block is not accessible in the inner block unless the identifier is qualified by the block name.
- Functions and procedures may be defined recursively.
- Items listed in parentheses after a function or procedure name when it is referenced are called actual parameters. Identifiers listed in the function or procedure header are called formal parameters.
- Parameters may be typed or untyped.
- Parameters may be passed by value or by reference.
- A variable parameter is preceded by the keyword **var** in the formal parameter list, and is passed by reference. A value parameter is not preceded by **var**, and is passed by value. The difference is that if a variable formal parameter is changed inside the procedure/function, the change is reflected in the corresponding actual parameter.
- Stubs (empty functions/procedures) can be used when developing large programs.
- Declarations, functions and procedures may be compiled independently of the main program in units.
- Programs or units may not use more than 64K of memory.
- TURBO.TPL is a file containing most of the standard units, which is loaded into memory when you enter Turbo Pascal.

- TPUMOVER may be used to move units in and out of TURBO.TPL.
- Overlays are parts of a program which share a common memory area. These should be used when a program gets too large for your PCs memory.
- .EXE files are produced when you compile a program to disk, and may subsequently be run directly from DOS.

EXERCISES

8.1 Write a program which uses the Newton quotient

$$[f(x + h) - f(x)]/h$$

to estimate the first derivative of $f(x) = x^3$ at $x = 1$, using successively smaller values of h: 1, 1e−1, 1e−2, etc., etc. Use a function for $f(x)$. See section 16.3 for the coding.

8.2 Write your own Turbo Pascal function to compute the exponential function directly from the Taylor series:

$$e^x = 1 + x + x^2/2! + x^3/3! + \dots$$

The series should end when the last term is less than 1e−6. Test your function against the standard Exp(X) function.

8.3 Write a function Bin(N, R) which returns the binomial coefficient,

$$n!/[r!(n-r)!],$$

as defined in Chapter 6.

8.4 Write a procedure

Quad(var X1, X2: real; A, B, C: real; var J:integer)

which computes the roots of the quadratic equation

$$ax^2 + bx + c = 0.$$

The parameters A, B and C (which may take any values) are the coefficients of the quadratic, and X1, X2 are the two roots (if they exist), which may be equal. See section 3.5 for the structure plan. J is a flag which must be set by the procedure as follows:

J = −1: imaginary roots (discriminant < 0);
J = 0: no solution ($a = b = 0, c <> 0$);
J = 1: one root ($a = 0, b <> 0$, so the root is $-c/b$);
J = 2: two roots (which could be equal);
J = 99: any x is a solution ($a = b = c = 0$).

8.5 If a random variable X is distributed normally with zero mean and unit standard deviation, the probability that $0 \leq X \leq x$ is given by the standard normal function $\Phi(x)$. This is usually looked up in tables, but it may be approximated as follows:

$$\Phi(x) = 0.5 - r(at + bt^2 + ct^3), \text{ where}$$
$$a = 0.4361836$$
$$b = -0.1201676$$
$$c = 0.937298$$
$$r = \exp(-0.5x^2)/\sqrt{(2\pi)}$$
$$t = 1/(1 + 0.3326x).$$

Write a function to compute $\Phi(x)$, and use it in a program to write out its values for $0 \leq x \leq 4$ in steps of 0.1.

8.6 The Fibonacci numbers are generated by the sequence

1, 1, 2, 3, 5, 8, 13, ...

Can you work out what the next term is? Write a recursive function to compute the Fibonacci numbers $F(0)$ to $F(20)$, using the relationship

$$F(n) = F(n-1) + F(n-2),$$

starting with $F(0) = F(1) = 1$.

8.7 Write a function **Time** which returns the number of seconds elapsed since midnight. Use the **GetTime** procedure in the **Dos** unit, as illustrated in section 4.4.

8.8 Write a program which uses **Time** (Exercise 8.7) to behave like a primitive stop-watch. It should prompt the user to hit any key to start, and any key to finish (using the **ReadKey** and **KeyPressed** functions).

8.9 Using the ideas of the previous problem write a program which measures your reaction time. This can be done by making the program sound a short note a random period of time after starting, and then measuring the time that elapses before you hit any key.

9 Arrays

Situations often arise in real problem solving where we need to handle a large amount of data in the same way, for example, to find the mean (average) of a set of numbers, or to sort a list of numbers or names, or to analyse a set of students' test results, or to solve a set of differential equations. To avoid an enormously clumsy program, where perhaps hundreds of identifiers are needed, we can use **indexed** (subscripted) variables, or **arrays**. These may be regarded as variables with components, rather like vectors or matrices. They are written in the normal way, except that the indices are enclosed in brackets after the variable name, for example, **X[3], Y[J + 2 * N]**.

9.1 MEAN AND STANDARD DEVIATION

To illustrate the basic principles, let's compute the sample mean and standard deviation of a set of N observations. The mean is defined as

$$\bar{X} = \sum_{i=1}^{N} X_i/N$$

where X_i is the ith observation. There are two ways of expressing the standard deviation. The less usual way (which doesn't require the use of an array) is

$$s^2 = (\sum_{i=1}^{N} X_i^2 - N\bar{X}^2) / (N-1) .$$

This form is used in the next program. The data are read from the disk file OBS. using the **Eof** boolean function to detect the end of the file.

```
program Average;
{ Here we go at Stats! }
const
  Mean : real  = 0;               { mean }
  N    : word  = 0;               { number of observations }
  Std  : real  = 0;               { standard deviation }
var
  F    : text;                    { data file }
  X    : real;                    { general observation }
begin
  Assign( F, 'OBS.' );
   Reset( F );

  while not Eof( F ) do           { read the data first }
  begin
    Read( F, X );
    N:= N + 1;
    Mean:= Mean + X;
    Std:= Std + X * X
  end;
  Mean:= Mean / N;                { now do the stats }
  Std:= Sqrt( (Std - N * Mean * Mean) / (N - 1) );
  Writeln( 'Mean:             ', Mean:6:2 );
```

```
  Writeln( 'Std deviation: ', Std:6:2 );
  Close( F )
end.
```

Try this with some sample data:

5.1 6.2 5.7 3.5 9.9 1.2 7.6 5.3 8.7 4.4

The output should be:

```
Mean:            5.76
Std deviation:   2.53
```

The assignment statements for **Mean** and **Std** in the **while** loop compute running totals, so **Mean**, for example, will take the successive values 5.1, 11.3, 17.0, etc.

A more familiar way of expressing the standard deviation is by the formula

$$s^2 = \sum_{i=1}^{N} (X_i - \bar{X})^2 / (N-1)$$

Programming this form introduces the use of an array. Suppose we still have 10 observations. They may be read into memory locations **X[1]**, **X[2]**, ..., **X[10]**, where **X** stands for any valid Turbo Pascal identifier. The mean may be computed while the observations are being read in, as before. When all the data have been read, they remain in variables **X[1]**, ..., **X[10]**, for further use later on in the program. The standard deviation may now be found by computing the deviation of each **X[I]** from the mean using the second formula quoted above. Try the following program out. It will work for up to 100 observations (bold type indicates changes from the previous program).

```
program Arrays;
{ Arrays for the first time! }
const
  MaxElt          = 100;      { maximum number of observations }
  Mean : real     = 0;        { mean }
  N    : word     = 0;        { number of observations }
  Std  : real     = 0;        { standard deviation }
var
  F    : text;                { data file }
  I    : word;                { loop counter }
  X    : array[ 1..MaxElt ] of real;                { array for all observations }
begin
  Assign( F, 'OBS.' );
  Reset( F );

  while not Eof( F ) do       { read the data first }
  begin
    N:= N + 1;
    Read( F, X[N] );
    Mean:= Mean + X[N]
  end;

  Mean:= Mean / N;            { now do the stats }

  for I:= 1 to N do
    Std:= Std + Sqr( (X[I] - Mean) );
  Std:= Sqrt( Std / (N - 1) );
  Writeln( 'Mean:          ', Mean:6:2 );
  Writeln( 'Std deviation: ', Std:6:2 );
  Close( F )
end.
```

After the data have been read, the array **X** will look as follows:

```
X[1] :    5.1
X[2] :    6.2
X[3] :    5.7
...
X[10] :   4.4
```

The declaration

X : array[1..MaxElt] of real; { array for all observations }

declares **X** to be an array with components of real type, numbered from 1 to **MaxElt** (=100)

If you are frequently involved with statistical work, for example, analysing results of experiments, you might need to find means and standard deviations in many programs. It therefore makes sense to write a general purpose procedure to do this. The following program includes such a procedure, **Stats**. It has two formal value parameters, **Y** and **Num**, and two formal variable parameters **Ybar** and **SDev**. **Y** is the array of data, and **Num** is the number of observations. They are value parameters to avoid the values of the actual parameters **X** and **N** being accidentally changed by sloppy coding in the procedure. **Ybar** and **SDev** are the mean and standard deviation of the data. They are variable parameters because the corresponding actual parameters **XBar** and **Std** *must* be changed.

It is important to note how an array is passed to a procedure. Its type declaration may *not* be included in the formal parameter list – this causes error 12 (Type identifier expected). Instead the type of the array to be passed must be defined in a **type** statement. In this example the type **ArrDat** is defined, and this definition is used as the type identifier in the formal parameter list.

```
program Statistician;
const
  MaxElt         = 100;           { maximum amount of data }
  Mean  : real   = 0;             { mean }
  N     : word   = 0;             { number of observations }
  Std   : real   = 0;             { standard deviation }
type
  ArrDat = array[ 1..MaxElt ] of real; { array type }
var
  F      : text;                  { data file }
  X      : ArrDat;                { array for all observations }

procedure Stats( Y: ArrDat; var YBar, SDev: real; Num: word );
{ reads data and returns mean and standard deviation }
var
  I      : word;                  { loop counter }
begin
  Ybar:= 0;                       { to remove any garbage }
  SDev:= 0;

  for I:= 1 to Num do
    Ybar:= Ybar + Y[I];

    Ybar:= Ybar / Num;

  for I:= 1 to N do               { run through the data again }
    SDev:= SDev + Sqr( Y[I] - Ybar );

  SDev:= Sqrt( SDev / (Num - 1) );
end; { Stats }

begin
  Assign( F, 'OBS.' );
  Reset( F );
```

```
  while not Eof( F ) do            { read the data first }
  begin
    N:= N + 1;
    Read( F, X[N] )
  end;
  Stats( X, Mean, Std, N );
  Writeln( 'Analysis of ', N, ' data:' );
  Writeln( 'Mean:          ', Mean:6:2 );
  Writeln( 'Std deviation: ', Std:6:2 );
  Close( F )
end.
```

If you are converting (at last) from languages like BASIC or FORTRAN, you will want to know if an array can be redimensioned to some variable length. In Pascal, the size of an array (ie the number of components) is fixed at compilation, and so its size must be a constant (for example **MaxElt** above). If a general purpose program is to be written, it must cater for the maximum possible array size. For this reason, it is a good idea to use constants for array bounds (lower or upper), since they can be found easily in a program if the bounds must be changed.

9.2 GENERAL RULES FOR ARRAYS

The following important points about arrays should be noted carefully.

X in the above program is called an **array**. An array is a **structured type**, meaning that it can hold more than one value. Other structured types are sets, files, records and objects.

Arrays have a fixed number of components, or elements, of a certain type – the **component type:**

array [*index type*, ...] **of** *component type*;

The index types, one for each **dimension** of the array (**X** above is one-dimensional), specify the number of components. Index types are all ordinal types except longint and subranges of longint. The array can be indexed in each dimension by all the values of the corresponding index type, or by a subrange. The number of dimensions is unlimited, although the maximum size allowed for an array is 65520 bytes. Different dimensions may have different *index* types. Some examples follow.

X: array[1..100] of real – the index type is the subrange 1..100 of integers, and these 100 elements of the array are of real type.

Y: array[shortint] of boolean – the index type is shortint (ie –128..127) and the component type is boolean, ie you can make the assignment

Y[–115]:= True;

Z: array[1..2, 1..3] of real – the array is two-dimensional. The first dimension has indices ranging from 1 to 2, while the second has indices from 1 to 3. So **Z** has 6 real components. This is how a (2×3) matrix can be represented. A component of **Z** is referenced thus: **Z[2, 1]**. A **multi-dimensional** array like this can also be treated as an array of arrays:

Z: array[1..2] of array[1..3] of real

A parenthesis and period may be used instead of brackets:

X(.I.):= 39;

An array cannot be read or written as a single entity, so this is *not* allowed:

Write(X). Instead use a **for** loop:

```
for I:= 1 to N do
  Write( X[I] );
```

However, arrays may be assigned as single entities, so this is allowed: **X:= Y**.

Turbo Pascal does not initialise variables to zero, as some languages do. This means that if you only use part of an array, the remaining elements will be garbage, and this could have disastrous consequences later if you reference one of them by accident. So it's best always to initialise arrays yourself:

```
for I:= 1 to MaxElts do
  X[I]:= 0;
```

For large arrays, this can be done much faster with the **FillChar** standard function:

```
FillChar( X, SizeOf(X), 0 );
```

In general, **FillChar(** *X*, *N*, *V* **)** puts the value *V* into *N* contiguous bytes of memory, starting at the first byte occupied by *X*. You cannot easily use this facility to set an entire array to a non-zero value, since individual bytes are set, and most arrays have elements longer than one byte.

SizeOf returns the number of bytes occupied by its argument.

Arrays may be declared as typed constants:

```
const
  HexDigits : array[0..15] of char = '0123456789ABCDEF';
  Vowels : array[1..5] of char = ('A', 'E', 'I', 'O', 'U' );
  TestData: array[1..5] of real = (1.1, 6.8, 8.9, 10, 4.6);
```

Note that arrays of char type may be expressed both as single characters and as strings.

An array can also be added to the Watch window (with **Ctrl-F7**), and its contents examined during or after execution. If an array is too large to fit into the Watch window, a range can be specified by giving the index and a repeat count,for example, entering

```
TestData[3],2
```

in the Watch window specifies 2 consecutive components starting at index 3.

If an index of an array goes out of bounds, Turbo Pascal does not report an error unless range-checking is on (use **O**ptions/**C**ompiler/**R**ange-Checking, or {**$R+**}). Since the default is off, you are advised to switch range-checking on while developing programs that use arrays. Terrible things can happen when an index goes out of range (like infinite loops, machine hang-ups, overwritten data, to name but a few). The price paid for range-checking is bigger, slower code, but once a program is thoroughly debugged you can switch it off.

When an array occurs in a formal parameter list, its type must be declared with a type identifier, ie the following will cause error 12 (Type identifier expected):

```
procedure Plonk( var X: array[1..100 of real );
```

Rather say

```
type
  ArrType = array[1..100] of real;
...
  procedure Plonk( var X: ArrType );
```

9.3 BAR CHARTS AND FREQUENCY DISTRIBUTION

It is possible to compute the mean and standard deviation without using an array – indeed we did so – although an array is essential for the general procedure written in the previous section. Our next example could be done without arrays only with great difficulty.

We will write a program to analyse the results of a test written by a class of students. We would like to know how many students obtained marks in the range 0% – 9%, 10% – 19%, ..., 100%+ (each of these ranges is called a decile). We will therefore need an array **F**, say, with 11 components, where each component stores the number of students with marks in that particular range, as follows:

number scoring 0% – 9% stored in **F[0]**: 0th decile;
number scoring 10% – 19% stored in **F[1]**: 1st decile;
...
number scoring 90% – 99% stored in **F[9]**: 9th decile;
number scoring 100% and over stored in **F[10]**: 10th decile.

So altogether there are *eleven* deciles. The program needs to read each mark (from a disk file MARKS) and decide to which of the 11 deciles that mark belongs:

```
program Bars;
var
  DFile  : text;
  F      : array[ 0..10 ] of integer;                    { frequencies }
  I, K   : byte;
  Mark   : real;
begin
  Assign( DFile, 'MARKS.' );
  Reset( DFile );
  FillChar( F, SizeOf( F ), 0 );                         { zero all components }
  while not Eof( DFile ) do
  begin
    Read( DFile, Mark );
    K:= Trunc( Mark / 10 );                              { decile }
    F[K]:= F[K] + 1
  end;
  for I:= 0 to 10 do
    Write( F[I]:3 )
end.
```

The output will be:

```
  3  0  1  4  8  7  7  3  4  2  1
```

This means that three students got marks in the range 0% – 9%, none in the range 10% – 19%, etc.

The results can be presented visually by changing the program to produce a bar chart of the frequencies **F[I]**. The statement

```
for I:= 0 to 10 do
  Write( F[I]:3 );
```

above should be replaced by the following statements:

```
for I:= 0 to 10 do
begin
  Write( 10 * I:3 );
  if I < 10 then
    Write( ' – ', 10 * I + 9:2 )
  else
    Write( ' +      ' );
  Write( ' ':3, F[I]:3, ': ' );
  for K:= 1 to F[I] do
    Write( '*' );
  Writeln
end;
```

The output now looks like this:

```
  0 –  9     3: ***
 10 – 19     0:
 20 – 29     1: *
 30 – 39     4: ****
 40 – 49     8: ********
 50 – 59     7: *******
 60 – 69     7: *******
 70 – 79     3: ***
 80 – 89     4: ****
 90 – 99     2: **
100 +        1: *
```

Note that **F[1]** is zero. The body of the **for** loop on **K** is therefore not executed for **K** = 1, so no asterisks are written for that decile. If you think asterisks are a bit dull, you can write solid bars instead of asterisks by replacing the Write('*') statement in the **for** loop with

```
Write( Chr( 219 ) )
```

where 219 is the ASCII code for a solid block.

Since a bar chart is something you may often need, it makes sense to write a procedure **BarChart** to produce the goods. It would also be useful (and better structured programming) to have a procedure **GetMarks** which open the data file and reads the marks. Your main program would then look just like a simple structure plan:

```
begin
  GetMarks;
  BarChart;
end.
```

Let's discuss **GetMarks** first (see below). Note that the parameters are explained in a comment section – this is essential for later use. **Name** is the (string) filename of the disk file where the data are. The type **Filename** must be defined in the main program. **X** is the array for the marks. Again its type **MarkType** must be defined in the main program.

```
{ ------GetMarks-----------------------------------------------------------------------}
{                                                                                      }
{  GetMarks opens the file Name, reads N marks into the array X,                      }
{  and then closes Name                                                                }
{                                                                                      }
{  Formal parameter types                                                              }
{                                                                                      }
{                 FileName = string[12];                                               }
{                 MarkType = array[ 1..MaxInClass ] of real;                           }
{--------------------------------------------------------------------------------------}

procedure GetMarks( Name: FileName; var X: MarkType; var N: word );

  var
    F : text;
  begin
    Assign( F, Name );
    Reset( F );
    N:= 0;

    while not Eof( F ) do
    begin
      N:= N + 1;
      Read( F, X[N] )
    end;
    Close( F )

  end; { GetMarks }
```

Now for **BarChart**. Note that it has been generalised to handle marks in the range 0 to **MaxMark** (a constant defined in the main program). Each row in the barchart can represent a variable range (**Width**) of marks. If **MaxMark** is not a multiple of **Width**, an error message is displayed, and the standard procedure **Exit** returns control to the main program. (In general, **Exit** causes an immediate exit from the current block.)

```
{------BarChart-----------------------------------------------------------------------}
{                                                                                      }
{  BarChart draws a barchart (frequency distribution) of the N                        }
{  marks in the array X. Width is the range of marks represented                      }
{  by each row of the chart. The maximum mark (MaxMark) must                          }
{  be an exact multiple of Width, otherwise the procedure returns an                  }
{  error message.                                                                      }
{                                                                                      }
{  Formal parameter type                                                               }
{                                                                                      }
{                 MarkType = array[ 1..MaxInClass ] of real;                           }
{--------------------------------------------------------------------------------------}
```

```
procedure BarChart( X: MarkType; N, Width: word );
  var
    F      : array[ 0..MaxMark ] of integer;                    {frequencies }
    I, K   : byte;
  begin
    ClrScr;
    if MaxMark mod Width <> 0 then
    begin
      Writeln( 'Sorry, MaxMark must be a multiple of Width.' );
      Exit
    end;
    FillChar( F, SizeOf( F ), 0 );
    for I:= 1 to N do
    begin
      K:= Trunc( X[I] / Width );                                 { decile }
      F[K]:= F[K] + 1
    end;
    for I:= 0 to MaxMark div Width do
    begin
      Write( Width * I:3 );
      if I < MaxMark div Width then
        Write( ' - ', Width * I + Width - 1:2 )
      else
        Write( ' +      ' );
      Write( ' ':3, F[I]:3, ': ' );
      for K:= 1 to F[I] do
        Write( Chr( 219 ) );
      Writeln
    end
  end; { BarChart }
```

Finally, the main program is as follows (the procedures are not repeated in full). Note that the **uses** clause must appear at the beginning of the main program, although the unit **(Crt)** is only used in **BarChart**.

```
  program Main;
  uses Crt;
  const
    MaxInClass = 200;
    MaxMark    = 100;
    Width = 10;
  type
    FileName = string[12];
    MarkType = array[ 0..MaxInClass ] of real;
  var
    DFile : text;
    NumMarks : word;
    Mark : MarkType;

  {------BarChart-----------------------------------------------------------}
    ...
  end; { BarChart }

  {------GetMarks-----------------------------------------------------------}
    ...
  end; { GetMarks }

  begin { Main }
    GetMarks( 'MARKS.', Mark, NumMarks );
    BarChart( Mark, NumMarks, Width );
  end. { Main }
```

9.4 SORTING A LIST: THE BUBBLE SORT

One of the standard application of arrays is in sorting a list of numbers into, let us say, ascending order. The basic idea is that the unsorted list is read into an array. The numbers are then ordered by a process which essentially passes through the list many times, swopping consecutive elements that are in the wrong order, until all the elements are in the right order. Such a process is called a **Bubble Sort**, because the smaller numbers rise to the top of the list, like bubbles of air in water. (In fact, in the version shown below, the largest number will sink to the bottom of the list after the first pass, which really makes it a Lead Ball sort.) There are many other methods of sorting, which may be found in most textbooks on computer science (one of them, the Quick Sort, is given in the next section). These are generally more efficient than the bubble sort, but its advantage is that it is by far the easiest method to program. A structure plan for the bubble sort is as follows:

1. Initialise N (length of list)
2. Read in the list X
3. Repeat $N-1$ times on counter K:
   3.1. Repeat $N-K$ times on counter J:
      3.1.1. If $X_j > X_{j+1}$ then
         3.1.1.1. Swop the contents of X_j and X_{j+1}
4. Write the list X, which is now sorted.

As an example, consider a list of five numbers: 27, 13, 9, 5 and 3. They are initially read into the array **X**. Part of the computer's memory for this problem is sketched in Table 9-1 below. Each column shows the list during each pass. A stroke (/) in a row indicates a change in that variable during the pass as the program works down the list. The number of tests (step 3.1.1) made on each pass is also shown in the table. Work through the table by hand with the structure plan until you understand how the algorithm works.

Pass:	1	2	3	4
X[1]:	27/13	13/ 9	9/ 5	5/ 3
X[2]:	13/27/ 9	9/13/ 5	5/ 9/ 3	3/ 5
X[3]:	9/27/ 5	5/13/ 3	3/ 9	9
X[4]:	5/27/ 3	3/13	13	13
X[5]:	3/27	27	27	27
Tests:	4	3	2	1

Table 9.1 Computer memory during a bubble sort

Sorting algorithms are compared by calculating the number of tests they execute (as in step 3.1.1 in the structure plan), since this takes up most of the execution time during the sort. On the Kth pass of the Bubble Sort there are exactly $N-K$ tests, so the total number of tests is

$$1 + 2 + 3 + \ldots + (N-1) = N(N-1)/2.$$

For a list of five numbers there are therefore ten tests, but for ten numbers there are 45 tests. The computer time needed goes up as the square of the length of the list.

The program below uses the procedure **BubbleSort** to sort 100 random numbers (random numbers are discussed in Chapter 14). It departs slightly from the structure plan above, which will make $N-1$ passes, *even if the list is sorted before then*. Since most real lists are partially sorted, it makes sense to check after each pass if any swops were made. If none were, the list must be sorted, so unnecessary and time-wasting tests should be eliminated. In the procedure, the boolean variable **Sorted** is used to detect swops, and the outer loop is coded instead as a **repeat-until** loop (since at least one pass must be made to determine whether the list is sorted).

```
program Sorter;
const
  MaxNum = 100;
type
```

```
  ArrType = array[ 1.. MaxNum ] of real;
var
  X       : ArrType;
  I, N    : word;
{------BubbleSort-------------------------------------------------------}
{                                                                       }
{  This procedure sorts an array X of N numbers into ascending          }
{  order using a Bubble Sort. The sorted list is returned               }
{  in the array X.                                                      }
{                                                                       }
{  Formal parameter types:                                              }
{                                                                       }
{              ArrType = array[ 1..MaxNum ] of real;                    }
{------BubbleSort-------------------------------------------------------}

  procedure Bubblesort( var X: ArrType; N: word );
  var
    J, K   : word;
    Temp   : real;
    Sorted : boolean;
    begin
    K:= 0;

    repeat                          { outer loop of bubble sort }
    K:= K + 1;                      { count the passes }
    Sorted:= true;                  { they might be sorted }
      for J:= 1 to N - K do           { count the tests }
        if X[J] > X[J+1] then         { are they in order? }
        begin                         { No ...           }
          Temp:= X[J];
          X[J]:= X[J+1];
            X[J+1]:= Temp;
          Sorted:= False              { a swop was made }
        end

    until Sorted                      { must be sorted now }

  end; { BubbleSort }

  begin { Main }
    Randomize;
    N:= 100;

    for I:= 1 to N do
      X[I]:= Trunc( 100 * Random );

    BubbleSort( X, N );

    for I:= 1 to N do
    begin
      Write( X[I]:3:0 );
      if I mod 25 = 0 then
        Writeln
    end

  end. { Main }
```

This program would be impossible to write without an array!

9.5 THE QUICK SORT

Try sorting 1000 numbers with the Bubble Sort. It takes quite a few minutes. Sorting 10000 numbers (a not inconceivable problem) would take about 100 times longer.

The famous Quick Sort algorithm, coded recursively below, is much faster. It was invented by C.A.R. Hoare. It is rather involved, and difficult to follow even by experienced programmers, so no explanation is given. A description of how it works may be found in Duntemann (1989). But you can use it without understanding how it works!

```
program QuickSortTest;
const
  MaxNum = 1000;
type
  ArrType = array[ 1..MaxNum ] of real;
var
  X      : ArrType;
  I, N   : word;
{------QuickSort-------------------------------------------------------}
{                                                                     }
{ This procedure sorts an array A of U numbers into ascending         }
{ order using C A R Hoare's QuickSort. The sorted list is             }
{ returned in the array A. The parameter L must be set to 1 on        }
{ entry                                                               }
{                                                                     }
{ Formal parameter types:                                             }
{                                                                     }
{               ArrType = array[ 1..MaxNum ] of real;                 }
{------QuickSort-------------------------------------------------------}

procedure QuickSort( var A: ArrType; L, U: word );
var
  J, K : word;
procedure Swop ( var A, B: real );
{ Swops the values of A and B }

var
  T : real;
begin
  T:= A;
  A:= B;
  B:= T
end; { Swop }

begin
  if L < U then
  begin
    J:= L;
    K:= U;

    repeat
      while (J < U) and (A[J] <= A[L]) do
        J:= J + 1;

      while (L < K) and (A[K] >= A[L]) do
        K:= K - 1;

      if J < K then
        Swop( A[J], A[K] )
    until J >= K;

    Swop ( A[L], A[K] );
    QuickSort( A, L, K-1 );
    QuickSort( A, K+1, U );
  end
end; { QuickSort }

begin { Main }
  Randomize;
  N:= 1000;

  for I:= 1 to N do
    X[I]:= Trunc( N * Random );
```

```
    QuickSort( X, 1, N );
  for I:= 1 to N do
  begin
    Write( X[I]:4:0 );
    if I mod 15 = 0 then
      Writeln
  end
end. { Main }
```

Try it out on 1000 numbers (as it stands). You should be impressed!

9.6 TOP OF THE CLASS

The program in section 5.1 to find the student with the highest mark in a class assumes that there is only one such student. We need to use an array if there is likely to be more than one name at the top:

```
program TopOfTheClass;
const
  MaxInClass = 100;
  TopMark    : real = -1;                         { someone must beat this! }
  NumTop     : word = 1;                          { there must be at least one! }
var
  F          : text;
  I          : word;
  Mark       : real;
  Name       : string[20];
  TopStudent : array[ 1..MaxInClass ] of string[20];
begin
  Assign( F, 'MARKS.' );
  Reset( F );
  while not Eof( F ) do
  begin
    Readln( F, Name, Mark );
    if Mark > TopMark then                        { new top mark here }
    begin
      TopMark:= Mark;                             { reset the top mark }
      NumTop:= 1;                                 { only one at the top now }
      TopStudent[1]:= Name                        { he must be at the top }
    end
    else
      if Mark = TopMark then                      { tie for top mark here }
      begin
        NumTop:= NumTop + 1;                      { advance counter }
        TopStudent[NumTop]:= Name                 {add his name to the list }
      end
    end;
    for I:= 1 to NumTop do
      Writeln( TopStudent[I]:20, TopMark:6:1 )
end.
```

As an exercise run through the program by hand with the following data:

Botha	58
De Klerk	72
Jones	72
Murray	72
Rogers	90
Tutu	90

Then run it as a check (the first 20 columns of each line in MARKS. must be reserved for the names). Note that at the end, the name Murray will still be in the array **TopStudent** (in component 3), but his name will not be written because **NumTop** has been reset to 2, and will prevent this. (You can examine the array **TopStudent** in the Watch window.)

9.7 GRAPHS WITH GRAPHICS

In Chapter 13 we will be looking at the graphics capabilities of Turbo Pascal. You may, however, not have a graphics card in your computer. The procedure **Grapher** in this section makes use of the **GoToXY** function to draw a rough graph of any function on the text screen. Its header is:

```
procedure Grapher( X, Y : ArrType; N: word; XF, XL, YD, YU: real; Symbol: char; Title: String80 );
```

The user must specify how many points (**N**) are to be plotted. These points are to be stored in the two one-dimensional arrays **X** and **Y**, where **X[I]** and **Y[I]** are the *x* and *y* co-ordinates of the *i*th point to be plotted. These arrays must be set up by the main program before entry. The user also supplies the smallest and largest *x* co-ordinates for the plot (**XF** and **XL**), the lowest and highest *y* co-ordinates (**YD** and **YU**), the plotting symbol (**Symbol**), and a title (**Title**), which will be centred.

Grapher draws the graph over a range of **MaxCol** columns and **MaxRow** rows on the screen. These are local variables declared in **Grapher**, although you could just as easily pass them as parameters. The elements of **X** and **Y** have to be scaled into these ranges before the graph can be drawn. This transformation requires some explanation.

The element **Y[I]** of the array **Y** must be transformed to a row number **IY**, giving the row on the screen where the plotting symbol must be written. Since we want a linear transformation (don't we?), we must have

$$IY = aY_i + b, \tag{1}$$

where the constants a and b must be determined. The highest point on the graph (YU) must be transformed into row 1 (the top of the screen), so

$$1 = aYU + b. \tag{2}$$

The lowest point on the graph (YD) must be transformed into row *MaxRow*, so

$$MaxRow = aYD + b. \tag{3}$$

Subtracting (2) from (3) immediately gives

$$a = (MaxRow - 1) / (YD - YU)$$

and substituting back into (2) gives

$$b = 1 - YU(MaxRow - 1)/(YD - YU).$$

These values for a and b may be used in (1) to give

$$IY = (Yi - YU)(MaxRow - 1)/(YD - YU) + 1.$$

A similar transformation is used to scale **X[I]** into a column **IX**. The test program below shows how **Grapher** may be used to plot the damped oscillations discussed in Chapter 6.

```
program TextGraph;
uses Crt;
const
   Pi          = 3.1415927;
   TwoPi       = 2 * Pi;
   Cycles      : real = 2;
   I           : real = 0;
   PerCy       : real = 10;
   T           : real = 0;
type
   ArrType = array[ 1..100 ] of real;
   String80 = string[80];
var
   A, C, Dt, F0, F1, L, Q, R: real;
   XF, XL, YD, YU : real;
   Symbol : char;
   Title : String80;
   IX, IY, K, Npts, Pad : integer;
X, Y : ArrType;
```

```
{------Grapher-----------------------------------------------------------------}
{                                                                             }
{ Grapher draws rough graphs on the text screen. The arrays                   }
{ X and Y contain the co-ordinates of the N points to be                      }
{ plotted. The drawing window is XF to XL (right to left)                     }
{ and YD to YU (bottom to top). Symbol is the single                          }
{ character to be drawn, and Title is the title.                              }
{                                                                             }
{ Formal parameter type:                                                      }
{                                                                             }
{               ArrType = array[ 1..100 ] of real;                            }
{-----------------------------------------------------------------------------}

  procedure Grapher( X, Y : ArrType; N: word; XF, XL, YD, YU: real;
                                   Symbol: char; Title: String80 );

  const
    MaxRow = 20;
    MaxCol = 80;
  var
    I : word;
    Line : string[ MaxCol ];
  begin
    ClrScr;
    for I:= 1 to MaxRow do
      Writeln( ':' );

    GoToXY( 1, MaxRow );

    for I:= 1 to MaxCol do
      Write( '-' );

    for I:= 1 to N do
    begin
      IX:= Round( (X[I] - XF) * (MaxCol - 1) / (XL - XF) + 1 );
      IY:= Round( (Y[I] - YU) * (MaxRow - 1) / (YD - YU) + 1 );
      GoToXY( IX, IY );
      Write( Symbol )
    end;

    GoToXY( 1, MaxRow + 5 );
    Pad:= Round( (MaxCol - Length( Title )) / 2 );
    Write( ' ': Pad, Title )                                { centre the title }

  end; { Grapher }
  begin
    Q:= 1e-5;
    R:= 1;
    C:= 1e-5;
    L:= 2e-3;
    Npts:= Round( Cycles * PerCy + 1 );
    F0:= Sqrt( 1 / (L * C) ) / TwoPi;
    F1:= Sqrt( 1 / (L * C) - Sqr( R ) / (4 * Sqr( L )) ) / TwoPi;
    A:= TwoPi * Sqr( F0 ) * Q / F1;
    Dt:= 1 / (PerCy * F1);

    for K:= 1 to Npts do
    begin
      T:= T + Dt; X[K]:= T;
      Y[K]:= A * Exp( - R * T / (2 * L) ) * Sin( TwoPi * F1 * T)
    end;

    XF:= 0;
    XL:= Cycles / F1;
    YD:= -1e-1;
```

```
  YU:= 1e-1;
  Symbol:= Chr( 249 );
  Title:= 'Current in a RLC circuit initially charged';
  Grapher( X, Y, Npts, XF, XL, YD, YU, Symbol, Title )
end.
```

Output:

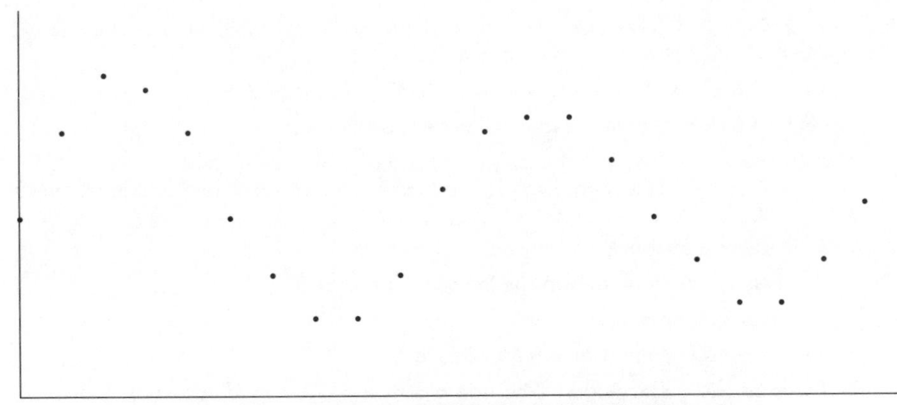

Figure 9.1 Current in a RLC Circuit Initially Charged

SUMMARY

- An array is a collection of components of the same type, and is an example of a structured data type.
- Arrays are useful for representing and processing large amounts of data.
- The size of the array must be specified in its declaration. Range checking should be switched on to detect indices which go out of bounds.
- Entire arrays may not be read or written.
- Entire arrays may be assigned.
- When an array appears as a formal parameter in a procedure or function, its type must be specified with a type identifier defined in the main program.

EXERCISES

9.1 If **Num** is an **array[1..100] of integer** write the lines of coding which will

(a) put the first 100 positive integers (1, 2, ... , 100) into the elements **Num[1]**, ... , **Num[100]**;

(b) put the first 50 positive even integers (2, ... , 100) into the elements **Num[1]**, ... , **Num[50]**;

(c) assign the integers in *reverse* order, ie assign 100 to **Num[1]**, 99 to **Num[2]**, etc.

9.2 Write some statements to put the first 100 Fibonacci numbers (1, 1, 2, 3, 5, 8, ...) into an array F[1], ... , F[100].

9.3 Salary levels at an educational institution are (in thousands of dollars): 9, 10, 12, 15, 20, 35 and 50. The number of employees at each level are, respectively, 3000, 2500, 1500, 1000, 400, 100, 25. Write a program which finds and writes:

(a) the average salary level;

(b) the number of employees above and below the average level;

(c) the average salary earned by an individual in the institution.

9.4 Write a program which will read in a positive integer (assumed less than 31, say) and write its binary representation on one line with no blanks between the digits. **Hint:** store each binary digit in a different component of an array.

9.5 Develop a structure plan for the problem of writing all the primes less than 1000 (1 and 2 are generally regarded as primes, and will probably have to be dealt with separately). **Hint:** use an array to store the primes as they are found.

9.6 Write the program for Exercise 9.5.

9.7 A formula, called Zeller's Congruence, may be used to compute the day of the week, given the date (within a certain range of dates). The formula is

$$f = ([2.6m - 0.2] + k + y + [y/4] + [c/4] - 2c) \bmod 7,$$

where the square brackets mean the integer part of and

m = month number, with January and February taken as months 11 and 12 of the preceding year, so March is then month 1, and December month 10;

k = day of the month;

c = first two digits of the year (ie the century number);

y = year in the century;

f = 0 means Sunday, 1 means Monday, etc.

For example: 23rd August 1963 has $m = 6, k = 23, c = 19, y = 63$;
1st January 1800 has $m = 11, k = 1, c = 17, y = 99$.

Write a program to read the date in the usual form (eg 30 9 1986 for 30th September 1986) and write the given date and the day of the week (in words) on which it falls. **Hint:** use an array of strings for the days of the week. Test your program on some known dates, like today's date, or your birthday, or 7th December 1941 (Sunday).

The formula will not work if you go too far back. Shakespeare and Cervantes both died on 23rd April 1616. Shakespeare died on a Tuesday, but Cervantes died on a Saturday! This is because England had not yet adopted the Gregorian calendar and was consequently ten days behind the rest of the world. The formula will also not work if you go too far forward, but I haven't been able to find out exactly how far.

9.8 In an experiment N pairs of observations (X_i, Y_i) are made. The best straight line that may be drawn through these points (using the method of **Least Squares**) has intercept A on the x-axis and slope B, where

$$B = (S_1 - S_2S_3/N) / (S_4 - S_2^2/N),$$
$$A = S_3/N - S_2B/N,$$
$$S_1 = \Sigma X_iY_i,$$
$$S_2 = \Sigma X_i,$$
$$S_3 = \Sigma Y_i,$$
$$S_4 = \Sigma X_i^2.$$

The correlation coefficient R is given by

$$R = \frac{NS_1 - S_2S_3}{\sqrt{(NS_4 - S_2^2)}\sqrt{(NS_5 - S_3^2)}}$$

where $S_5 = \Sigma Y_i^2$.

($R = 1$ implies a perfect linear relationship between X_i and Y_i. This fact can be used to test your program.) All the summations are over the range 1 to N. The observations are stored in a text file. It is not known how many observations there are. Write a program to read the data and compute A, B and R.

9.9 If a set of points (X_i, Y_i) are joined by straight lines, the value of Y corresponding to a value X which lies on a straight line between X_i and X_{i+1} is given by

$$Y = Y_i + (X - X_i) \frac{(Y_{i+1} - Y_i)}{(X_{i+1} - X_i)}$$

This process is called **linear interpolation**. Suppose no more than 100 sets of data pairs are stored, in ascending order of X_i, in a text file. Write a program which will compute an interpolated value of Y given an arbitrary value of X keyed in at the keyboard. It is assumed that X is in the range covered by the data. Note that the data must be sorted into ascending order with respect to the X_i values. If this were not so, it would be necessary to sort them first.

10 Strings

In this chapter we look at strings in more detail.

10.1 SORTING STRINGS

Strings (eg words or names) can be arranged very easily into alphabetical order in Turbo Pascal. It has a **lexical collating sequence** such that the string **N** is less than the string **M** if **N** is alphabetically ahead of **M**. The following program segment reads two strings, **A** and **B**, and writes them in alphabetical order:

```
Readln( A );
Readln( B );
if A < B then
  Writeln( A, ' ', B )
else
  Writeln( B, ' ', A );
```

Turbo Pascal uses the ASCII (American Standard Code for Information Interchange) lexical collating sequence, which is set out in full in Appendix C. The sequence is based on the computer's internal binary representation of its character set. The ASCII codes for the letters A to Z are the consecutive integers 65 to 90, while the codes for a to z run from 97 to 122. This sensible arrangement allows for alphabetical sorting, because the following Boolean expressions, for example, are all true:

```
'A' < 'B'
' A' < 'A'
'A ' < 'AA'
' MCBEAN' < 'McBEAN'
'MC BEAN' < 'MCBEAN'
```

Note that the space precedes 'A' in the collating sequence, and that the uppercase letters all precede the lowercase ones. (Turbo Pascal is only "case sensitive" with regard to strings.)

As an exercise amend the Bubble Sort in section 9.4 to sort words (of up to, say, 20 letters) instead of numbers. You will need to redefine **ArrType** as **array[1..MaxNum] of string[20]**, and declare **Temp** as **string[20]**. You will also have to read the words in (instead of generating random numbers), and change the **Write** statement to write the sorted words one to a line.

10.2 GENERAL INFORMATION

It is important to distinguish between the physical length and the logical length of a string. The **physical length** is the number of bytes indicated in the string's declaration (the default length is 255 bytes). This is the amount of memory allocated to the string. So in

```
var
  A : string;
  B : string[20];
```

A has a physical length of 255, while **B** has a physical length of 20.

The **logical length**, however, is the number of bytes currently occupied by the string. So if **B** is declared as above, the statement

```
B:= 'Mortimer';
```

results in a logical length of 8 bytes for **B**.

Particular bytes in a string may be accessed with an index, rather as if the string were an array (it is in fact a **packed** array of char). So **B[4]** returns the value 't'. Referencing a byte beyond the logical length of a string may result in garbage. There's a further surprise. The first byte of **B** is not **B[1]**, as you might reasonably expect. It is **B[0]**, and holds the *string representation* of the current logical length of the string, which can be useful. So **Length(B)** and **Ord(B[0])** both have the value 8 in this example.

The standard function **ReadKey** (in the **Crt** unit) reads a single character of type char from the keyboard, without echoing it to the screen. The syntax is

```
Ch:= ReadKey;
```

This is useful for extracting single-letter options from a nervous user who might not be able to find the **Return** key too easily. See section 11.7 for an example. If the boolean function **KeyPressed** was True before the call to **ReadKey**, the character that made **KeyPressed** true is returned immediately, otherwise **ReadKey** waits for a character to be typed.

Some keys and key combinations on the keyboard (eg the cursor movement keys) are represented not by single ASCII codes, but by *two* codes called **extended key codes.** These extended codes are given in Appendix C, and the description of **ReadKey** in Appendix B explains how to read them.

Relational operators may be used to compare strings, as we saw in the previous section. Strings of any type may be so compared, because all string types are compatible. Strings may also be compared with char types.

The type identity rule for function and procedure parameters (section 8.4) normally requires that strings passed as parameters must be declared with a type identifier. The header

```
procedure Plink( Name: string[12] );
```

will therefore generate an error (incidentally, the error is not no. 12: Type identifier expected – but no. 89: ") " expected).

The problem may be solved by declaring:

```
type
  StringType = string[12];
...
procedure Plink( Name: StringType );
```

In this case the *actual* array parameter must be declared with the same type identifier, so the following will cause a type mismatch error:

```
var
  Title : string[12];
...
begin
  Plink( Title );
```

Title must also be a **StringType** variable.

The type identity rule may be relaxed in the case of strings if the **{$V–}** compiler directive is used (Var String Checking off). Any string variable is then allowed as an actual parameter.

The only string operator is +, which may be used in string expressions to concatenate. For example, the string expression

```
'ich' + 'thus'
```

produces the result 'ichthus' (Greek for fish).

10.3 STANDARD STRING FUNCTIONS AND PROCEDURES

The standard string functions and procedures are discussed briefly in this section.

Functions

Concat(*String*1, *String*2, ... **)** concatenates its string parameters (of which there may be any number, for example,

```
Concat( 'Nap', 'ole', 'on' )
```

Copy(*String, Start, N* **)** copies *N* bytes from *String*, beginning at byte *Start*, for example,

```
Copy( 'Napoleon', 5, 4 )
```

returns 'leon'.

Length(*String* **)** returns the logical length of its string parameter.

Pos(*Substring, String* **)** returns the index of the first character of *Substring* in *String* (zero if *Substring* does not occur), for example

```
Pos( 'pole', 'Napoleon' )
```

returns 3. This is useful for detecting the presence of a character, for example

Pos('.', St) > 0 is true if **St** contains a period.

UpCase(*Char* **)** converts its char parameter to uppercase, if it is a lowercase letter. Otherwise it has no effect.

Procedures

Delete(*String, Start, N* **)** deletes *N* characters from *String*, starting at index *Start*, for example:

```
St:= 'Napoleon'
Delete( St, 1, 4 );
```

changes **St** to 'leon'.

Insert(*Substring, String, N* **)** inserts *Substring* into *String*, beginning at index *N* of *String*, for example:

```
Insert( 'Napo', St, 1 );
```

restores **St** to 'Napoleon'.

Str(*X, String* **)** converts a numeric value *X, formatted as in* **Write,** into its string equivalent, for example:

```
X:= 1; { real }
Str( X:4:1, St)
```

returns **St** with the value ' 1.0'.

Val(*String, X, Index* **)** is the reverse of **Str,** and converts *String* into its numerical equivalent *X*. *String* must be a sequence of characters that correctly define a signed whole number. *X* must be real or integer. If *String* is not correct, the position of the first offending character is returned in *Index*.

10.4 COUNTING WORDS

It's very easy to manipulate text in Turbo Pascal. The next two problems will give you a taste of what's possible. The procedure **WordsInStr** counts the number of words in its string argument **Line**. The number of words is returned in **Words**. The procedure is as simple as possible to show you the basic ideas. Words are separated by any number of blanks, and a word is defined as any string of one or more non-blank characters. So punctuation marks like commas and periods will not be counted as separate words as long as they are not preceded by blanks.

The real work of the procedure is done in the **while** loop. It takes time to think out a problem like this. It often helps to think how you would explain the problem (not even the answer) to someone who didn't know the first thing about it. Imagine a stream of letters and blanks coming past you. How would you know when a complete word has passed? Surely, when a non-blank changes to a blank – it's the change from non-blank to blank that signals the end of a word. Realising this will give you the Aha! experience that problem solvers rave about. So the essence of the solution is to move through the string one character at a time, keeping a record of the *previous* character **(OldCh)** in order to compare it with the *current* character **(Ch)**. If the previous character is non-blank when the current one is blank, we've found another word.

The rest of the procedure is just a bit of mopping up. **OldCh** must be initialised to a blank, to start the ball rolling. If the last character in the string is a non-blank the argument above will not catch that word, so it's necessary to check for this after completion of the **while** loop.

```
{------WordsInStr-----------------------------------------------------------}
{                                                                          }
{  Counts words, separated by any number of blanks,                        }
{  in a string Line. Words consist of anything except blanks.              }

procedure WordsInStr( Line: string; var Words: word );
const
  Blank = ' ';
var
  Ch, OldCh : char;
  I, Len : word;

begin
  Words:= 0;
  Len:= Length( Line );
  I:= 0;                                { count the characters in the string }
  OldCh:= Blank;

  while I < Len do
  begin
    I:= I + 1;
    Ch:= Line[I];
    if (Ch = ' ') and (OldCh <> ' ') then             { arrival of blank... }
      Words:= Words + 1;                          { ...signals end of word }
    OldCh:= Ch
  end;
  if Ch <> ' ' then                             { if last char is non-blank... }
    Words:= Words + 1                             { ...count another word }
end; { WordsInStr }
```

In Chapter 2 this procedure is altered slightly to count the words in a text file.

10.5 A XHOSA-ENGLISH TRANSLATION TEST

The program in this section subjects the user to a translation test – Xhosa phrases are presented, and the user is invited to enter the English translation. The program exploits Turbo Pascal's ability to compare strings. In the true spirit of structured programming, the problem is broken down into a number of procedures (the divide and conquer approach!). They are discussed in logical order, although they are declared below in alphabetical order (this necessitates a **forward** declaration of **Xhosa**).

The data are in a text file WORDS. Each line in the file has an English word or phrase, followed by a backslash (\), called the separator, followed by its Xhosa equivalent. For example:

```
teacher \ titshala
pupils \ bafundi
how are you? \ usaphila?
window \ ifestile
bird \ intaka
open \ vula
close \ vala
stand \ yima
Tuesday \ uLwesibini
```

The main program's first action is to open the data file and read it a line at a time (it's assumed that no line is longer than 80 characters, so the type **string80 = string[80]** is used). This could also be in a procedure if you like.

Each line of data, **LineOfText,** is sent to **UpperCase,** where each character in the line is converted to uppercase. Turbo Pascal is case sensitive only with regard to strings, so an entry given in uppercase would not match a lowercase solution. The best way out is to convert everything to uppercase.

The next task is to separate **LineOfText** into its English and Xhosa parts. **Separate** does this, placing the parts in the *N*th components of the arrays **Eng** and **Xho** respectively, where *N* is an increasing line counter. **Separate** uses the standard function **Pos** to search for the backslash separator. Now this is where you have to decide how foolproof you want to make the program. What happens if the separator was left out? You can code strategies of varying degrees of complexity to handle situations like this. For example, you could refuse to accept the line (so the line counter *N* must be prevented from being incremented in some way). In our case, the string '@@@' is inserted as the English/Xhosa phrase. But this has implications for the user's score. He must reply '@@@', or lose a mark! See what I mean? The bulk of user-friendly software development goes into coping with the user's mistakes. If it finds the separator, **Separate** uses **Copy** to copy the English and Xhosa halves of the line.

The procedure **Menu** then offers the user some choices. Single letter options are read from the keyboard with **ReadKey**, and not echoed to the screen. The standard function **UpCase** is used to convert the single character reply into uppercase. The basic structure is **repeat-until**. The procedures **English** or **Xhosa** are activated, according to the user's choice. Note that **English** is only a stub, to make the program as realistic as possible during development.

If the user chooses to translate from Xhosa to English, the procedure **Xhosa** is activated. A Xhosa phrase is selected at random. **BlankTrim** removes blanks from the user's answer, and from a copy of the correct answer. This is to avoid an answer being judged as wrong because it has too many blanks between words. The user's answer is also converted to uppercase. This is compared with the trimmed correct answer, and appropriate action is taken. If the answer is wrong, the correct (untrimmed) one is written.

There are also various frills, like asking how many questions the user wants, keeping track of the score, and highlighting certain phrases.

```
program EnglishXhosa;
{ English - Xhosa translation test }

uses Crt;
const
  MaxNum     = 100;
  N : word   = 0;                    { number of phrases }
type
  String80 = string[80];
  ArrString = array[ 1..MaxNum ] of String80;
var
  I : word;
  Ans, LineOfText : String80;
  Eng, Xho : ArrString;
  F : text;

procedure Xhosa; forward; {to keep procedure alphabetical }

{------BlankTrim-----------------------------------------------------------------}
{                                                                                 }
{                                                                                 }
{  Removes all blanks from the string St                                          }

procedure BlankTrim( var St: string80 );
var
  I : word;
  Temp : string80;
begin
  Temp:= '';
  for I:= 1 to Length( St ) do
    if St[I] <> ' ' then
```

```
    Temp:= Temp + St[I];
  { make a copy with no blanks }
    St:= Temp
  end; { BlankTrim }

{------English ----------------------------------------------------------------}
{                                                                              }
{                                                                              }
{   EnglishXhosa test        <<<<Not operational>>>>                           }
  procedure English;
  begin
  end; { English }

{------Menu -------------------------------------------------------------------}
{                                                                              }
{                                                                              }
{   Presents user with menu of options.                                        }

  procedure Menu;
  var
    Ans : char;
    begin
    repeat
      ClrScr; Writeln( 'ENGLISH/XHOSA TRANSLATION TEST' );
      Writeln;
      Writeln( 'Indicate your choice with a single letter:' );
      Writeln;
      Writeln( 'English-Xhosa (E) (not operational yet!)' );
      Writeln( 'Xhosa-English (X)' );
      Writeln( 'Stop (S)' );
      Writeln;
      Writeln( 'What do you want? ' );
      Ans:= ReadKey;
      Ans:= UpCase( Ans );                                         { just in case }
      if Ans = 'X' then
        Xhosa
      else
        English;
    until Ans = 'S'

  end; { Menu }

  {------Separate ---------------------------------------------------------------}
  {                                                                              }
  {                                                                              }
  {   Splits St into St1 and St2 (before and after '\')                          }
  procedure Separate( St: string80; var St1, St2: string80 );
  var
    Separator: word;
  begin
    Separator:= Pos( '\', St );
    if Separator = 0 then                       { no separator }
    begin
      St1:= '@@@';
                                                { keep the show on the road }
      St2:= '@@@';
      Exit
    end;
    St1:= Copy( St, 1, Separator - 1 );
    St2:= Copy( St, Separator + 1, Length( St ) - Separator );
  end; { Separate }
```

```
{------UpperCase----------------------------------------------------------------------------}
{                                                                                          }
{                                                                                          }
{ Converts St to uppercase.                                                                }

  procedure UpperCase( var St: string80 );
  var
    I : word;
  begin
    for I:= 1 to Length( St ) do
      St[I]:= UpCase( St[I]                        { change every char to uppercase }
  end; { UpperCase }

{------Xhosa--------------------------------------------------------------------------------}
{                                                                                          }
{                                                                                          }
{ Xhosa/English test                                                                       }

  procedure Xhosa;
  var
    I, J, Marks, Num : word;
    Ans, Right : string80;
  begin
    Marks:= 1;
    ClrScr;
    Writeln( 'XHOSA/ENGLISH' );
    Writeln;
    Write( 'How many questions do you want? ' );
    Readln( Num );
    Writeln;

    for I:= 1 to Num do
    begin
      J:= Trunc( N * Random + 1 );                 { choose a random phrase }
      Write( 'Xhosa: ' );
      HighVideo;
      Writeln( Xho[J] );
      NormVideo;
      Write( 'English: ' );
      Readln( Ans );
      BlankTrim( Ans );                            { strip the blanks }
      UpperCase( Ans );                            { convert to uppercase }
      Right:= Eng[J];                              { keep blanks in correct answer }
      BlankTrim( Right );
      if Ans = Right then
      begin
        Marks:= Marks + 1;
        Writeln( 'Correct' )
      end
      else
      begin
        Sound( 200 );
        Delay( 500 );
        NoSound;
        Write( 'Wrong - answer is: ' );
        HighVideo;
        Writeln( Eng[J] );
        NormVideo
      end;
      Writeln
    end;
    Writeln;
    Writeln( 'You got ', Marks, ' out of ', Num );
    Writeln( 'Press any key to continue...' );
```

```
   Ans:= ReadKey
end; { Xhosa }

begin { English __ Xhosa }
   Randomize;
Assign( F, 'WORDS.' );                                              { open file }
Reset( F );

while not Eof( F ) do { get and separate English/Xhosa phrases }
begin
   Readln( F, LineOfText );
   UpperCase( LineOfText );
   N:= N + 1;
   Separate( LineOfText, Eng[N], Xho[N] );
end;
   Close( F );
   Menu;
end. { English __ Xhosa }
```

It is left as an exercise to program the English-Xhosa test. Perhaps it would be more economical to have them in one procedure, since the only difference is the prompt to the user, and whether **Eng** or **Xho** is used. You might also like to think about how to prevent a correctly answered question from being asked again in the same session (see section 14.8 for the solution to a similar problem).

SUMMARY

- The physical length of a string is the amount of memory allocated to it by the compiler. Its logical length is the number of characters in it at any given moment.
- A string may be indexed, rather like an array, to access particular characters. The first byte, with index zero, holds the string representation of the current logical length of the string.
- Characters are represented by ASCII codes. This is the basis of word sorts.
- If Var String Checking is off – **{$V–}** – actual string parameters of any length may be passed to formal string parameters, although if the string type passed is longer than the formal parameter type, data may be overwritten.

EXERCISES

10.1 Write a program which reads a one-line sentence ending with a period and writes the sentence backwards, without the period. Hint: use the position indices of the string.

10.2 Write a program which will read a number in binary code of arbitrary length (eg 1100 – no blanks between the digits) and write its decimal value (12 in this case). Hint: read the number as a string, and use Val to convert the individual characters into numbers.

11 Advanced Input and Output

We have already seen how data for a program can be read from a disk file. It should come as no surprise to you that *output* from a program can also be *written* to a disk file. The word *file* has in fact two distinct meanings. It can mean a DOS file on a disk – we can call this a **physical** file. It can also mean a stream of bytes in a Turbo Pascal program, which exists in a universe of its own – the program's memory – and which does not necessarily have any connection with the real world. Such a file can be called a **logical** file. Turbo Pascal, furthermore, allows two fundamentally different types of logical files: **text files**, and **binary files**. We are going to look at text files in detail in this chapter. Binary files will be discussed in Chapter 12.

11.1 TEXT FILES

A text file is nothing more than a stream of characters which may be displayed on a computer monitor (ie the printable ASCII characters) plus what are called **whitespace** characters. These include the carriage return ($0D – hexadecimal for 13), linefeed ($0A), formfeed ($0C), horizontal tab ($09), and backspace ($08). The bell character ($07) is also permitted in text files. This is why you can get a linefeed on the monitor with the statement

```
Writeln( Chr( $0A ) )
```

Because text files consist of these characters they may be typed on the monitor or printer with the DOS command TYPE (you can't type a .EXE file like TURBO.EXE because it's a binary file with non-printable characters – so don't try!).

Another special control character allowed in a text file created under DOS is the **end-of-file marker** (EOF). This marker, **Ctrl-Z** ($1A), is automatically inserted at the end of a text file by DOS, and can be detected by the **Eof** standard function.

Turbo Pascal text files are declared as follows:

```
var
  InFile : text;                    { both forms are valid }
  OutFile : file of text;
```

The file variable so declared may also be thought of as a file *buffer*, or *window* into the file. So when you read from the file **InFile** with

```
Read( InFile, X )
```

you can think of the file as a tape moving under a window. Once the item **X** has been read from it, the tape moves on, and the next item comes to rest under the window, waiting to be read. The same applies to writing:

```
Write( OutFile, Y )
```

So far we have said nothing about connecting Turbo Pascal's logical files to the physical files on a disk in the outside world. This is done with the **Assign** procedure:

Assign(InFile, *Filename* **)**

This statement connects the file variable **InFile** with the disk file *Filename* (which may be a string variable or constant).

The file is still not ready for input or output. The file has a **file pointer** or logical marker (not to be confused with the Turbo Pascal pointer variable), which indicates which element in the file is to be read or written to next. In the case of reading, the procedure call

```
Reset( InFile )
```

places the file pointer at the beginning of the file. The file is then said to be **open** for reading. The procedure call

```
Rewrite( OutFile )
```

opens a file for writing by placing the pointer at the beginning of the file. ***When* Rewrite *is executed on a text file, all previous contents of the file is lost.*** A text file cannot be *partially* rewritten. We will see below, however, how to update a text file.

There are two standard text files that are always open for reading and writing: **Input** and **Output**. They are the default files for use with **Read<ln>** and **Write<ln>**. The statement

```
Writeln( X )
```

actually means

```
Writeln( Output, X )
```

In some versions of Pascal (not Turbo) these default files must be named in the program statement:

```
program Quaint( Input, Output )
```

A text file is read or written to sequentially, starting from the beginning each time. The file pointer cannot be positioned to any other place in the file. This is not the case with binary files, which may be read and written to at any place in the file.

When you have finished with a file, it should be closed with

```
Close( MyFile )
```

This ensures that all the data in the file buffer are physically transferred to the disk (in the case of write files). It's a good habit to make sure *all* files are closed before a program terminates. If a file which is not open is closed, runtime error 103 (File not open) occurs.

Although a text file is a continuous one-dimensional stream of characters, the standard procedures **Readln** and **Writeln**, which work only on text files, introduce the concept of the **end-of-line** (EOL) marker. When you enter text in the Turbo Pascal Edit window, or with any word processor, the end-of-line marker is inserted at the end of each line of text. **Writeln** does the same on the monitor or to a text file. **Readln** reads a line of text, terminating in the end-of-line marker, from the keyboard or a text file.

The EOL marker is usually two characters: \$0D/\$0A. This harks back to the days of the teletype printer, when one character (\$0D) was needed for a carriage return, and another (\$0A) to advance the paper one line.

You can find out what the EOL marker is on your computer as follows. Use the Edit window to create a text file which has only two lines, say, with one character on each line (no blanks), for example:

```
A
B
```

Save it under the name TEXT. Then run the following simple program:

```
...
var
  F : text;
  Ch : char;
  I : word;
begin
Assign( F, 'TEXT.' );
Reset( F );

I:= 0;
repeat
```

```
  I:= I + 1;
  Read( F, Ch );
  Write( Ord( Ch ):4 )
until eof( F );
Writeln( I:6 );
...
```

The output (on my Olivetti M24) is:

```
    65    13    10    66    4
```

65 is the ASCII code for A, so 13 10 ($0D $0A in hex) must be the code for the EOL marker. 66 is the code for B. The counter **I** records that there are 4 characters in the file – two letters and the two characters for the EOL marker. Note that the end-of-*file* marker (**Ctrl-Z** – 26) is not read, precisely because it exists only to mark the end of the file. (See section 12.3 on how to read the EOF marker with **BlockRead**.)

The standard boolean function **Eoln(MyFile)** returns True if the current file pointer in **MyFile** is at the EOL marker. If the parentheses and file variable are omitted, the standard **Input** file is assumed.

We have already seen that the standard boolean function **Eof(MyFile)** detects the end-of-file marker.

A file variable which is a formal parameter of a procedure or function must be a *variable* parameter, otherwise error 126 (Files must be var parameters) occurs.

11.2 COUNTING WORDS IN A TEXT FILE

In section 10.4 we wrote a procedure **WordsInStr** to count words in a single line of text (in a string variable). This procedure may easily be changed to do the same for a text file. It is shown here with a calling program, which passes the text file to it as a *variable* parameter:

```
program WordCount;
var
  N : word;
  F : text;
{------WordsInText-----------------------------------------------------------------}
{                                                                                  }
{ Counts words, separated by any number of blanks,                                 }
{ in a text file F. Words consist of anything except blanks.                       }
procedure WordsInText( var F: text; var Words: word );
const
  Blank = ' ';
var
  Ch, OldCh : char;
  I, Len : word;
begin
  Words:= 0;
  OldCh:= Blank;
  while not eof( F ) do
  begin
    Read( F, Ch );
    if (Ch = Blank) and (OldCh <> Blank) then
      Words:= Words + 1; { arrival of blank signals end of word }
    OldCh:= Ch
  end;
  if Ch <> Blank then                          { if last char is non-blank... }
    Words:= Words + 1                                  { ...count another word }
end; { WordsInText }
begin
  Assign( F, 'TEXT.' );
  Reset( F );
  WordsInText( F, N );
  Close( F );
```

```
  Writeln( N )
end.
```

11.3 SWITCHING OUTPUT BETWEEN SCREEN AND PRINTER

Sooner or later you may want to write a large program which will print masses of output on a printer. It's a terrible waste of time and paper for it to print all the output each time you run the program while you go through the traumatic development and debugging process. So obviously, during development you will direct all the output to the screen. However, when the program is finally ready it's a great nuisance to have to change every **Write(** *rhubarb* **)** to **Write(Lst,** *rhubarb* **)** (and to remember to add a **uses Printer** clause too).

The following program, however, enables you to switch an entire program's output from the screen to the printer, and vice versa, with a single keystroke. Try it out (make sure your printer is connected).

```
program OutSwitch;
uses Crt;
var
  Out : text;
  Ch : char;
begin
  Writeln( 'Output to Screen (S) or Printer (P)? ' );
  Ch:= ReadKey;
  Ch:= UpCase( Ch );
  if Ch = 'S' then
    Assign( Out, 'CON' )
  else
    Assign( Out, 'PRN' );
  Rewrite( Out );

  Writeln( Out, 'Output is on chosen device!' );
  Close( Out )
end.
```

How this works in explained in the next section.

11.4 DEVICE FILES

CON and PRN are the names of two special DOS **device files** which are recognised by Turbo Pascal. A device file is really a third type of file (neither logical nor physical) in that it is a special operating system file that has one end in your program (if it is **Assigned**) and the other end in a physical piece of computer hardware, like a keyboard, monitor, printer, modem, etc.
CON refers to the **con**sole device, in which output is sent to the monitor and input is read from the keyboard. It is connected by default to the standard files **Input** and **Output**, and to all files assigned an empty name, unless input/output is redirected.

PRN is a synonym for LPT1, the line printer device. You may use a further two printers, with device names LPT2 and LPT3.

COM1 and COM2 refer to the two standard serial communication ports. Be careful with them. If you try to read one of these devices when no character is ready, it will wait for a character and hang up the system. AUX is the synonym for COM1.

NUL is the null device. It ignores everything written to it, and generates an immediate EOF marker if read. So what's the point of it? You can use it when you don't want to create a particular file, but the program syntax requires a filename.

11.5 OPENING FILES: ERROR INTERCEPTION

A large program might require the user to enter the name of a file to be read for data. He types by mistake the name of a non-existent file, and the whole show comes crashing down. A general system failure like this can be prevented with the **{$I}** Input/Output Checking compiler directive. When this is switched off, a runtime I/O error will not be fatal. Instead the standard function **IOResult** will return the number of the error, for example, 2 (File not found), 103 (File not open), etc. It returns the value zero if the operation is successful. Its value is reset on its next call. An error can be detected, therefore, from the value returned by **IOResult**, and appropriate action coded.

The procedure **OpenFile** below attempts to open a given file for reading or writing according to the parameter **Mode**. If **Mode** is incorrectly set (ie neither 'R' nor 'W') **IOCode** is set to −1, otherwise it is set to **IOResult**. Note the use of a set constant **GoodMode** in determining whether **Mode** is valid (sets are discussed in Chapter 12). In the example below an incorrect **Mode** is sent to **OpenFile**. The value of **IOCode** returned is used to avoid attempting to close a file that has not been opened.

```
program ErrorTest;
type
  Str80 = string[80];
var
  F : text;
  FName : Str80;
  IOC : shortint;
{------OpenFile-------------------------------------------------------------}
{ Traps I/O error when attempting to read/write files.                      }
{                                                                           }
{ F          : text file variable                                           }
{ Name       : disk filename                                                }
{ Mode       : 'R' (read) or 'W' (write)                                    }
{ IOCode     : IOResult; if Mode is incorrect, IOCode is                    }
{                returned as -1                                             }
{                                                                           }
{ Formal parameter type:                                                    }
{                  Str80 = string[80]                                       }
{---------------------------------------------------------------------------}

procedure OpenFile( var F: text; Name: Str80; Mode: char;
                    var IOCode: shortint );
const
  GoodMode = ['R', 'W'];

begin
  if not (Mode in GoodMode) then
  begin
    IOCode:= -1;
    Exit
  end;
  {$I-}
  Assign( F, Name );
  if Mode = 'R' then
    Reset( F )
  else
    if Mode = 'W' then
      Rewrite( F )
    else
      IOCode:= -1;
  {$I+}
  IOCode:= IOResult
end; { OpenFile }
begin
  Write( 'Filename? ' );
  Readln( FName );
  OpenFile( F, FName, 'I', IOC );
  If IOC = 0 then
    Close( F )
end.
```

11.6 UPDATING STUDENT RECORDS

It's time we had a real example of text files. The following problem examines their use in maintaining and updating students' marks. Text files are not necessarily the most efficient vehicle for this (the problem is reworked with binary files in Chapter 12), but their great advantage is that you can view them with a text editor and see exactly what's going on. So they're good to start with.

What we would like to do first is to write a list of students' names to a text file MARKS.TXT. We could use a text editor or spreadsheet to do this directly, but it's more instructive to write a program to do it. The program **Names** accepts strings of up to 20 characters from the keyboard and writes them to MARKS.TXT. It stops when a null name is entered. Note that a copy of part of the body of the **repeat** loop must appear before the loop, to get things rolling. Otherwise the null name will be written to the disk file.

```
program Names;
{ Sends names of 20 chars or fewer to a text file }
uses Crt;
const
  MaxChars = 20;
var
  F : text;
  Name : string[MaxChars];
begin
  ClrScr;
  Assign( F, 'MARKS.TXT' );
  Rewrite( F );
  Write( 'Name: ' );                              { start the ball rolling }
  Readln( Name );

  repeat
    Writeln( F, Name );
    Write( 'Name: ' );
    Readln( Name )
  until Name = '';

  Close( F )
end.
```

Try it out with the following names, for example:

```
ABLE ER
BOTHA FW
SMITH ZZ
```

When you've run the program you can load MARKS.TXT in the Turbo Pascal Edit window to check that it's correct. That's the nice thing about text files.

The next thing to do is to update the file MARKS.TXT by writing some marks to it. Unfortunately, a text file cannot be updated directly by reading from and writing to it at the same time. You can only rewrite it completely, or add new data on at the end of it with **Append**. The way out is to read the students' names one at a time from MARKS.TXT, read a mark for each from the keyboard, and write the name with the mark to a new text file which we shall call SCRATCH.TXT. When all the marks have been typed in, MARKS.TXT must be erased, and SCRATCH.TXT renamed MARKS.TXT. Before MARKS.TXT is erased (a rather drastic step) a backup copy of SCRATCH.TXT should be made in case of a power failure at the crucial moment. This is done with the procedure **BackUp** below, which makes a copy of any text file, under the same name, but with the extension BAK. Note the use of the function **Pos** to find the position of the period in the filename.

```
program AddOne;
{ Updates Student Record by adding marks for one offering }
uses Crt;
const
  MaxChars = 20;
type
```

```
  Str80 = string[80];
var
  F : text;
  Inp, Out : text;
  Mk : word;
  Name : string[MaxChars];
{------BackUp-------------------------------------------------------------------}
{                                                                               }
{  Makes a backup copy of the text file Name, with ext                          }
{  .BAK                                                                         }
{                                                                               }
{  Formal parameter type:                                                       }
{                   Str80 = string[80]                                          }
{-------------------------------------------------------------------------------}
  procedure BackUp( Name: Str80 );
  var
    BackUpName : Str80;
    Dot : word;
    Ch : char;
    Inp, Out : text;
  begin
    Dot:= Pos( '.', Name );
    BackUpName:= Copy( Name, 1, Dot - 1 ) + '.BAK';

    Assign( Inp, Name );
    Reset( Inp );
    Assign( Out, BackUpName );
    Rewrite( Out );

    while not Eof( Inp ) do
    begin
      Read( Inp, Ch );
      Write( Out, Ch )
    end;

    Close( Inp );
    Close( Out )
  end; { BackUp }

  begin { AddOne }
    ClrScr;
    Assign( Inp, 'MARKS.TXT' );                              { Master file }
    Reset( Inp );
    Assign( Out, 'SCRATCH.TXT' );                           { Scratch file }
    Rewrite( Out );
    while not Eof( Inp) do
    begin
      Readln( Inp, Name );
      Write( Name, ': ' );
      Read( Mk );
      Writeln( Out, Name, ' ':MaxChars - Length( Name ), Mk:4 )
    end;

    Close( Inp );
    Close( Out );
    BackUp( 'SCRATCH.TXT' );                      { make a backup just in case! }
    Assign( F, 'MARKS.TXT' );
    Erase( F );                                             { Erase MARKS.TXT }
    Assign( F, 'SCRATCH.TXT' );
    Rename( F, 'MARKS.TXT' )                         { Rename SCRATCH.TXT }
  end. { AddOne }
```

If you try out the program **Addone** with some sample data, MARKS.TXT could end up looking like this:

```
ABLE ER           78
BOTHA FW           0
SMITH ZZ          99
```

The line

```
Writeln( Out, Name, ' ':MaxChars - Length( Name ), Mk:4 )
```

needs some explanation. Each line in the output file must be padded with blanks from the right, to make sure that the name occupies the first 20 characters. This ensures that the mark will be beyond the 20th character in each line. Otherwise, when the file is read again, any marks in the first 20 positions of the line will be read as part of the name (since **Readln** will insist on finding 20 characters for **Name**, whether they are letters or numbers).

Note the use of the two standard functions **Erase** and **Rename**.

Erase(*FileVar* **)** erases the disk file to which the file variable *FileVar* has been assigned. The file must not be open, and must have been assigned.

Rename(*FileVar* , *NewName* **)** changes the name of the disk file, to which *FileVar* is assigned, to *NewName*. The file must not be open, and must have been assigned.

A More General Solution

The problem with **AddOne** is that it can't be used exactly as it stands to add a second offering to MARKS.TXT. The part that reads names from MARKS.TXT and writes names and marks to SCRATCH.TXT is:

```
Readln( Inp, Name );
Write( Name, ': ' );
Read( Mk );
Writeln( Out, Name, ' ':MaxChars - Length( Name ), Mk:4 )
```

If we want to add a second offering we will need something like

```
Readln( Inp, Name, Mk1 );
Write( Name, ': ' );
Read( Mk2 );
Writeln( Out, Name, ' ':MaxChars - Length( Name ), Mk1:4, Mk2:4 )
```

(since we don't want to lose the first mark).

But then similar changes will be needed to add a third offering. The program will have to be changed every time we want to enter another offering. A much better solution is to write a general purpose program that uses the first **Offerings** components of an *array* **Mark** to read the existing marks for each student from the file, and then to read the latest mark from the keyboard into the element **Mark[Offerings + 1]** . The entire array **Mark** is then written back to the file. This way the same program can be used again and again. The file will need some extra information, namely, the number of offerings (tests) currently in the file. For good measure, we may as well also write to the file the maximum mark for each offering, since these won't all necessarily be the same.

Before we start, we need to change the program **Names** to record the current number of offerings (none to start with) in the first line of the file. The new initialising program, **Initial** does this:

```
program Initial;
{ Sends names of 20 chars or less to MARKS. }
{ Also number of offerings - none at first }
uses Crt;
const
  MaxChars = 20;
  Offerings : byte = 0;                              { no offerings at first }
var
  F : text;
  Name : string[MaxChars];
begin
  ClrScr;
```

```
Assign( F, 'MARKS.' );
Rewrite( F );
Writeln( F, Offerings );                                    { in first line }
Write( 'Name: ' );                                     { start the ball rolling }
Readln( Name );
repeat
  Writeln( F, Name );
  Write( 'Name: ' );
  Readln( Name )
   until Name = '';
   Close( F )
 end. { Initial }
```

Run this program with some sample data again, for example:

```
ABLE ER
BOTHA FW
SMITH ZZ
```

and verify that the first line of MARKS contains a zero. Note that we are no longer using MARKS.TXT as the text file.

Now for the general purpose program, which is called **StudentMarks**. It has a number of procedures. It uses **BackUp** and **OpenFile** as defined above. They are not given in full again below. Since these two procedures are likely to be used quite often it might be a good idea to compile them into a unit.

Any filename may be used for the data. **GetMarksFile** ensures that an existing file is opened for read.

Update arranges the entry of the new offering and the update of the existing file. Any name may be used for the scratch file, but this carries the danger of possibly overwriting a valuable file.

Note how **Update** warns against this. To see if a file is already on the disk, an attempt is made to open it for *reading*. If the attempt succeeds (**IOCode** returned as zero), the user is asked whether it can be overwritten. Only when the appropriate action has been decided is the scratch file opened for *writing*.

Display writes all the names and marks (with maxima) neatly on the screen.

The main program takes the form of a menu.

Note that the new procedures (**Display, GetMarksFile** and **Update**) are written without parameters since they are specific to this application and are not likely to be used in any other program. They also have no local variables. **BackUp** and **OpenFile**, however, were defined with parameters to make them usable in any program.

```
program StudentMarks;
{ U: Updates marks in text file MarksFile with new offering          }
{ D: Displays all names and marks                                    }
uses Crt;
const
  MaxChars = 20;
  MaxOfferings = 20;
type
  ArrMarks = 1..MaxOfferings;
  Str80    = string[80];
var
  Ch        : char;                                   { reply to question }
  F         : text;                               { general file variable }
  I         : byte;                                     { general counter }
  InFile    : text;                                  { read file variable}
  IOCode    : shortint;                  {I/O error returned by OpenFile }
  Mark      : array[ ArrMarks ] of real;                  { all the marks }
  MarksFile : str80;                                    { marks file name }
  Max       : array[ ArrMarks ] of real;                  { max of each... }
```

```
                                                           { ...offering }
  Name      : string[MaxChars];                            { student name }
  NewMax    : real;                                  { max of new offering }
  Offerings : byte;                                  { number of offerings }
  OK        : Boolean;                                 { flag for I/O check }
  OutFile   : text;                                   { write file variable }
  Scratch   : str80;                                   { scratch file name }
procedure GetMarksFile; forward;
procedure OpenFile( var F: text; Name: Str80; Mode: char;
                    var IOCode: shortint ); forward;

procedure BackUp( Name: Str80 );
  ...
end; { BackUp }
{------Display ------------------------------------------------------------}
{                                                                          }
{ Displays all names and marks on screen                                   }
{--------------------------------------------------------------------------}
procedure Display;
begin
  GetMarksFile;
  ClrScr;
  Read( InFile, Offerings );                          { get no. of offerings }
  Write( 'Maximum mark:', ' ':8 );

  for I:= 1 to Offerings do
  begin
    Read( InFile, Max[ I ] );                              { ... and maxima }
    Write( Max[ I ]:5:0 )                           { ... and display them }
  end;
  Readln( InFile );                                             { new line }
  Writeln;
  Writeln;
                                  { now get names and marks and display them }
  while not Eof( InFile ) do
  begin
    Read( InFile, Name );
    Write( Name, ' ': MaxChars - Length( Name ) );

    for I:= 1 to Offerings do
    begin
      Read( InFile, Mark[ I ] );
      Write( Mark[ I ]:5:0 )
    end;

    Writeln;
    Readln( InFile )                                            { new line }
  end;

  Close( InFile );
  Writeln;
  Write( 'Press any key to continue...' );
  Ch:= ReadKey;
  ClrScr;
end; { Display }

{------GetMarksFile -------------------------------------------------------}
{                                                                          }
{ Keeps trying until user gives name of existing file                      }
{--------------------------------------------------------------------------}

procedure GetMarksFile;
begin
  repeat                                { first make sure that marks file exists }
    OK:= False;                                        { flag to detect error }
```

```
    Write( 'Name of marks file? ' );
    Readln( MarksFile );
      OpenFile( InFile, MarksFile, 'R', IOCode );
      if IOCode <> 0 then
        Writeln( #7'I/O error ', IOCode, ' - please try again. ' )
      else
        OK:= True
    until OK                                                        { no error }
  end; { GetMarks }

  procedure OpenFile;
    ...
  end; { OpenFile }

{------Update---------------------------------------------------------------------}
{                                                                                 }
{  Updates marks file with new offering                                           }
{  Does all necessary house-keeping                                               }
{---------------------------------------------------------------------------------}

  procedure Update;
  begin
    ClrScr;
    Writeln( 'Updating student marks ...' );
    GetMarksFile;                                  { get name of valid marks file }
    repeat                                           { now ask for Scratch file }
    OK:= False;
    Write( 'Name of scratch file? ' );
    Readln( Scratch );
    OpenFile( OutFile, Scratch, 'R', IOCode );
                                                   { check if it's already there }
    if IOCode = 0 then                                            { it is there }
    begin
      Write( #7'There is another file on the disk' );
      Writeln( ' with the same name' );
      Write( 'Do you want to overwrite it? (Y/N) ' );
      Ch:= ReadKey;
      Writeln( Ch );                                          { echo to screen }
      Ch:= UpCase( Ch );
      if Ch = 'Y' then
        OK:= True;
      Close( OutFile )                        { we didn't really want to read it }
    end
    else                                                        { it isn't there }
      OK:= True;
    if OK then                                  { now we can open it for writing }
      OpenFile( OutFile, Scratch, 'W', IOCode )
    until OK;

    Read( InFile, Offerings );                            { get no. of offerings }
    for I:= 1 to Offerings do                             { then get the maxima }
      Read( InFile, Max[ I ] );

    Readln( InFile );                                                { new line }
    Write( 'Maximum for new offering: ' );
    Readln( NewMax );
    Max[ Offerings + 1 ]:= NewMax;
    Write( OutFile, Offerings + 1 );                        { update # offerings }

    for I:= 1 to Offerings + 1 do                           { maxima to Scratch }
      Write( OutFile, ' ', Max[ I ]:4:0 );

    Writeln( OutFile );                                              { new line }

    while not Eof( InFile ) do
    begin
    Read( InFile, Name );                          { now get names, old marks }
```

```
  for I:= 1 to Offerings do
    Read( InFile, Mark[ I ] );                    { them's his old marks }
  Readln( InFile );                               { new line }
  Write( Name );
     GoToXY( 21, WhereY );
     Write( 'Mark: ' );
     Readln( Mark[ Offerings + 1 ] );             { get new mark }
     Write( OutFile, Name, ' ':MaxChars - Length( Name ) );
                                                  { write his padded name... }
     for I:= 1 to Offerings + 1 do                { ..and all his marks }
       Write( OutFile, ' ', Mark[ I ]:4:0 );
     if not Eof( InFile ) then
       Writeln( OutFile )                         { new line except at end }
   end;
   Close( OutFile );
   Close( InFile );
   BackUp( Scratch );                             { now tidy up }
   Assign( F, MarksFile );
   Erase( F );
   Assign( F, Scratch );
   Rename( F, MarksFile )
 end; { Update }
 begin { StudentMarks }
   ClrScr;
   Writeln( 'Student Mark System' );
   Writeln;
   repeat
     Write( 'Display (D), Quit (Q) or Update (U)? ' );
     Ch:= ReadKey;
     Ch:= UpCase( Ch );
     Writeln;
     if Ch = 'D' then
       Display
     else
       if Ch = 'U' then
         Update
   until Ch = 'Q'
 end. { StudentMarks }
```

Try this program out on MARKS. After entering two offerings, the output of **Display** should look something like this:

```
Maximum mark:     100    25

ABLE ER            98    12
BOTHA FW           43     0
SMITH ZZ           76    23
```

11.7 BUDGETING PROCEDURES

In this section we develop a menu-driven program to compare monthly budgets and expenditures. You could easily adapt it for use at work or at home. The menu has four options. The **Initialise** option enables you to set up categories of expenses you want to allow for (for example, household, transport, etc.) and how much you want to budget for each category. This information is stored in a text file which is named with the first three letters of the month in question. Whenever you incur expenses during that month you can use the **Transaction** option to enter for each transaction a pre-defined single letter code for the expense category, and the amount to be debited to that category. Only valid expense codes are accepted. The **Statement** option writes a statement for the month showing expenditures for the categories, and their variance from budget. Finally, there is a **Quit** option.

The problem is fairly involved, so it is wise to draw up a structure plan before plunging into the code:

1. Start up
2. Repeat until asked to *Quit*:
   2.1. Display Menu and ask for option
   2.2. If *Initialise* then
      2.2.1. Open a new file
      2.2.2. Read expense codes, explanation and budget, and write them to the file
      2.2.3. Close the file
   2.3. If *Transaction* then
      2.3.1. Open the file and set the pointer to the end of the file
      2.3.2. Repeat until (@ 0) entered:
         2.3.2.1. Read expense code and amount
         2.3.2.2. Write them to the file
      2.3.3. Close the file
   2.4. If *Statement* then
      2.4.1. Open the file
      2.4.2. Get budget data from the file
      2.4.3. While more data in the file repeat:
         2.4.3.1. Get transactions from file
         2.4.3.2. Total the expenditure
      2.4.4. Produce and write the statement
      2.4.5. Close the file
3. Stop.

A text file is the appropriate kind of file to use here. It is easy to handle, and may be viewed on the screen and corrected. When new transactions are to be added, the **Append** procedure is used to add additional text at the end of the file.

Each menu option is handled by a different procedure. These are unlikely to be used in any other application, so it is convenient to dispense with parameters and local variables. Consequently the scope of all variables covers the whole program, with the exception of one variable in **HighLight**. This procedure uses some of the special features of the **Crt** unit to highlight a string when writing it on the screen, and has been written with parameters so that it can be used in any program (the details of the **Crt** unit are discussed in section 11.10).

BudgetData and **Transaction** use a new data structure – a set – to check if the expense code entered with a transaction is valid. Sets are discussed in section 12.1.

Note how the format of the monthly statement produced by **Statement** depends on a single constant **N**.

An important feature of **Read** with text files needs explanation. **Initialise** writes the budget information to the file with the statement

```
Writeln( F, Bud[I]:10:2, ' ', Code[I], Expln[I] )
                                        { blank after Bud must be read ! }
```

ie a number, a blank, a single character and a string. The blank is necessary to avoid an error when the file is read in **BudgetData** with

```
Readln( F, Bud[I], Ch, Code[I], Expln[I] );
                                        { Ch is the separator }
```

When **Read** is reading a number it expects a blank, a tab or an EOLN marker to end the number. The blank, however, is not read as part of the number. It must be read into the dummy variable **Ch** to get it out of the way so that the one-character expense code can be read into **Code[I]**. If the blank is omitted after **Bud[I]** error 106 (Invalid numeric format) occurs since the number is incorrectly delimited.

The complete program is as follows:

```
program Budget;
{ A household budget planner }
```

```
uses Crt;
const
  ExpWidth  = 15;                                  { length of explanation }
    MaxCodes= 20;                                  { maximum number of codes }
    N       = 15;                                  { width of numerical output }
  type
    Codes   = 1..MaxCodes;                         { array index }
    CodeSet = set of char;
    ExpStr  = string[ ExpWidth ];                  { explanation type }
  const
    LegalCd : CodeSet = [ '@' ];                   { set of expense codes }
  var
    Bud      : array[ Codes ] of real;             { budgets }
    Ch       : char;                               { general character }
    Code     : array[ Codes ] of char;             { expense codes }
    DskFil   : string[9];                          { disk file name }
    ExpCode: char;                                 { transaction expense code }
    Expln    : array[ Codes ] of ExpStr;           { explanations }
    F        : text;                               { general file variable }
    I        : word;                               { general counter }
    Month    : string[12];                         { month name }
    NumCodes:word;                                 { number of expense codes }
    OneCd    : CodeSet;                            { set for single expense code }
    Opt      : char;                               { user's option }
    Spend    : array[ Codes ] of real;             { expenses }
    TotBud   : real;                               { total budget }
    TotEx    : real;                               { total expenses }
    TransAmt: real;                                { transaction amount }
{------BudgetData--------------------------------------------------------------}
{                                                                              }
{  Get budget data from opened file F and compute total                        }
{  budget                                                                      }
{------------------------------------------------------------------------------}
  procedure BudgetData;
  begin
    Readln( F, NumCodes );
    TotBud:= 0;

    for I:= 1 to NumCodes do
    begin
      Readln( F, Bud[I], Ch, Code[I], Expln[I] );
                                                   { Ch is the separator }
      TotBud:= TotBud + Bud[I];
      OneCd:= [ Code[I] ];
      LegalCd:= LegalCd + OneCd;                   { set of expense codes }
    end

  end; { BudgetData }
{------HighLight---------------------------------------------------------------}
{                                                                              }
{  Writes string St with foreground colour ForeCol and                         }
{  background colour BackCol. Original text attributes                         }
{  (OldText) are restored.                                                     }
{------------------------------------------------------------------------------}
  procedure Highlight( St: string; ForeCol, BackCol: word );
  var
    Blinking : byte;
    OldBack: byte;
    OldFore : byte;
    OldText : byte;
  begin
    OldText:= TextAttr;                            { present text attributes }
```

```
    OldFore:= byte( OldText shl 4 );                              { type casting... }
    OldFore:= OldFore shr 4;                                  { ...handles overflow }
    OldBack:= OldText shr 4;
    if OldText shr 7 = 1 then
      Blinking:= 128;
    TextColor( ForeCol );
    TextBackGround( BackCol );
    Write( St );
    TextColor( OldFore + Blinking );                            { restore original }
    TextBackGround( OldBack )
  end; { Highlight }
{------Initialize---------------------------------------------------------------}
{                                                                               }
{  Gets codes, explanations, budgets and writes them                            }
{  to DskFil                                                                    }
{-------------------------------------------------------------------------------}
  procedure Initialize;
  begin
    Assign( F, DskFil );
    Rewrite( F );
    ClrScr;
    Write( 'How many codes? ' );
    Readln( NumCodes );
    Writeln( F, NumCodes );
    for I:= 1 to NumCodes do
    begin
      Write( 'Code', I:3, ': ' );
      Readln( Code[I] );
      GoToXY( 13, WhereY - 1 );
      Write( 'Explanation: ' );
      Readln( Expln[I] );
      GoToXY( 60, WhereY - 1 );
      Write( 'Budget: ' );
      Readln( Bud[I] );
      Writeln( F, Bud[I]:10:2, ' ', Code[I], Expln[I] )
                                                    { blank after Bud must be read ! }
    end;
    Close( F )
  end; { Initialize }
{------Statement----------------------------------------------------------------}
{                                                                               }
{  Prepares and writes monthly statement                                        }
{-------------------------------------------------------------------------------}
  procedure Statement;
  begin
    FillChar( Spend, SizeOf( Spend ), 0 );                             { all zeros }
    TotEx:= 0;
    ClrScr;
    Assign( F, DskFil );
    Reset( F );
    BudgetData;                                                  { get budget data }
    while not Eof( F ) do                                  { read all transactions }
    begin
      Readln( F, ExpCode, TransAmt );
      for I:= 1 to NumCodes do                           { find expense category }
        if ExpCode = Code[I] then
        begin
          Spend[I]:= Spend[I] + TransAmt;                              { allocate it }
          TotEx:= TotEx + TransAmt                             { keep running total}
```

```
      end
    end;
                                                      { now write the statement }
    Writeln( 'Statement for the month of ', Month );
    Writeln; Writeln( ' ': ExpWidth, 'BUDGET':N, 'ACTUAL':N, 'VARIANCE':N );
    Writeln;

    for I:= 1 to NumCodes do
    begin
      Write( Expln[I], ' ':ExpWidth - Length( Expln[I] ) );
      Writeln( Bud[I]:N:2, Spend[I]:N:2, Bud[I] - Spend[I]:N:2 )
    end;
    Writeln;
    Write( 'TOTAL:', ' ':ExpWidth - 6, TotBud:N:2, TotEx:N:2,
                                                     TotBud - TotEx:N:2 );

    Close( F );
    GoToXY( 1, WhereY + 3 );
    Write( 'Press any key to continue ...' );
    Ch:= ReadKey
  end; { Statement }
{------Transaction--------------------------------------------------------------------}
{                                                                                     }
{  Accepts transactions in the form Code, Amount                                      }
{  (@ 0 to end)                                                                       }
{-------------------------------------------------------------------------------------}

  procedure Transaction;
  begin
    Assign( F, DskFil );                                   { get budget data first }
    Reset( F );
    BudgetData;
    Close( F );
    Assign( F, DskFil );                                   { get ready to add new }
    Append( F );                                { ...transactions at end of text file }
    ClrScr;
    Writeln( 'Enter expense code and amount (@ 0 to end)' );
    Writeln;

    repeat
      Write( 'Transaction: ' );
      Readln( ExpCode, TransAmt );
      ExpCode:= UpCase( ExpCode );
      if ExpCode in LegalCd then                            { check for legal code }
        Writeln( F, ExpCode, ' ', TransAmt:10:2 )
                                       { blank after code is essential for later Read }
      else
      begin
        Writeln( 'Unknown expense code - legal codes are: ' );

        for Ch:= 'A' to 'Z' do                                { show legal codes }
          if Ch in LegalCd then
            Write( Ch, ' ' );

        Writeln
      end
    until ExpCode = '@';

    Close( F );                                  { don't forget to close the file! }
  end; { Transaction }

  begin { Budget }
    TextColor( LightGrey );
    Write( 'Month? ' );
    Readln( Month );
    DskFil:= Copy( Month, 1, 3 ) + '.';
                                                    { first three letters of month }
```

```
repeat                                                    { display menu }
  ClrScr;
  Write( 'Budget for the month of ' );
  HighLight( Month, Yellow + Blink, Blue );
  GoToXY( 1, 5 );
  Writeln( 'Month Initialisation: I' );
  Writeln;
  Writeln( 'Transaction Entry: T' );
  Writeln;
  Writeln( 'Monthly Statement: S' );
  Writeln;
  Writeln( 'Quit: Q' );
  Writeln;
  Write( 'Which option (' );
  Highlight( 'do NOT press ENTER', Black + Blink, Magenta );
  Write( ')? ' );
  Opt:= ReadKey;
  Opt:= UpCase( Opt );
  case Opt of
   'I'  : Initialise;
   'S'  : Statement;
   'T'  : Transaction;
   end;
  until Opt = 'Q';
  ClrScr
end. { Budget }
```

The program is demonstrated with some sample sessions below. First, initialisation (**I** option):

```
How many codes? 5
Code   1: C    Explanation:   Clothing        Budget: 75
Code   2: E    Explanation:   Entertainment   Budget: 50
Code   3: H    Explanation:   Household       Budget: 500
Code   4: G    Explanation:   General         Budget: 300
Code   5: T    Explanation:   Transport       Budget: 80
```

Next, some transactions (**T** option):

```
Enter expense code and amount (@ 0 to end)

Transaction: h 120
Transaction: t 20
Transaction: c 25
Transaction: e 12.5
Transaction: t 75
Transaction: @ 0
```

Finally, a monthly statement (**S** option):

```
Statement for the month of May
                      BUDGET      ACTUAL    VARIANCE
Clothing               75.00       25.00       50.00
Entertainment          50.00       12.50       37.50
Household             500.00      120.00      380.00
General               300.00        0.00      300.00
Transport              80.00       95.00      -15.00

TOTAL:               1005.00      252.50      752.50

Press any key to continue ...
```

The **Append** procedure may be used instead of **Rewrite** if you don't want to lose the contents of a file.

Append(*FileVar* **)** where *FileVar* has been assigned to a physical file, opens the file for writing at the current EOF marker. New text is added to the file with **Write** and **Writeln**, at and beyond the EOF marker.

11.8 PRINTING A TEXT FILE

The following program asks the user for the name of a text file and prints it on the line printer:

```
program PrfText;
uses Printer;
var
  Ch       : char;
  F        : text;
  Name     : string;
begin
  Write( 'Name of text file to print? ' );
  Readln( Name );
  Assign( F, Name );
  Reset (F);
  while not Eof( F ) do
  begin
    Read( F, Ch );
    Write( Lst, Ch )
  end;
  close( F )
end.
```

Since a Pascal program is a text file, this is one way of printing programs (another is to mark the whole program and to print the marked block with **Ctrl-KP**).

11.9 STANDARD I/O FUNCTIONS AND PROCEDURES

There are some further I/O standard functions and procedures that are useful.

ChDir(*String* **)** changes the current directory to a path specified by the string expression *String*. The path may include a drive letter.

Flush(*FileVar* **)** empties the file variable buffer, forcing the data to the physical disk file. *FileVar* should be a file variable opened for output. *Flush* should only be used on an open file. It has no effect on a file opened for input.

GetDir(*Integer, String* **)** returns the current directory of the *Integer* in *String*. *Integer* = 0 indicates the current drive, 1 indicates drive A, 2 indicates drive B, and so on.

MkDir(*String* **)** creates a subdirectory with the path specified by *String*.

RmDir(*String* **)** removes the empty subdirectory with the path specified by *String*.

The function **SeekEof(** *FileVar* **)** is similar to **Eof** except that it skips all blanks, tabs and EOL markers before returning EOF status. It is useful when reading numeric values from a text file. In the same way, **SeekEoln** skips blanks and tabs before returning EOL status.

Of the standard functions and procedures mentioned in this chapter, **Append, Eoln, Flush, Readln** and **Writeln**, operate on *text* files *only*. The rest operate on binary files as well.

11.10 THE CRT UNIT

The **Crt** unit has a number of facilities for enhancing screen output. We have already come across some of them, like **ClrScr**, **HighVideo**, etc. The declaration part of the unit is on your Turbo Pascal disk under the name \DOC\CRT.DOC. You should display or print it. You will see that there are predeclared constants and variables, as well as functions and procedures.

Text modes

Different text **modes** may be selected by the procedure **TextMode(** *Mode* **)**. The modes available on the IBM standard display adapters are:

```
BW40    = 0;                    { 40x25 B/W on Colour Adapter }
CO40    = 1;                { 40x25 Colour on Colour Adapter }
BW80    = 2;                    { 80x25 B/W on Colour Adapter }
```

```
CO80     = 3;                    { 80x25 Colour on Colour Adapter }
Mono     = 7;                    { 80x25 on Monochrome Adapter }
Font8x8  = 256;                  { Add-in for ROM font }
```

These are all constants defined in the **Crt** unit. For example, the statement **TextMode(BW80)** selects the mode **BW80**. (Incidentally, you can't disable colour if you are using an EGA or a VGA card, or if you are using the RGB outputs of the CGA.)

In addition the predeclared variable **LastMode** can be used to select the last active text mode. This can be useful if you want to return to the original text mode after using a graphics package, for example:

```
uses Crt;
var
  OldMode : word;
begin
  OldMode:= LastMode;
  ...
  TextMode( OldMode );
```

Note that **TextMode** does not support graphics modes.

Text colours

If you have a colour graphics card you can use **TextColor(** *Colour*) and **TextBackground(** *Colour*) to select the text foreground and background colours, and you can also make a character blink. The relevant constants in the **Crt** unit are:

```
{ Foreground and background color constants }
  Black          = 0;
  Blue           = 1;
  Green          = 2;
  Cyan           = 3;
  Red            = 4;
  Magenta        = 5;
  Brown          = 6;
  LightGrey      = 7;
{ Foreground color constants }
  DarkGrey       = 8;
  LightBlue      = 9;
  LightGreen     = 10;
  LightCyan      = 11;
  LightRed       = 12;
  LightMagenta   = 13;
  Yellow         = 14;
  White          = 15;
{ Add-in for blinking }
  Blink          = 128;
```

For example, **TextColor(Red + Blink)** selects red blinking characters. The following program illustrates the text colours:

```
program Joseph;
uses Crt;
var
  I, J : byte;
  OldMode: byte;
begin
  OldMode:= LastMode;
  ClrScr;
  for I:= 1 to 24 do
  begin
    TextBackground( I - 1 );
    TextColor( I );
```

```
    Write( I:4, ' Here is some pretty text!' );
    for J:= 1 to 30 do
      Write( Chr( 219 ) );
    Writeln
    end;
  Readln;
  TextMode( OldMode )
end.
```

Note that if *Colour* > 15 the foreground colour blinks.

The predeclared **Crt** byte variable **TextAttr** stores the currently selected text attributes, and can also be used to set them directly. The colour information is encoded in the eight bits of **TextAttr** as follows:

7	6	5	4	3	2	1	0
B	b	b	b	f	f	f	f

B is the blink-enable bit (ie 128), *bbb* is the 3-bit background colour, and *ffff* is the 4-bit foreground colour. So, for example, the background colour can be extracted with the operation

```
TextAttr shr 4
```

(although this retains the blink-bit the background colour is not affected, since only eight colours are available). This facility is used in the procedure **HighLight** in section 11.7.

Windows

Try the following program:

```
...
uses Crt;
var
  I : byte;

begin
  ClrScr;
  Window( 1, 1, 40, 10 );
  TextBackground( Blue );
  ClrScr;
  Writeln( 'Top window' );
  Window( 5, 12, 45, 20 );
  TextBackground( White );
  ClrScr;
  TextColor( Blue );
  for I:= 65 to 95 do
    Writeln( Chr( I ) );
  Writeln( 'Bottom window' );
  Readln
...
```

The procedure

```
Window( X1, Y1, X2, Y2 )
```

defines a text window on the screen. **X1, Y1** are the column and row of the upper left corner of the window. **X2** and **Y2** define the lower right corner of the window. All output from **Write** and **Writeln** will go into this window, which will scroll in the same way as the whole screen does. Note that **ClrScr** actually fills the window with the background colour.

The cursor movement function **GoToXY** operates *relative* to the current window, ie **GoToXY(1, 1)** puts the cursor in the top left corner of the current window, no matter what its *absolute* co-ordinates are.

The quickest way to clear an area of the screen is with **Window**:

```
procedure ClearSpace( X1, X2, Y1, Y2 : byte );
```

```
begin
  Window( X1, X2, Y1, Y2 );
  ClrScr;
  Window( 1, 1, 80, 25 )
end; { ClearSpace }
```

This is much faster than writing lines of spaces. The co-ordinates of the current window are available in the predeclared variables **WindMin** and **WindMax**. **WindMin** contains the upper left co-ordinates, and **WindMax** the lower right ones. The *X* co-ordinate is stored in the **low byte**, and the *Y* co-ordinate in the **high byte**. They can be accessed with the standard functions **Lo** and **Hi**. For example, **Hi(WindMax)** returns the *Y* co-ordinate of the lower right corner. Note that the values returned by **WindMin** and **WindMax** are actually *relative to zero*, and not to (1, 1). So with the window defined by

```
Window( 5, 12, 45, 20 );
```

WindMin will return (4, 11) and **WindMax** will return (44, 19).

Other standard Crt functions and procedures

AssignCrt(*FileVar* **)** associates the text file *FileVar* with the screen, and works just like **Assign** except that no physical file is mentioned, the CRT being assumed. This allows faster output (and input).

ClearEol changes all characters to blanks (in the background colour) from the cursor position to the end of the line, without moving the cursor.

DelLine deletes the line containing the cursor. An empty line in the background colour is inserted at the bottom of the screen.

InsLine inserts a line of blanks, in the current background colour, at the cursor position.

SUMMARY

- A physical file is a collection of data on a disk. A logical file is a Turbo Pascal variable which may be connected to a physical file with the **Assign** procedure.
- Logical files are either binary files or text files.
- Text files are lines of printable characters.
- A text file can either be completely overwritten (the previous contents are lost) or appended to (previous contents retained). Material cannot be inserted into the middle of a text file (with a Turbo Pascal program).
- A device file is a piece of hardware such as a printer or a keyboard, and may also be connected to a logical file.

EXERCISES

11.1 Write a procedure UpperCase(var Name: string) to replace all the lowercase letters in the disk text file Name with uppercase letters.

11.2 When a message is prepared for enciphering, all blanks are removed and it is transmitted in groups of five letters, with one blank between each group. Write a program which reads the following extract from *Jabberwocky* by Lewis Carroll, removes all the blanks, and writes it out in uppercase in groups of five letters:

Twas brillig and the slithy toves
Did gyre and gimble in the wabe

The output should look like this:

TWASB RILLI GANDT HESLI THYTO VESDI DGYRE ANDGI MBLEI NTHEW ABE

The program should input any number of lines from a disk file.

11.3 A fair indication of the authorship of prose can sometimes be obtained by calculating the average number of words per sentence (mean sentence length) and the standard deviation of this statistic. I once found, for example, that with samples of about 700 lines,

G.K. Chesterton is easily distinguishable from Lord Macaulay, the former having a significantly shorter mean sentence length, with a larger standard deviation. Write a program that reads some text from a text file and computes these statistics. Assume, to make things a little easier, that sentences are delimited by periods or exclamation marks only, and that periods occur nowhere else in the text.

11.4 Rewrite the program PrtText in section 11.8 as a procedure TextPrint(Name: string) to print the text file with filename Name. Include I/O error handling to cope with non-existent files.

12 Structured Types

A structured type is characterised by its component type being able to hold more than one value. We have already seen two structured types: arrays and files. In this chapter we look at the remaining structured types in Turbo Pascal: sets, records, pointers and objects (a new type available in Turbo Pascal 5.5). We will also discuss binary files.

12.1 SETS

Sets are fun, and very useful. We have already seen an example of them in section 11.7 in checking for legal expense codes. Here is another example:

```
...
uses Crt;
const
  Replies = ['y', 'Y', 'n', 'N'];
var
  ch : char;
begin
  repeat
  Write( 'Do you want to continue? (y/n) ' );
  Ch:= ReadKey;
  Writeln;
  if not (Ch in Replies) then
    Writeln( 'Answer the question!' )
  until Ch in Replies
...
```

It doesn't do very much, but it illustrates the point that sets help to make concise, readable code. The alternative is;

```
if (Ch <> 'y') and (Ch <> 'Y') and (Ch <> 'n') and (Ch <> 'N') then
  Writeln( 'Answer the question!' )
until (Ch = 'y') or (Ch = 'Y') or (Ch = 'n') or (Ch = 'N')
```

which is a great deal longer (and also takes more computer time to execute).

In this example, the set is **Replies** (actually it is a constant set). It is defined by enclosing a list of elements of simple type in square brackets. In this context the pair of square brackets is called a **set constructor**.

A set in Turbo Pascal is defined as a collection of values **(elements)** of any simple type which has 256 or fewer values. This is the **base type** of the set. For example, the base type of **Replies** above is char, since it is a collection of characters. Furthermore, the ordinal values of the base type must lie in the range 0 to 255. So the base type of a set cannot be shortint, integer, longint or word. It can however be a subrange or an enumerated type.

Some examples follow:

```
const
  EmptySet = [ ];
type
  CharSet = set of char;
```

```
  GradeRange = 1..10;
var
  Grade          : set of GradeRange;
  Consonants     : CharSet;
  Punctuations   : CharSet;
  Single         : CharSet;
  Vowels         : CharSet;
begin
  Consonants:= [ 'b'..'d', 'v'..'z', 'f'..'h', 'j'..'n', 'p'..'t' ];
  Punctuations:= [ ',', '.', '''', '?' ];
  Vowels:= [ 'a', 'e', 'i', 'o', 'u' ];
  Single:= [ '?' ];
  Punctuations:= Punctuations + Single;
  Grade:= [ 1, 3..6, 9 ];
  Grade:= Grade - [6..10];
  if not (9 in Grade) then write( 'no' );
```

Note that the empty set has no elements.

You might be tempted to define a set as

```
Grade : [ 1..10 ];
```

but this is not allowed. The base type must be defined in a type declaration if it is not a standard type (ie char, byte or boolean);

Set operators

There are three operations allowed on sets:

- `+` : the **union** of two sets contains all the elements of both sets;
- `*` : the **intersection** of two sets contains only those elements present in *both* sets;
- `–` : the **difference** of two sets **A** and **B** contains only the elements of **A** that are not also in **B**. It's rather like subtraction in a way. So [**1..5**] – [**4..10**] returns [**1..3**]

If you want to add an element to a set (as in adding further punctuation marks to the set **Punctuations** above) a set must first be defined containing the element to be added, otherwise a type mismatch occurs (only sets can be added to sets):

```
Single:= [ '?' ];
Punctuations:= Punctuations + Single;
```

This is also done in the procedure **BudgetData** in section 11.7 to construct a set of legal expense codes.

Set relational operators

There are five set relational operators, which can be used to construct Boolean expressions involving sets and their elements:

- **in** : true if the element on the left is in the set on the right, for example, **if Ch in ['a', 'e', 'i', 'o', 'u'] then ...**
- = : true if both sets contain the same elements;
- <> : true if the two sets do not contain the same elements;
- <= : true if all the elements in the set on the left are present in (is a subset of) the set on the right;
- >= : true if all the elements in the set on the right are present in (is a subset of) the set on the left.

Fruit sundae

The following extracts show the use of a set of enumerated type:

```
uses Crt;
```

```
type
Ingredients    = ( Apples, Strawberries, Bananas, Nuts, Icecream,
                   ChocolateSauce, Cream, Pastry, Sugar, Ice );
  Pudding      = set of Ingredients;
 var
  Goodies    : Ingredients;                          { var of base type }
  AppleCrumble: Pudding;                             { var of set type }
  Feast      : Pudding;
  Sundae     : Pudding;

 begin
  ClrScr;
  Sundae:= [ Strawberries..Cream ];                  { consecutive elements }
  Feast:= Sundae + [ Apples, Sugar, Pastry ];        { set union }
  ...
  if Bananas in AppleCrumble then
    Writeln( 'What strange apple crumble!' );
  ...
  Goodies:= Apples;
  while Goodies <> Ice do                            { examine contents of Sundae }
  begin
    if Goodies in Sundae then
      case Goodies of
        Apples    : write( 'apples ' );
        Bananas   : write( 'bananas ' );
        Cream     : write( 'cream ' );
      end;
    Goodies:= Succ( Goodies )
  end;
```

Note the use of the **Succ** function on the dummy set **Goodies** to list the elements of the set **Sundae**.

12.2 RECORDS

The structured types we have seen so far, like arrays and sets, have been characterised by the fact that their component types have been the same. So **array[1..100] of real** declares all the components of the array to be real. However, there are many applications where the basic entity has components of *different* types. Consider, for example, a student record system at a school or university. Each student has a number of associated data items, like name, address, telephone number, course, marks, etc. These are all most conveniently represented in Turbo Pascal by variables of different type – strings of different lengths for personal particulars and reals or integers for the marks.

One of Pascal many distinguishing features is that it has a structured data type called a **record** which allows components of different type, and which can handle this situation very easily.

Let's take a simple example to start with. Suppose each student has only a name and one mark. Then a record type **PersonRec** can be defined as follows:

```
type
  PersonRec = record
                Name : string[20];
                Mark : real
              end;
```

A variable **Person** can then be declared with this type:

```
var
  Person : PersonRec;
```

This record has two components or **fields, Name** and **Mark**. These can be referenced for assignment, reading or writing, etc., by **dotting**, for example:

```
Person.Name:= 'Bombadil';
Readln( Person.Mark );
```

(Technically, **Person.Name** is a qualified identifier.) Furthermore, records of the same type are assignment compatible, so if **OldPerson** is also of type **PersonRec**, we can say

```
OldPerson:= Person;
```

This copies the data in each field of **Person** to the corresponding field of **OldPerson**, and so is equivalent to

```
OldPerson.Name:= Person.Name;
OldPerson.Mark:= Person.Mark;
```

If there are a large number of fields, this makes for very concise coding.

Updating student marks again

The fields of a record may be structured types themselves, like arrays, or even other records. This can get very complicated! In the program **StudentMarks** in section 11.6, each student has a name **(string[MaxChars])** and an array of marks **(array[1..MaxOfferings] of real)** so we could construct a record type **StudentRec** with one field for the name, and another field for the array of marks:

```
StudentRec = record
               Name : string[MaxChars];                { student's name }
               Mark : array[ ArrMarks ] of real;       { his marks }
             end;
```

What's the point of this added complication? Well, suppose we want to produce an order of merit list, based on a particular offering, ie a list of students in descending order of mark. We could read all the names from the disk file (MARKS) into a string array, and all the marks of the offering to be sorted into a real array. Then we could sort the offering array (using a Bubble Sort to keep things simple). However, the crux of the sort is the swopping of items which are not in the correct order:

```
if X[J] > X[J+1] then
begin
  Temp:= X[J];
  X[J]:= X[J+1];
  X[J+1]:= Temp;
...
```

But every time two marks are swopped we would have to *remember* to *swop the corresponding names also*, otherwise at the end of the day the marks will be in descending order, but the names will still be in the original order.

A much neater solution is to declare an *array* of records of type **StudentRec**, and then when the marks are in the wrong order to swop entire records. So the basic variable to declare is

```
var
  Student : array[ 1..200 ] of StudentRec;
```

It helps to visualise what is going on:

```
Student[1]   :     Name;
                   Mark[1], Mark[2], ..., Mark[20];

Student[2]   :     Name;
                   Mark[1], Mark[2], ..., Mark[20];
...
Student[200] :     Name;
                   Mark[1], Mark[2], ..., Mark[20];
```

The following program reads the data from the disk file MARKS into the array **Student**, asks the user which offering is to be sorted **(SortOff)**, uses an amended Bubble Sort procedure **RecordSort** to sort the required offering, and writes the names and marks in order of merit. To economise on coding, the program uses a **with** statement which is explained below.

```
program Merit;
{ performs order of merit on given offering }
uses Crt;
```

```
const
  MaxChars = 20;
  MaxOfferings = 20;
  MaxStu    = 200;
type
  ArrMarks = 1..MaxOfferings;
  StudentRec= record
                  Name : string[MaxChars];                    { student's name }
                  Mark : array[ ArrMarks ] of real;                { his marks }
              end;
  ArrType   = array[ 1..MaxStu ] of StudentRec;
var
  I          : byte;                                        { general counter }
  InFile     : text;                                       { read file variable}
  Max        : array[ ArrMarks ] of real;               { max of each offering }
  Num        : word;                                   { number of students }
  Offerings  : byte;                                   { number of offerings }
  SortOff    : byte;                                    { offering to sort on }
  Student    : ArrType;                                { array of StudentRec }

{------RecordSort--------------------------------------------------------------}
{ This procedure sorts the SortOff offering in the Mark field                  }
{ of the record array X into descending order (order of merit)                 }
{ using a Bubble Sort.                                                          }
{ N is the number of records to be sorted.                                      }
{                                                                               }
{ Formal parameter type:                                                        }
{                                                                               }
{ StudentRec = record                                                           }
{                  Name : string[MaxChars];                                     }
{                  Mark : array[ ArrMarks ] of real;                            }
{              end;                                                             }
{ ArrType    = array[ 1..MaxStu ] of StudentRec;                                }
{                                                                               }
{------RecordSort--------------------------------------------------------------}
procedure Recordsort( var X: ArrType; N, SortOff: word );
var
  J, K      : word;
  Temp      : StudentRec;
  Sorted    : boolean;
begin
  K:= 0;

  repeat                                              { outer loop of bubble sort }
  K:= K + 1;                                                  { count the passes }
  Sorted:= true;                                          { they might be sorted }
  for J:= 1 to N - K do                                        { count the tests }
    if X[J].Mark[SortOff] < X[J+1].Mark[SortOff] then
    begin
      Temp:= X[J];
      X[J]:= X[J+1];
      X[J+1]:= Temp;
      Sorted:= False                                          { a swop was made }
      end

  until Sorted                                              { must be sorted now }

end; { RecordSort }

begin { Merit }
  ClrScr;
  Assign( InFile, 'MARKS.' );
  Reset( InFile );
  Read( InFile, Offerings );                              { get no. of offerings }
```

```
for I:= 1 to Offerings do                              { then get the maxima }
  Read( InFile, Max[ I ] );
Readln( InFile );                                      { new line }
Num:= 1;        { start counting }
   while not Eof( InFile ) do
     with Student[ Num ] do
     begin
       Read( InFile, Name );                           { now get names, old marks }
       for I:= 1 to Offerings do
         Read( InFile, Mark[ I ] );                    { these are his old marks }
       Readln( InFile );                               { new line }
       if not Eof( InFile ) then
         Num:= Num + 1                                 { otherwise Num will be 1 too big }
     end;
   Write( 'Order of Merit on which offering? ' );
   Readln( SortOff );
   RecordSort( Student, Num, SortOff );
   for I:= 1 to Num do
     with Student[ I ] do
       Writeln( Name, ' ', Mark[ SortOff ]:4:0 );
   Close( InFile )
 end. { Merit }
```

The changes made to the **BubbleSort** procedure of section 9.4 have been highlighted. Note how few there are. Note in particular that the statements

```
Temp:= X[J];
X[J]:= X[J+1];
X[J+1]:= Temp;
```

now actually swop entire records – the name and **MaxOfferings** marks. (This can be very time consuming if there is a great deal of data – see section 12.3 for an alternative approach using the concept of a *keyfile*.)

Note also how a field of a record which is a component of an array is referenced. For example, the name field of the fifth record in the array **Student** is referenced as

```
Student[5].Name
```

(the field comes *after* the array index).

The **with** statement introduced above needs some explanation. Referencing records can become rather cumbersome, for example:

```
Readln( Student.Name, Student.Address, Student.Phone )
```

The **with-do** statement allows you to reference a record's fields without mentioning its name each time:

```
with Student do
  Readln( Name, Address, Phone );
```

This makes for much easier coding. **with-do** may be followed by a compound statement, as in the main program above. In a **with** statement, Turbo Pascal checks first whether a variable is a record field, and will treat it as such if it is, even if another variable of the same name is accessible.

Records may be nested, ie records may themselves be fields of larger records.

Transfer functions with complex arithmetic

A criticism sometimes levelled at Pascal is that it can't handle complex numbers directly, as a language like FORTRAN can. However, complex arithmetic can be defined quite easily using records. (If you are not familiar with complex numbers you can skip this section.)

A complex number z may be represented as

$$z = x + iy$$

where x is its real part, y its imaginary part, and i is the unit imaginary number $\sqrt{-1}$. A natural notation for z is also (x, y).

The arithmetic operations of addition, multiplication and division for two complex numbers $z_1 = (x_1, y_1)$ and $z_2 = (x_2, y_2)$ may then be defined using the rules of ordinary (real) arithmetic and the fact that $i^2 = -1$.

The sum $z_1 + z_2$ is $(x_1 + x_2, y_1 + y_2)$. This also covers the difference since the signs of the numbers have not been specified.

The product $z_1 z_2$ is $(x_1 x_2 - y_1 y_2, y_1 x_2 + x_1 y_2)$, ie the real part of the product is $x_1 x_2 - y_1 y_2$ and the imaginary part is $y_1 x_2 + x_1 y_2$.

The quotient z_1 / z_2 has a real part of $(x_2 x_2 + y_1 y_2) / (x_2{}^2 + y_2{}^2)$ and and an imaginary part of $(y_1 x_2 + x_1 y_2) / (x_2{}^2 + y_2{}^2)$. (This form may be obtained by multiplying $(x_1 + iy_1)/(x_2 + iy_2)$ by $(x_2 - iy_2)/(x_2 - iy_2)$ in order to make the denominator real.)

To represent complex numbers in Turbo Pascal we can define a type **Complex** as a record with two fields, for the real and imaginary parts:

```
type
   Complex = record
                  Re : real;
                  Im : real
              end;
```

The procedure **CompAdd** can then be defined to add two complex numbers **A** and **B**, returning the sum in **C**:

```
procedure CompAdd( var A, B, C: Complex );
{ complex sum of A and B, returned in C }
begin
   C.Re:= A.Re + B.Re;                        { sum of the real parts }
   C.Im:= A.Im + B.Im                         { sum of the imaginary parts}
end; { CompAdd }
```

CompMult returns the product of **A** and **B**:

```
procedure CompMult( var A, B, C: Complex );
{ complex product of A and B, returned in C }
begin
   C.Re:= A.Re * B.Re - A.Im * B.Im;
   C.Im:= A.Im * B.Re + A.Re * B.Im
end; { CompMult }
```

CompDiv returns the quotient:

```
procedure CompDiv( var A, B, C: Complex );
{ complex quotient of A and B, returned in C }
var
   Den : real;
begin
   Den:= B.Re * B.Re + B.Im * B.Im;
   C.Re:= (A.Re * B.Re + A.Im * B.Im) / Den;
   C.Im:= (A.Im * B.Re - A.Re * B.Im) / Den
end; { CompDiv }
```

One further procedure, **CompAsg**, is needed to assign the real and imaginary parts, **A** and **B**, to the complex number **C**:

```
procedure CompAsg( A, B: real; var C: Complex );
{ assigns real (A) and imaginary (B) parts to C }
begin
   C.Re:= A;
   C.Im:= B
end; { CompAsg }
```

So the complex value $1 + 0.4i$ may be assigned to the complex variable **X** with the call **CompAsg(1, 0.4, X)**.

Flushed with excitement at our complex achievements we can apply this to the standard electrical engineering problem of calculating a **transfer function.**

The response (output) of a linear system, which may be thought of as a black box, is characterised in electrical engineering by its transfer function. An input signal with a given angular frequency (ω radians/sec) is applied at one end of the box. The output from the other end is then given by the input multiplied by the absolute value of the transfer function, with its phase shifted by the phase angle of the transfer function.

Suppose a servomechanism is characterised by the transfer function:

$$T(i\omega) = \frac{K(1 + 0.4i\omega)(1 + 0.2i\omega)}{i\omega(1 + 2.5i\omega)(1 + 1.43i\omega)(1 + 0.02i\omega)^2}$$

where K is an amplification factor. $T(i\omega)$ is a complex number. If its real and imaginary parts are a and b respectively then its absolute value is $\sqrt{(a^2 + b^2)}$ and its phase angle θ is given by $\arctan(b/a)$.

This raises a slight problem because the standard function **ArcTan** returns an angle in the range $-\pi/2$ to $\pi/2$ (first and fourth quadrants) whereas the angle might actually be in the second or third quadrants. The quadrant may be determined from the signs of a and b. The function **Atan** below returns an angle in the correct quadrant:

```
function Atan( Im, Re: real ): real;
{ returns correct quadrant of arctangent ( Im / Re ) }
begin
  if (Re >= 0) and (Im >= 0) or (Re >= 0) and (Im <= 0) then
    Atan:= ArcTan( Im / Re )                          { 1st and 4th quadrants }
  else
    if (Re <= 0) and (Im <= 0) then
      Atan:= ArcTan( Im / Re ) - Pi                   { 3rd quadrant }
    else
      Atan:= Pi + ArcTan( Im / Re )                   { 2nd quadrant }
end; { Atan }
```

The program below shows how the servomechanism responds to different input frequencies ω. This information is necessary in the design of stable feedback control devices. The initial input frequency **Omega** is 0.02 radians/sec. This is multiplied by a factor **(Fact)** of 1.25 each time for a given number of steps. The amplification factor K is 900. The phase shift θ of the output is given in degrees.

$T(i\omega)$ has to be computed in stages, as a running product **T**. **CompAsg(K, 0, T)** gives **T** the real value K, and **CompAsg(1, 0.4 * Omega, X)** gives **X** the complex value $1 + 0.4i\omega$. **CompMult(T, X, Y)** forms the product $K(1 + 0.4i\omega)$ in **Y**, which is assigned directly to **T** in the next statement. In this way **T** is built up using the two intermediate variables **X** and **Y**.

If you think this coding is too involved, try calculating the real and imaginary parts of the transfer function by hand. You need to start by multiplying the numerator and denominator by the complex conjugate of the denominator:

$$-\ i\omega(1 - 2.5i\omega)(1 - 1.43i\omega)(1 - 0.02i\omega)^2$$

Good luck! I think the coding is easier!

The complete program to compute the transfer function is as follows:

```
program Servo;
{ Servomechanism frequency response }
type
  Complex = record
              Re : real;
              Im : real
            end;
var
  I                               : word;
  Fact, K, Omega, Phase, TAbs     : real;
  Iom, T, X, Y                    : complex;
```

```
function Atan( Im, Re: real ): real;
  ...
end; { Atan }
procedure CompAsg( A, B: real; var C: Complex );
  ...
end; { CompAsg }
procedure CompAdd( var A, B, C: Complex );
  ...
end; { CompAdd }
procedure CompMult( var A, B, C: Complex );
  ...
end; { CompMult }
procedure CompDiv( var A, B, C: Complex );
  ...
end; { CompDiv }
begin
  K:= 900;
  Omega:= 0.02;
  Fact:= 1.25;
  Writeln( 'Omega':10, 'Real T':14, 'Imag T':14, 'Abs T':14,
           'Phase':11 );
  Writeln;
  for I:= 1 to 41 do
  begin
    CompAsg( K, 0, T );
    CompAsg( 1, 0.4 * Omega, X );
    CompMult( T, X, Y ); T:= Y;
    CompAsg( 1, 0.2 * Omega, X );
    CompMult( T, X, Y );
    T:= Y;
    CompAsg( 0, Omega, X );
    CompDiv( T, X, Y );
    T:= Y;
    CompAsg( 1, 2.5 * Omega, X );
    CompDiv( T, X, Y );
    T:= Y;
    CompAsg( 1, 1.43 * Omega, X );
    CompDiv( T, X, Y );
    T:= Y;
    CompAsg( 1, 0.02 * Omega, X );
    CompDiv( T, X, Y );
    T:= Y;
    CompDiv( T, X, Y );
    T:= Y;
    TAbs:= Sqrt( T.Re * T.Re + T.Im * T.Im );
    Phase:= Atan( T.Im, T.Re ) * 180 / Pi;
    Writeln( Omega:10, T.Re:14:3, T.Im:14:3, TAbs:14:3, Phase:11:2 );
    Omega:= Omega * Fact
  end
end.
```

Output:

```
     Omega        Real T        Imag T        Abs T      Phase

 2.000E-02     -3023.601    -44825.416    44927.275     -93.86
 2.500E-02     -3018.335    -35782.112    35909.190     -94.82
 3.125E-02     -3010.140    -28528.307    28686.673     -96.02
 3.906E-02     -2997.410    -22701.678    22898.704     -97.52
 4.883E-02     -2977.703    -18011.603    18256.082     -99.39
 6.104E-02     -2947.352    -14224.928    14527.060    -101.71
```

7.629E−02	−2900.974	−11154.862	11525.910	−104.58
9.537E−02	−2830.962	−8652.581	9103.928	−108.12
1.192E−01	−2727.186	−6601.316	7142.473	−112.45
1.490E−01	−2577.495	−4912.678	5547.783	−117.68
1.863E−01	−2369.930	−3524.578	4247.260	−123.92
2.328E−01	−2097.603	−2399.070	3186.766	−131.16
2.910E−01	−1765.784	−1517.136	2328.024	−139.33
3.638E−01	−1397.490	−867.698	1644.955	−148.16
4.547E−01	−1031.195	−432.703	1118.300	−157.24
5.684E−01	−707.927	−176.772	729.664	−165.98
7.105E−01	−454.856	−49.785	457.573	−173.75
8.882E−01	−277.357	−0.270	277.357	−179.94
1.110E+00	−163.647	11.616	164.058	175.94
1.388E+00	−95.371	9.705	95.863	174.19
1.735E+00	−55.858	5.028	56.084	174.86
2.168E+00	−33.256	1.311	33.282	177.74
2.711E+00	−20.240	−0.859	20.258	−177.57
3.388E+00	−12.615	−1.850	12.749	−171.66
4.235E+00	−8.056	−2.129	8.332	−165.20
5.294E+00	−5.278	−2.038	5.657	−158.88
6.617E+00	−3.556	−1.784	3.978	−153.36
8.272E+00	−2.472	−1.476	2.879	−149.15
1.034E+01	−1.778	−1.169	2.128	−146.68
1.292E+01	−1.323	−0.885	1.592	−146.21
1.616E+01	−1.012	−0.634	1.194	−147.91
2.019E+01	−0.784	−0.420	0.889	−151.83
2.524E+01	−0.603	−0.244	0.651	−157.94
3.155E+01	−0.450	−0.112	0.463	−166.05
3.944E+01	−0.317	−0.023	0.318	−175.79
4.930E+01	−0.207	0.024	0.208	173.39
6.163E+01	−0.124	0.040	0.130	162.17
7.704E+01	−0.068	0.037	0.078	151.22
9.630E+01	−0.035	0.028	0.044	141.07
1.204E+02	−0.017	0.018	0.025	132.07
1.505E+02	−0.008	0.011	0.013	124.33

Note how the signal is amplified at first, but then attenuated. The phase shift starts at about −90° and moves gradually to about −180°, after which it swings back and forth across the real axis as the input frequency increases.

Variant records

The records we have seen so far have all been fixed records in the sense that the fields of a given record type are always the same. This means that all situations must be catered for at all times, which can waste valuable memory. For example, suppose students collect 20 marks each year. By their third year they would have 60 marks, if we wanted to keep them all. But allocating space for 60 marks to first-year students doesn't make sense – we know we only need a third of the space.

The following declaration gives every student a **Name** field (since they all have names) and a first-year mark field (**First**), since all students must start in their first year. However, second-year students get an additional mark field (**Second**), while only third-year students get a third mark field (**Third**).

```
type
  ArrMark     = array[ 1..20 ] of real;
  StudentRec  = record
                  Name : string[20];
                  First : ArrMark;
                  case Year : byte of
                    2, 3 :
                            (Second : ArrMark);
                    3    :
                            (Third : ArrMark)
                end;
```

This structure is known as a **variant record**. It consists of a fixed part, which must come first, followed by the variant part in the form of a **case** statement. There may be no further fixed fields after the variant part. The variant fields actually used are selected according to the value of the **tag field (Year** in this example) when the record is referenced during execution.

Note that parentheses must surround the field definitions of each variant part. The tag field must *not* be included in the parentheses. Note that variant parts of a variant record *not* selected by the tag field are *inaccessible*, and their values are *undefined*.
Another example may be helpful:

```
type
  Employee = record
               Name : string[30];
               case Foreign : boolean of
                 True :
                       (Country: string[20];
                       EntryDate : string[6];
                       Status : string[12])
             end;
```

In this case the fixed part of the record has one field while the variant part has three. The tag field, **Foreign**, is boolean. The records of domestic employees therefore only have **Name** fields.

For the record, so to speak, the tag field (eg **Foreign**) may be absent, but not the tag field *type* (eg **boolean**). In this case the program selects a variant by another criterion, as the *Turbo Pascal Reference Guide* mysteriously puts it. Such a variant record, without a tag field, is called a **free union** variant record, to distinguish it from the sort above, which is called a **discriminated union** in some circles. To use this form successfully you need to know that free union variant fields are all mapped onto the *same region of memory*. Consider the example:

```
type
  dirty = record
            case byte of
              0 : (Full : word);
              1 : (Low : Byte;                    { same as Lo(Full) }
                   High : Byte)                   { same as Hi(Full) }
          end;
var
  X : dirty;
```

There is no tag field, only a tag field type (**byte** in this case). The tag field type must be an ordinal type with 256 or fewer values. The two variant parts here (case 0 and case 1) are mapped onto the same memory area. Because **Low** and **High** are each one byte long, **Low** will occupy the same memory as the low byte of **Full**, while **High** will occupy the high byte of **Full**. So the assignment:

```
X.Full:= 256
```

will effectively give **X.Low** the value 0 and **X.High** the value 1. (The same result is returned by using the standard functions **Hi** and **Lo**, but this method is faster.)

Free unions basically allow you to force variables of one type into variables of another type regardless of Pascal's strict typing regulations. They should be used with great care, and only as a last resort.

The **absolute** clause can also be used to declare variables on top of each other:

```
YLo, YHi: byte;
Y: word absolute YLo;
```

YLo and **YHi** will be in contiguous bytes of memory. **Y** will start at the same address as **Ylo,** but because it is two bytes long it will overlap **YHi** as well. This has exactly the same effect as the free union example above. You can verify this by using the **Ofs** standard function to find the offset parts of the addresses of these variables.

12.3 BINARY FILES

So far the only kind of files we have looked at are text files, which may effectively contain data items of different types. Text files may only be accessed *sequentially*, ie you can only read from (or write to) where the file pointer is, and the file pointer must be advanced one position at a time.

In contrast to a text file, a **binary file** may be accessed at random. A **random access** file is one in which *any* item may be read or written after opening. Binary files in Turbo Pascal are random access files, and are either **typed** or **untyped**.

If a file is typed, its components must all be of the same type (the component type). The components may be any type except a file type or a structured type with a file type component. Such file variables are declared as follows:

```
var
  IntFile : file of integer;
  ArrFile : file of array[1..10] of real;
```

The following program creates a file of integers, reads them back, and writes them on the screen:

```
program FileTest;
var
  IntFile: file of integer;
  I : integer;
begin
  Assign( IntFile, 'D:Junk.' );
  Rewrite( IntFile );
  for I:= 1 to 10 do
    Write( IntFile, I );                    { write them to the file }
  Readln;
  Reset( IntFile );                    { reset the pointer to the front }
  while not Eof( IntFile ) do
  begin
    Read( IntFile, I );                     { read them back again }
    Write( I:3 )                                  { and write them }
  end;
     Close(
IntFile )
end.
```

The file is assigned in the normal way with **Assign**, and opened for writing with **Rewrite** (which causes all the previous contents of the file to be lost). When writing is complete, the file pointer is at the end of the file. **Reset** moves it back to the beginning of the file, so that it can be read from the beginning. A file opened with **Reset** may also be written to while it is open.

Data are written to (and read from) a binary file with the standard procedures **Read** and **Write** (**Readln** and **Writeln** apply only to text files):

Read(*FileVar, Var* **);**
Write(*FileVar, Var* **);**

FileVar's component type must be *identical* to *Var's* type. The following will generate error 26 (Type mismatch):

```
var
  F : file of string[4];
  X : string[4];
begin
  Assign( F, 'Junk.' );
  Rewrite( F );
  X:= 'abcd';
  Write( F, X )      { 26 - Type mismatch }
```

Rather define a type:

```
type
  Str4 = string[4];
var
  F : file of Str4;
  X : Str4;
```

Each data item in the file is referred to as a **record**. This is ***not*** to be confused with the Turbo Pascal record data type. Typed binary files must be records of fixed length (as opposed to text files), which is why each record must contain the same data type. In the case of **ArrFile** above, each record contains an array of 10 real elements, and this entire array is read or written.

A file's records are numbered sequentially from zero, so the first record is number 0. **Read** or **Write** advances the file pointer one record, so if you read a record and immediately want to overwrite it, you have to move the pointer back one record. This may be done with **FilePos** and **Seek**:

Seek (*FileVar*, **FilePos(** *FileVar* **) − 1);**

FilePos(*FileVar* **)** returns the record number of the next item in *FileVar* to be read or written. **Seek(** *FileVar*, *RecNum* **)** moves the *FileVar's* pointer in such a way that record *RecNum* is the next record to be read or written. Neither **FilePos** nor **Seek** may be used with text files.

You should never try to write a binary file on the screen. At best you'll get garbage, and at worst your machine will hang up.

Student records yet again

We have seen the use of text files in updating student records in sections 11.6 and 12.2. Binary files provide a neater and more efficient way of handling this problem. What we will do is to set up a file where each record in the file contains a student's name and all his marks. So each record in the file should be a data item of type **StudentRec**, where:

```
StudentRec = record
               Name : string[MaxChars];              { student's name }
               Mark : array[ ArrMarks ] of real;     { his marks }
             end;
```

In other words, each record (in the file sense) will be a record (in the Turbo Pascal sense). We therefore need a file of type **StudentFile**, where

```
StudentFile = file of StudentRec;
```

If the declarations

```
RecFile   : StudentFile;                 { general file variable }
Student   : StudentRec;                  { individual record }
```

are made, the statement

```
Read( RecFile, Student )
```

will read a particular student's name and marks from the next record of the file. His name will then be in **Student.Name**, and his marks in **Student.Mark[1]**, etc.

The program **RecordFile** below assigns the variable **RecFile** to the disk file MARKS.REC. It has a number of options, each of which moves the file pointer to the beginning of the file. The main program closes the file. The file is created initially by the procedure **SetUp**:

```
procedure SetUp;
{ writes names to new file until null name is entered }
begin
  Rewrite( RecFile );
  ClrScr;
  with Student do
  begin
    Offerings:= 0;                          { no. of offerings ... }
    Str( Offerings, Name );                 { ... coded into Name }
    Write( RecFile, Student);
    repeat
   Write( 'Name: ' );
   Readln( Name );
   if Name <> '' then
     Write( RecFile, Student )
      until Name = ''
  end
end; { SetUp }
```

This is the only procedure to use **Rewrite**, since the file is being created. Because each record in the file must now be of the same type we cannot directly store the number of offerings in the first record, as we did in the case of the text file. So instead we have to use **Str** to convert the number of offerings into a string, which can be assigned to **Student.Name** in the first record (number 0) of the file. The procedure then simply asks the user for a name and writes it to the file until a null string is entered for a name.

UpDate allows the user to key in the marks of an offering, updating the file accordingly:

```
procedure UpDate;
{ Updates record file by adding marks for new offering }
begin
  ClrScr;
  Reset( RecFile );
  Read( RecFile, Student );
  with Student do
  begin
    Val( Name, Offerings, Code );
    Write( 'Enter maximum mark for new offering: ' );
    Readln( Max );
    Mark[ Offerings + 1 ]:= Max;                      { get new max }
    Offerings:= Offerings + 1;
    Str( Offerings, Name )                   { encode no. of offerings }
  end;
  Seek( RecFile, 0 );                        { re-position file pointer }
  Write( RecFile, Student );                   { write new info to file }
  while not Eof( RecFile ) do
  begin
    Read( RecFile, Student );
    with Student do
    begin
      Write( Name );
      GoToXY( 21, WhereY );
      Write( 'Mark: ' );
      Readln( Mark[ Offerings ] );                   { get new mark }
    end;
   Seek( RecFile, FilePos( RecFile ) - 1 );           { pointer back }
   Write( RecFile, Student );          { write the new mark to the file }
  end
end; { UpDate }
```

Note that the number of offerings, encoded as a string in the first record, must first be decoded with **Val**, then incremented by one, and encoded again with **Str**. The maximum of the new offering is assigned to the next element of **Student.Mark** (also in the first record). The updated first record is rewritten.

The **Mark** field of each subsequent record in the file is then updated with the new offering. The statement

```
Seek( RecFile, FilePos( RecFile ) - 1 );               { pointer back }
```

is used to make sure that the pointer is moved back each time after reading. Otherwise a particular mark goes into the *next* record!

Display presents all names and marks (with maxima) on the screen:

```
procedure Display;
{ displays names and marks }
begin
  ClrScr;
  with Student do
  begin
    Reset( RecFile );
    Read( RecFile, Student );
    Val( Name, Offerings, Code );
    if Offerings > 0 then
    begin
      Write( 'Maximum mark:', ' ':7 );
      for I:= 1 to Offerings do
```

```
        Write( Mark[ I ]:5:0 );                                     { display maxima }
      Writeln;
      Writeln
      end;
      while not Eof( RecFile ) do
      begin
        Read( RecFile, Student );
        Write( Name, ' ': MaxChars - Length( Name ) );                       { name }
        for I:= 1 to Offerings do
          Write( Mark[ I ]:5:0 );                                            { marks }
        Writeln
      end
    end;
    GoToXY( 1, WhereY + 2 );
    Write( 'Press any key to continue ... ' );
    Ch:= ReadKey
  end; { Display }
```

Again, the name in the first record must be decoded to get the number of offerings.

The program with all the declarations is as follows. Note the use of a stub for the procedure **Search**. This is developed in the next section to implement a binary search.

```
program RecordFile;
uses Crt;
const
  MaxChars     = 20;
  MaxOfferings = 20;
type
  ArrMarks     = 1..MaxOfferings;
  ItemType     = string[MaxChars];                                   { search item }
  StudentRec   = record
                   Name : string[MaxChars];                       { student's name }
                   Mark : array[ ArrMarks ] of real;                   { his marks }
                 end;
  StudentFile = file of StudentRec;
var
  Ch           : char;                                     { general character }
  Code         : integer;                    { dummy argument returned by Val }
  I            : byte;                                       { general counter }
  Item         : ItemType;                                 { Item to search for }
  Max          : real;                                { maximum of new offering }
  Offerings    : byte;                                   { number of offerings }
  Posn         : longint;                          { record number of found item }
  RecFile      : StudentFile;                           { general file variable }
  Student      : StudentRec;                                { individual record }
procedure Display;
  ...
end; { Display }
procedure Search;
  ...
end; { Search }
procedure SetUp;
  ...
end; { SetUp }
procedure UpDate;
  ...
end; { UpDate }
begin { RecordFile }
  Assign( RecFile, 'MARKS.REC' );
  repeat
    ClrScr;
```

```
    Writeln( 'Student Record System: Main Menu' );
    Writeln;
    Write( 'Display (D), Initialize(I), Quit (Q), ' );
    Write( 'Search(S) or Update (U)? ' );
    Ch:= ReadKey;
    Ch:= UpCase( Ch );
    Writeln;
    if Ch = 'D' then
      Display
    else if Ch = 'I' then
      SetUp
    else if Ch = 'S' then
      Search
    else if Ch = 'U' then
         Update
      until Ch = 'Q';

      Reset( RecFile );                          { in case it wasn't opened }
      Close( RecFile )
  end. { RecordFile }
```

About the only disadvantage of this approach as opposed to using text files, is the possible waste of memory and disk space. Since the record length of a file is fixed, each record must be big enough to hold the maximum number of offerings (20 in this case). You may never use most of these, but the space for them must still be allocated. With the text file, however, this problem does not arise. The records (lines) simply get longer each time a new offering is entered. One way round the problem, however, is to create a new binary file each time, with room for one additional mark, and to rename it, as was done with the text file in section 11.6.

A binary search

We have seen already how to sort numbers and words. Items are invariably sorted in order to be able subsequently to search through them for a particular item. An obvious (and easy) method of searching is to go through the list of items one by one comparing them with the search item. The process stops either when the search item is found, or when the search has gone past the place where the item would normally be (eg its alphabetical position). This is called a **linear** search. Its disadvantage is that it can be very time consuming if the list is long. A much more cunning method is the **binary search**.

Suppose you want to find the page in a telephone directory that has a particular name on it. A linear search would examine each page in turn from page 1 to determine whether the name is on it. This could clearly take a long time. A binary search is as follows. Find the middle of the directory (by consulting the page numbers), and tear it in half. By looking at the last name in the lefthand half (or the first name in the righthand half), determine which half the required name is in. Throw away the unwanted half, and repeat the process with the half that contains the name, by halving it. After a surprisingly low number of halvings, you will be left with one page containing the required name. Although this can be a little heavy on telephone directories, it illustrates the principle of a binary search quite well.

The method is very efficient. For example, my local directory has 1243 pages with subscribers' names and numbers. Since the method halves the number of pages each time, the number of halvings (or **bisections**) required to find a name will be the smallest power of 2 that exceeds 1243, ie 11, since

$$2^{10} = 1024 < 1243 < 2^{11} = 2048.$$

The smart way to find the maximum number of bisections N required is to observe that N must be the smallest integer such that

$$2^N > 1243,$$

ie $$N > \log_2(1243).$$

In the worst possible case, the required name would be the last one in the directory (Zywica). A linear search would involve examining all 1243 pages, whereas a binary search requires you to look at only 11 pages!

Suppose our student record file MARKS.REC contains **NumRecs** records altogether. The first one (number 0) contains the offering maxima, and all subsequent ones contain one name each, assumed in alphabetical order. We would like to search for a given student (eg in order to be able to view his marks, and change them if necessary). A binary search through the file must try to find the record number **(Mid)** of the required student's name **(Item)**. The lower and upper bounds of the record numbers for the search are **Low** and **High** respectively. **Mid** is the average of these two values. Successive bisections change the value of either **Low** or **High**, keeping the alphabetical position of **Item** between these bounds each time. Since each bisection takes the integer part of **Mid**, the starting value of **Hi** must be 1 more than the last record number, or the last student can never be found. The maximum number of bisections required, **NumBis**, is found as described above. This requires computing a logarithm to the base 2, which may be done as follows. Suppose we wish to calculate $\log_2(a)$, ie we want x, where

$$a = 2^x.$$

Taking the natural logarithm of both sides gives

$$\log_e(a) = x\log_e(2).$$

Solving for x yields

$$x = \log_e(a)/\log_e(2),$$

which is what we want.

The coding for the binary search is as follows:

```
{------BinSearch----------------------------------------------------------------}
{  Does a binary search for Item through all records of RecFile                 }
{  except the first. Record of found item returned in Posn,                     }
{  which is set to zero if item is not found.                                   }
{                                                                               }
{  Formal parameter types:                                                      }
{                                                                               }
{  ItemType      = string[MaxChars];                                            }
{  (* StudentRec = record                                                       }
{                    Name : string[MaxChars];                                   }
{                    Mark : array[ ArrMarks ] of real;                          }
{                  end; *)                                                      }
{  StudentFile = File of StudentRec                                             }
{-------------------------------------------------------------------------------}
  procedure BinSearch( var RecFile: StudentFile;
                       Item: ItemType; var Posn: longint );
  var
    Count,                                            { bisection counter }
    High,                                                         { upper }
    Low,                                                          { lower }
    Mid,                                                       { midpoint }
    NumBis,                                            { no. of bisections }
    NumRecs : longint;                                    { no. of records }
  Found     : boolean;                                              { flag }
  begin
    NumRecs:= FileSize( RecFile );
    NumBis:= Trunc( Ln( NumRecs - 1 ) / Ln( 2 ) ) + 1;
    Count:= 0;
    Found:= False;
    Posn:= 0;                                         { item not found yet }
    Low:= 1;                                   { first name in second record }
    High:= NumRecs;                                         { last name + 1 }

    repeat                                            { now for the search }
      Mid:= Trunc( (High + Low) / 2 );                   { first bisection }
      Seek( RecFile, Mid );                           { move to record Mid.. }
      Read( RecFile, Student );                           { ..and read it }
      with Student do
        if Item = Name then
          Found:= True
```

```
      else if Item < Name then
        High:= Mid
      else
        Low:= Mid;
      Count:= Count + 1
  until (Found) or (Count = NumBis);
    if Found then
      Posn:= Mid
  end; { BinSearch }
```

The standard function **FileSize** returns the number of records in a binary file. It may *not* be used on a text file.

The binary search may be integrated into the student record program **RecordFile** with the prodecure **Search**:

```
procedure Search;
{ initiates binary search }
begin
  Reset( RecFile );
  ClrScr;
  Write( 'Name to search for: ' );
  Readln( Item );
  BinSearch( RecFile, Item, Posn );
  if Posn = 0 then
    Writeln( Item, ' not found' )
  else
    Writeln( Item, ' found in record ', Posn );
  Writeln;
  Write( 'Press any key to continue ... ' );
  Ch:= ReadKey
end; { Search }
```

Keyed files

An obvious extension to the program **RecordFile** above is to sort a particular offering, as in the program **Merit** in section 12.2, and to save the sorted file. If the records in the data file are long (ie many offerings in the **Mark** field), this can be both time-consuming (because of all the swopping involved) and risky (disk errors are more likely to occur during the rewrite of a large file). The concept of a **keyed file** provides a neat solution to both these potential problems.

Suppose we want to sort the first offering in MARKS.REC (the data file used above). We really only need the **Mark[1]** field (the **key field**) of each student, plus a **reference field** to point to the student's name in the original file MARKS.REC once the key field has been sorted. We therefore create a key file, MARKS.KEY, which is a file of Turbo Pascal records. The field **KeyField** has the offering to be sorted (the first in this case), while the field **RecNum** gives the position (record number) of that student in MARKS.REC (bearing in mind that the first record, number zero, has the number of offerings and the maxima). Now a sort need only be performed on the much smaller file MARKS.KEY. Figure 12.1 shows the position after sorting MARKS.KEY.

	MARKS.REC				MARKS.KEY	
#	**Name**	**Mark[1]**	**Mark[2]**	...	**RecNum**	**KeyField**
1.	Jack	23	67	...	3	89
2.	Ann	34	63	...	4	76
3.	Bill	89	45	...	2	34
4.	Jim	76	78	...	1	23

Figure 12.1 Keyed files

The **RecNum** field gives the names of the students in order of merit: 3 (Bill), 4 (Jim), 2 (Ann) and 1 (Jack).

The program **KeyTest** below reads MARKS.REC and creates the key file MARKS.KEY based on which offering is to be sorted. It then reads the key file into the array **KeyArr**, which is passed to **KeySort**. **KeySort** is an amendment of **RecordSort** in section 12.2. After sorting, **KeyArr** is written back to MARKS.KEY. The sorted key file is then used with the original data file to write the names of the students and marks, in order of merit.

```
program KeyTest;
const
  MaxChars      = 20;
  MaxOfferings  = 20;
  MaxStu        = 200;
type
  ArrMarks      = 1..MaxOfferings;
  Key           = record
                    RecNum: longint;                              { record number }
                    KeyField: real;
                  end;
  StudentRec    = record
                    Name : string[MaxChars];                       { student's name }
                    Mark : array[ ArrMarks ] of real;                   { his marks }
                  end;
  StudentFile = file of StudentRec;
  ArrType     = array[1..MaxStu] of Key;
var
  I         : byte;                                             { general counter }
  KeyArr    : ArrType;
  KeyFile   : file of Key;
  Num       : word;                                          { number of students }
  RecFile   : StudentFile;
  RecKey    : Key;
  Sort      : word;                                  { element in Mark to be sorted }
  Student   : StudentRec;                                     { individual record }
{------KeySort-----------------------------------------------------------------------}
{  This procedure sorts the KeyField field of the record array X                    }
{ into descending order (order of merit) using a Bubble Sort.                       }
{ N is the number of records to be sorted.                                          }
{                                                                                   }
{ Formal parameter type:                                                            }
{                                                                                   }
{ Key          = record                                                             }
{                   RecNum     : longint;                                           }
{                   KeyField    : real;                                             }
{                end;                                                               }
{ ArrType      = array[1..MaxStu] of Key;                                           }
{-----------------------------------------------------------------------------------}
  procedure KeySort( var X: ArrType; N: word );
  var
    J, K      : word;
    Temp      : Key;
    Sorted    : boolean;
  begin
    K:= 0;
    repeat                                                { outer loop of bubble sort }
    K:= K + 1;                                                      { count the passes }
    Sorted:= true;                                             { they might be sorted }
      for J:= 1 to N - K do                                           { count the tests }
        if X[J].KeyField < X[J+1].KeyField then
        begin
          Temp:= X[J];
          X[J]:= X[J+1];
          X[J+1]:= Temp;
          Sorted:= False                                             { a swop was made }
          end
    until Sorted                                                 { must be sorted now }
```

```
end; { KeySort }

begin { KeyTest }
  Assign( RecFile, 'MARKS.REC' );
  Assign( KeyFile, 'MARKS.KEY' );
  Reset( RecFile );
  Rewrite( KeyFile );
  Write( 'Which offering must be sorted? ' );
  Readln( Sort );
  Seek( RecFile, 1 );                                   { start at 2nd record }
  Num:= 1;

  while not Eof( RecFile ) do                           { create the key file }
  begin
    Read( RecFile, Student );
    RecKey.RecNum:= Num;
    RecKey.KeyField:= Student.Mark[ Sort ];
    Write( KeyFile, RecKey );
    Num:= Num + 1
  end;
  Num:= 1;                                              { now sort the key file }
  Reset( KeyFile );

  while not Eof( KeyFile ) do
  begin
    Read( KeyFile, RecKey );                            { first read it into an array }
    KeyArr[ Num ]:= RecKey;
    Num:= Num + 1
  end;

  Num:= Num - 1;                                        { correct the overcount }
  KeySort( KeyArr, Num );                               { then sort the array }
  Reset( KeyFile );
  I:= 1;

  while not Eof( KeyFile ) do                           { now write the sorted array back }
  begin
    Write( KeyFile, KeyArr[ I ] );
    I:= I + 1
  end;

  Reset( KeyFile );                                     { pointer back to beginning }
  while not Eof( KeyFile ) do                           { use sorted keyfile to write list }
  begin
    Read( KeyFile, RecKey );                            { read the keyfile }
    Seek( RecFile, RecKey.RecNum );                     { find record no. RecNum }
    Read( RecFile, Student );                           { read that record }
    Writeln( Student.Name:20, Student.Mark[ Sort ]:4:0 )
  end;

  Close( RecFile );
  Close( KeyFile );
  readln
end. { KeyTest }
```

If a key file is set up with names as the key field, it can be sorted on the names (with slight adjustments to **KeySort**). A binary search for a name can then be conducted on the key file, with reference to the original data file for all that student's marks, if necessary.

Hashing

One problem with a binary search is that the items must be *sorted*. This means that if additional items are added to the list, the entire list must be resorted before a search can be conducted. The method discussed in this section does *not* require the items to be sorted, and is one of the most efficient methods of searching: hashing. If you are a programming novice, you might like to skip this section and come back later when you have more programming under your belt.

NAMES	INDEX
[1] Ann [2] Jack [3] Bill [4] Tony [5] David [6] Andre ...	[1] 4 (Tony) [2] −100 (empty) ... [42] −100 (empty) [43] 1 (Ann)

Figure 12.2 Hashing

Suppose we have an array **Names**, as in Figure 12.2. Take the first element Ann, and perform some operation on the characters in the name to produce a positive integer, for example add up the ASCII codes of the characters. This process is called **hashing**, the operation is called the **hash function**, and the resultant unsigned integer is called the **hashed index**. Let's call it **K**. Now set up a second array **Index**, and store in **Index[K]** Ann's position in **Names**, ie 1. Suppose K has the value 43. Then Index[43] will have the value 1, as in Figure 12.2. (The name Ann is inserted for clarity.) Now take some other item in **Names**, for example Tony, and hash it with the same hash function (whatever it is). Suppose the hashed index is 1. Then store Tony's address in **Names** (4) in **Index[1]**, as in the figure. Obviously **K** is going to have to be a reduced modulo the length of the array **Index**, for example if **Index** has indices from 1 to 53, say, and **K** turns out to be 4575, it must be reduced by the operation

K:= K mod 53 + 1

to put it in the range 1 to 53.

We continue this process for all the items in **Names**. You might have thought of an objection by now. It is most unlikely that the hash function will produce a *unique* value of **K** for each item in the list. So when setting up the hashed list in **Index**, a particular hashed position might be found to be occupied already (the elements of **Index** should be initialised to some negative value, say −100, to indicate that they are all unoccupied at first). This is called a **collision**. There are various ways of dealing with collisions, like just using the next position, but this causes **clumping** of the hashed list, which is inefficient. A more imaginative solution to collisions is to use **double hashing**.

At this stage we need a little more notation. Let's call the original hash value **H**. For best results, the length of the **Index** array needs to be a prime number. Let's call it **Mn**. So **K** is in fact given by

K:= (H mod Mn) + 1

For double hashing, choose another prime **Mn2**, which is slightly less than **Mn**. If position **K** is occupied, look in position **K + InK** where

InK:= H mod Mn2;

Continue increasing **K** like this (modulo **Mn**) until an unoccupied position is found. When we have finished we will have a hashed list in **Index**. To find a particular item, hash it and probe at **K, K + InK, ...,** until either an unoccupied position (not found) or a match is found. For the best results, the total number of items in **Names** should not exceed 0.75**Mn**.

The program below, **TestHash**, demonstrates hashing on a list of names in the disk file NAMES., which is set up separately as a file of 20 character strings. The file is read into the array **Names**, which is hashed into **Index** by the procedure **Place** and the function **Find**. Items supplied by the user are then searched for with **Find**. If the item is found, it is displayed with its position in **Names**. If it is not found, **Find** returns minus the position it would occupy in **Index** if it was there.

Mn and **Mn2** are taken as 103 and 89 respectively, and the actual hashing function used, at the beginning of **Find**, computes the sums of the squares of the ASCII codes of the characters in the item. Different hashing functions could be used, depending on the nature of the list to be searched. Some experimentation might be necessary on a dummy list to find a hashing function which causes the least clumping (this reduces the number of probes needed to find an item).

```
program TestHash;
{ demonstrates search by hashing }
const
  MaxLen     = 75;                                  { about 0.75Mn for best results }
  Mn         = 103;                                            { prime for hashing }
  Mn2        = 89;                                             {       ditto       }
type
  Str20      = string[20];
  IndexType  = array[ 1..Mn ] of shortint;
  NamesType  = array[ 1..MaxLen ] of Str20;
var
  F      : file of Str20;                                         { file of names }
  H,                                                              { value of Find }
  I,                                                                    { counter }
  N      : integer;                       { length of list - should be <= MaxLen }
  Index  : IndexType;                                               { hashed list }
  Item   : Str20;                                           { name to search for }
  Names  : NamesType;                                             { list of names }
{------Find-----------------------------------------------------------------------}
{                                                                                 }
{    Find hashes Item to the integer K, which is increased by InK                 }
{    if necessary, until either an unused position (Index [K] =                   }
{    -100) or a match (Item = Names[ Index[K] ]) is found.                        }
{    If no match is found, -K is returned. If a match is found,                   }
{    Index[K] is returned.                                                        }
{---------------------------------------------------------------------------------}

function Find( var Index: IndexType; var Names: NamesType;
               Item: Str20 ): integer;
var
  Asc, F, H, I, Ink, K : longint;
begin
  H:= 0;
  for I:= 1 to Length( Item ) do                                       { hash it }
  begin
    Asc:= Ord( Item[I] );
    H:= H + Asc * Asc
  end;
  if H < 0 then                                                   { just in case }
    H:= - H;
  K:= (H mod Mn) + 1;
  InK:= H mod Mn2;
  { we look until we find an unused position or a match }
  F:= -1;
  while F = -1 do
  begin
    if Index[K] = -100 then
      F:= -K
    else if Item = Names[ Index[K] ] then
      F:= Index[K];
    K:= (K + InK) mod Mn + 1;
  end;
  Find:= F
end; { Find }
{------Place----------------------------------------------------------------------}
{                                                                                 }
{    Place is used to set up the hashed list Index from the list                  }
{    of items in Names. The item in Names[J] is hashed to the                     }
{    integer K. The item's position J in Names is placed in                       }
{    Index[K].                                                                    }
{    A positive value should never be returned here by Find, since                }
{    a match is not being sought from Place. A positive value                     }
{    means a duplicate item in Names.                                             }
{---------------------------------------------------------------------------------}
```

```
procedure Place( J: shortint; var Index: IndexType;
                 Names: NamesType );
var
  K: integer;
begin
  K:= Find( Index, Names, Names[J] );
  if K > 0 then { position occupied - we should never get here! }
  begin
    Writeln( Names[J], ' already known at hash position ', K );
    Writeln( 'New simple position ', J, ' will be inaccessible' )
  end
  else
  begin
    K:= - K;
    Index[K]:= J
  end
end; { Place }

begin { TestHash }
  Assign( F, 'NAMES.' );
  Reset( F );
  I:= 1;
  while not Eof( F ) do                          { Read list of names }
  begin
    Read( F, Names[ I ] );
    I:= I + 1
  end;
  N:= I - 1;
  for I:= 1 to Mn do
    Index[I]:= -100;          { -100 means that position is unoccupied }
  for I:= 1 to N do
    Place( I, Index, Names );
{
  for I:= 1 to Mn do                       (* display the index array *)
    Write( Index[I]:4 );
  Writeln;
} repeat Write( 'Item? ' );
    Readln( Item );
    H:= Find( Index, Names, Item );
    if H > 0 then
      Writeln( H:4, Names[ H ]:20 )
    else
      Writeln( H )
  until Item = ''
end.
```

Dealing with additional items is simple. Just add them on at the end of the disk file, and rehash the enlarged array **Names**.

There are more detailed discussions of hashing in standard data processing texts, such as Kruse (1984).

Untyped files

An **untyped file** is simply a continuous stream of bytes, regardless of the component type of the disk file associated with it. Its declaration omits the type:

```
var
  Blurb : file;
```

The advantage of untyped files is that they may be used to move information around very quickly, with the help of the standard procedures **BlockRead** and **BlockWrite**.

Hexadecimal Dump

As an example, try the following program. It reads the disk file TEXT as an untyped file, writing each byte in hexadecimal notation, after Duntemann (1989). The disk file may be of any type, but it's interesting if it's a text file, because then you can see what the EOL and EOF markers are.

```
const
  HexDigits : array[0..15] of char = '0123456789ABCDEF';
var
  F          : file;
  Ch         : char;
  FS         : word;
  BT, BZ     : byte;
begin
  Assign( F, 'TEXT.' );
  Reset( F, 1 );
  FS:= FileSize( F );
  Writeln( FS );

  while not eof( F ) do
  begin
    BlockRead( F, Ch, 1 );
    BT:= Ord( Ch );
    begin
      BZ:= BT and $0F;                         { and between corresponding bits }
      BT:= BT shr 4;                           { all bits 4 places to the right }
      Write( ' ', HexDigits[BT], HexDigits[BZ] )
    end
  end;

  Close( F );
```

BlockRead(*FileVar, Var, Blocks* <, *Result*>)

reads *Blocks* records into any variable *Var* from the untyped file *FileVar*. *Result* is an optional parameter, which may be omitted. The default length of a record is 128 bytes. This record length can be changed with an optional parameter in the **Reset** statement:

Reset(*FileVar, BlockSize*)

Using this optional parameter with a typed file generates error 89 (")" expected). In the above example, the record length was set to 1 byte, so that the file could be read one byte at a time. Bigger blocks will result in faster handling (see below).

Remember that bitwise **and** (between 1- or 2-byte items) operates on the corresponding bits of each operand separately. **shr** shifts all bits one place to the right. The best way to follow how the conversion to hexadecimal works is to do a few examples by hand, for example $1A = 26 (see Appendix C). (The Evaluate window of the Debug menu can be used to evaluate hex numbers directly.)

BlockWrite and **Rewrite** work just like **BlockRead** and **Reset**, except that data flow in the other direction.

Saving a graphics image to disk

The following program, suggested by Duntemann (1989), uses a record length of 16384 bytes with **BlockRead** to save a graphics image to disk. The graphics image on the CGA card takes up this amount of RAM (the image size is different on some other cards). The starting address of the image on the CGA card is segment $B800 and offset 0000. The **absolute** clause ensures that the variable **GBuff** (an array of byte) uses the same memory as the image, so that at any given moment the *current* graphics image will be accessible in **GBuff**.

The program shades in a circle, saves it to disk, clears the screen, and reads the image back from the disk.

```
program PicSave;
uses Graph;
const
  PicSize = 16384;
```

```
type
  ScreenBuff = array[1..PicSize] of byte;
var
  GrDriver, GrMode : integer;
  GBuff : ScreenBuff absolute $B800:0000;
  GFile : File;
begin
  GrDriver:= Detect;
  InitGraph( GrDriver, GrMode, '\tp5' );
  Assign( GFile, 'PIC.' );
  Rewrite( GFile, PicSize );
  PieSlice( 320, 100, 0, 360, 200 );
  BlockWrite( GFile, GBuff, 1 );
  readln;
  ClearViewPort;
  readln;
  Reset( GFile, PicSize );
  BlockRead( GFile, GBuff, 1 );
  Readln;
  CloseGraph
end.
```

Note that the time taken to BlockRead the image from disk is considerably less than the time taken to draw it originally!

12.4 DYNAMIC VARIABLES: POINTERS

This section covers a more advanced topic, so if you are a beginner you may like to come back to it later. Up until now all the variables we have used in our programs have been **static variables**, although this has never been mentioned. This means that when the variable is declared, the compiler allocates it to a certain address in memory, and there it stays as long as the program is running. You can in fact find out the address of any variable in a program with the **Seg** and **Ofs** functions, which give the address segment and offset respectively, for example:

```
var
  X : real;
  ...
  Writeln( Seg( X ), ':', Ofs( X ) );
```

This address remains the same while the program executes, and the memory allocated cannot be used for anything else, hence the term *static* variable. You can generate a memory map of a program, showing the addresses of all variables used, with the **O**ptions/**L**inker/**M**ap File menu. If you choose a value other than **O**ff in the **M**ap File menu a .MAP file is generated with the memory map. The **C**ompile/**D**estination must be set to **D**isk. The .MAP file will be in your .EXE directory.

Static variables are stored in the area of memory called the **stack**, which word is meant to conjure up images of neat stacks of memory locations used in order, as plates might be taken from a pile in a canteen. In contrast to the stack, Turbo Pascal has a fearsome thing called the **heap**. Memory is grabbed from the heap, in any old order, when it is needed for a variable, and thrown back on to heap when it is no longer needed, ***while the program is still running***. Such a variable is called a **dynamic** variable. The only way dynamic variables differ from static variables is how they are created, and how they are accessed. Dynamic variables introduce a new type of data item: the **pointer**.

Run the following program:

```
...
type
  EType = array[1..20000] of byte;
var
  EPt : ^EType;
begin
  Writeln( MemAvail );
  EPt:= Nil;                                  { points to nothing }
```

```
New( EPt );                                   { now it points to EPt^ }
Writeln( MemAvail );
Dispose( EPt );                               { now it's gone }
Writeln( MemAvail ); ...
```

EPt is called a pointer. The notation ^ **EType** in its declaration means that it can point to an area of memory on the heap of type **EType** (an array of 20000 bytes in this example). The pointer variable actually contains the address of the variable it points to - a handle with which to grab some memory off the stack.

However, in the same way that a static variable is undefined immediately after compilation, before any assignments, a pointer is also undefined – it doesn't even point to nothing. Undefined pointers are dangerous – they should never be left lying around, as they can make horrible things happen to your program. The statement:

```
EPt:= Nil;
```

defines the pointer as pointing to nothing. As a safety measure, **Nil** should be assigned to all pointers in a program as soon as execution starts.

To make the pointer actually point to some memory on the heap, the **New** procedure is used:

```
New( EPt )
```

This allocates some heap memory (20000 bytes in fact) to a dynamic variable. This variable has a rather curious name. It is referred to simply as **EPt^**. So while **Ept** can be spoken of as a pointer to a dynamic variable of type **EType**, the dynamic variable itself can only be spoken of as the variable to which **EPt** points, or **EPt's referent** (which is better).

Note that the circumflex (^) is used only in the pointer's type definition (**^EType**) and in the referent's name (**EPt^**).

The **MemAvail** standard function returns the amount of unused memory on the heap. Its use in the above program shows 20000 bytes of heap disappearing, and then re-appearing when the memory occupied by **EPt^** is released by **Dispose**, and made available for use later in the program.

An attempt to **Dispose** a **Nil** pointer generates error 204 (Invalid pointer operation).

Since a pointer has no value in the usual sense it cannot be written, but the address it points to is returned by **Seg** and **Ofs** with the pointer as argument, for example **Ofs(EPt)**.

Pointers may point to any type (the pointer's **base type**) except a file type.

Pointers may be compared for equality, which means they point to the same dynamic variable, or they have the value **Nil**.

Pointers of the same base type may be assigned to one another, but you need to think carefully what this means.

```
var
  EPt, FPt : ^EType;
...
  EPt:= Nil;
  FPt:= EPt;                                  { nil also }
  New( EPt );                                 { EPt^ created }
  New( FPt );                                 { FPt^ created }
  FPt:= EPt;                                  { both point to EPt^ now! )
```

Since a pointer points to a dynamic variable, an assignment means the pointer on the left now points to the dynamic variable pointed to on the right. So

```
FPt:= EPt;
```

means that both pointers now point to the dynamic variable pointed to by **EPt**, ie to **EPt^**. Consequently, ***nothing points to*** **FPt^**! **FPt**'s dynamic variable is now completely inaccessible, and what is worse, still occupies 20000 bytes of heap memory (or **heapspace** as it is also called). There is no way of getting hold of a dynamic variable, or of returning the memory it uses to the heap, once its pointer has been cut loose from it.

Of what possible use could these strange animals be? Pointers are useful whenever you only want to use a chunk of memory for *part* of the time a program is executing. Pointers make for good memory management. The following program uses a pointer to copy a graphics image to an area on the heap until it's needed later (without saving it do disk):

```
program PicCopy;
uses Graph;
const
  PicSize = 16384;
type
  ScreenBuff = array[1..PicSize] of byte;
var
  GrDriver, GrMode : integer;
  GBuff : ScreenBuff absolute $B800:0000;
  GrPt : ^ScreenBuff;
begin
  New( GrPt );
  GrDriver:= Detect;
  InitGraph( GrDriver, GrMode, '\tp5' );
  PieSlice( 320, 100, 0, 360, 200 );                    { now you see it }
  GrPt^:= GBuff;
  Readln;
  ClearViewPort;                                        { now you don't }
  Readln;
  GBuff:= GrPt^;                                        { there it is again }
  Dispose( GrPt );
  Readln;
  CloseGraph
end.
```

Incidentally, the same approach can be used to copy the *text* screen, which resides at the same address on the CGA card, although less memory is needed:

```
program TextCopy;
uses Crt;
const
  ScrSize = 4000;
type
  ScreenBuff = array[1..ScrSize] of byte;
var
  GBuff : ScreenBuff absolute $B800:0000;
  GrPt : ^ScreenBuff;
begin
  TextBackGround( Blue );
  ClrScr;                                               { now you see it }
  New( GrPt );
  GrPt^:= GBuff;
  Readln;
  TextBackGround( Black );
  ClrScr;                                               { now you don't }
  Readln;
  GBuff:= GrPt^;                                        { there it is again }
  Dispose( GrPt )
end.
```

Can you see why 4000 bytes are needed for 25 rows of 80 columns? Each character needs a byte ($80 \times 25 = 2000$), but in colour, each character needs an additional byte (4 bits for the foreground, 3 for the background and 1 for blinking – see the discussion of the **Crt** unit variable **TextAttr** in section 11.9).

Generic pointers

For the record, you should know that Turbo Pascal allows **generic** pointers, which have no base type, but which are simply variables of pointer type:

```
Var
  ScreenBuffer : pointer;
```

The generic equivalents of New and Dispose are GetMem and FreeMem:

GetMem(*Pointer, Size* **);**
FreeMem(*Pointer, Size* **);**

Since a generic pointer has no base type, the size of its dynamic variable is not fixed at compilation. **GetMem** does this during execution, according the needs of the moment. In this way, the same pointer identifier can be made to point to dynamic variables of different sizes at different times. An example of this is with the use of **GetImage** to save a *portion* of a graphics image to disk (see Chapter 13).

Linked lists

Dynamic variables really come into their own when data structures are required which vary from execution to execution of the same program. The classical application of dynamic variables is in constructing **linked lists**. This is a vast subject, leading up to such topics as (binary) trees, tries and B-trees, which are dealt with in many standard texts, for example Kruse (1984). The purpose here is simply to give you a hint of what it's about.

Pointers are rather strange beasts. Their most peculiar property is that a pointer may be defined as pointing to a type which itself has not yet been defined. It is precisely this property which allows for the construction of linked lists. Consider the following:

```
type
  ListPtr = ^ListRec;
  ListRec = record
              Name : string[20];
              Next  : ListPtr
            end;
```

This is a circular definition! **ListRec** is a record type with two fields, a string (**Name**) and a pointer (**Next**) to type **ListRec**. The idea is to be able to create a lot of dynamic variables of type **ListRec**, where each variable's **Next** field ***points to the next variable***, as shown in Figure 12.3, of which more below.

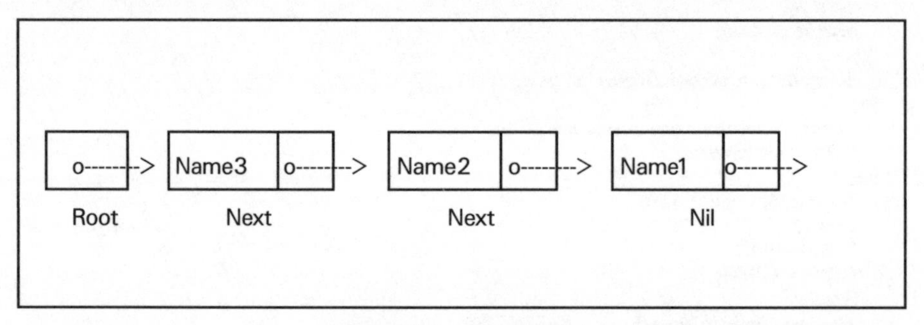

Figure 12.3 A linked list

The program below reads a list of names from the binary file NAMES and builds them into a linked list. It then traverses the list, writing each name, and finally disposes of the list, releasing its memory to the heap.

```
program Linked;
type
  Str20     = string[20];
  ListPtr   = ^ListRec;
  ListRec   = record
                Name : Str20;
                Next  : ListPtr
              end;
var
  List : ListRec;
  Current, Root : ListPtr;
  F : file of Str20;
begin
```

```
    Writeln( MemAvail );
    Assign( F, 'names.' );
    Reset( F );
    Root:= Nil;                                  { list ends nowhere }
    while not Eof( F ) do
    begin
      List.Next:= Root;                          { copy end of list }
      Read( F, List.Name );                      { fill the static record }
      New( Current );                            { create new dynamic variable }
      Current^:= List;                           { copy static record into Current^ }
      Root:= Current;                            { point Root to end of list again }
    end;
    readln;
    Close( F );
    Current:= Root;                              { start at the end of the list }
    while Current <> Nil do                      { traverse the list }
    begin
      Writeln( Current^.Name );
      Current:= Current^.Next                    { move up one each time }
    end;
    readln;
Current:= Root;                                  { Root still points to end of list }
    repeat                                       { now dispose of the list }
      Root:= Current^.Next;                      { copy pointer to next item ... }
      Dispose( Current );                        { ... before destroying it }
      Current:= Root                             { end of list has moved up }
    until Current = Nil;
    Writeln( MemAvail )
  end.
```

Note that there is only one static variable (apart from the file variable) in the program: **List**. This remains to the end, and in fact holds the last name in the list at the end of the day.

The pointer in the first record (on the right in Figure 12.3) is **Nil**, to indicate the top of the list. The pointer **Root** points to the last record in the list (on the left), and is the list's lifeline to the real world. If its value is lost, the list will be left hanging in the air, utterly inaccessible, and its memory will be irretrievable.

Note that the list is traversed from the bottom (left), because all the pointers point up (right). The program also shows the proper way to dispose of a list: again from the bottom up.

This list is in fact a *singly* linked list; it can only be traversed in one direction. A doubly linked list has two pointers in each record – one pointing in each direction – and can therefore be traversed in either direction.

With a little ingenuity, items can be inserted and removed from linked lists, which may or may not be ordered. Linked lists also provide a means of sorting. Start with one record in the list. Get the next record, and insert it above or below the first one, as the case may be. Get the next record. Traverse the list until its correct position is found, and insert it. This is called sorting by insertion.

See Duntemann (1989) and Kruse(1984) for some interesting applications of linked lists.

12.5 OBJECTS

Object-oriented programming (OOP) is one of the most fashionable programming phrases at the moment, and many think it is the way forward in the 1990s. In spite of the comment by Edsger Dijkstra (winner of virtually every computer science award there is) that "object oriented programming is an exceptionally bad idea which could only have originated in California" (in conversation with Bob Crawford, reported in *TUG Lines*, no. 32), you should take a look at OOP if you are serious about programming. It is however an advanced topic, and you may wish to skip this section for the moment.

Turbo Pascal 5.5 introduces a new type, **object**, which is further developed in version 6.0. What follows here is just the slightest hint of what can be done.

The classical way of thinking of computer programs is that they are collections of data, which have things done to them, for example a list of numbers which may be initialised, written, sorted, etc. A dichotomy has developed between the data, on the one hand, and the procedures for handling them, on the other. Object-oriented programming, however, attempts to think of the data, and the code that does the things to them, as a *single object*. So a list may be thought of as an active entity which can get some data, arrange itself into order, write itself, find its largest member, etc.

Let's follow up the example of a list. In classical Pascal we could define it as an array, and then perhaps define a procedure **Init** to get values for it, a procedure **Show** to write it, and a function **Max** to find its largest member. The **object** type of Turbo Pascal 5.5 and 6.0 allows these procedures and function to be bundled together in the type declaration of the object **List**:

```
type
  List = object
           Member : array[1..100] of real;
           procedure Init( Nums: word );
           function Max: real;
           procedure Show;
         end;
```

This actually looks very like the definition of a Turbo Pascal record, but we will see that there are some rather interesting differences. In the OOP context, **Init, Max** and **Show** are called the object's **methods**. This process of bundling data (**Member**) together with methods (**Init, Max** and **Show**) is called **encapsulation**, which is one of the big three keywords of OOP, the other two being inheritance and polymorphism.

The methods are defined in much the same way as procedures and functions, except for the headers, which must be qualified by the object type identifier (we'll see why in a moment). So the method **Init** can be declared as follows:

```
procedure List.Init;
var
  I: word;
begin
  Randomize;
  for I:= 1 to Nums do
    Member[I]:= 100 * Random;
  for I:= Nums + 1 to MaxNum do
    Member[I]:= -1
end; { List.Init }
```

In this example we are initialising the first **Nums** elements of **Member** randomly, the rest being set to −1. They could equally well have been read from a disk file.

Max and **Show** are defined similarly:

```
function List.Max;
var
  I: word;
  LocMax : real;
begin
  LocMax:= -1;
  for I:= 1 to MaxNum do
    if Member[I] > LocMax then
      LocMax:= Member[I];
  Max:= LocMax
end; { List.Max }

procedure List.Show;
var
  I: word;
begin
  I:= 1;
  repeat
    if Member[I] >= 0 then
      Write( Member[I]:4:0 );
    I:= I + 1
  until Member[I] < 0
end; { List.Show }
```

What next? Well, remember that all this is the type definition of the object **List**. We have to declare a variable:

```
var
  Marks : List;
```

To generate, say, 10 random marks, all we need is:

```
Marks.Init( 10 );
```

OOP enthusiasts (fanatics, some would say) like to think of objects as actors on a stage, with a set of lines (methods) memorised. When you as the director give the word, the actor recites his lines. So you can think of the statement:

```
Marks.Init( 10 );
```

as you giving an order to the object **Marks**: Get yourself 10 random members.

To write the list and its maximum is equally simple:

```
Marks.Show;
Writeln( Marks.Max );
```

Notice that to use the object **Marks** successfully you don't need to know how the **Member** field is constructed, *because no parameters are passed*. It could equally well be a linked list or a binary file. This is a consequence of encapsulation: data and the code for handling it are bundled together.

You might think that the improvements in ease of notation are very slight advantages. Objects, however, can pass on their properties (data fields and methods) to their descendants. This startling feature is called **inheritance**. Suppose we want to define a type such as we have used in the student mark programs. We used a record with two fields: a string for the name, and an array for the marks. However, using objects, we can do the following:

```
PersonRec = object( List )                          { descendant of List }
               Name : string[20];
               procedure Init( Nums: word );
               procedure Show;
             end;
```

The type **PersonRec** is now a descendant of the object type **List**, which means ***it inherits all* List's *data fields and methods***. In other words, type **PersonRec** has *two* data fields: the inherited **Member** array, and the new string field **Name**. It also inherits the methods **List.Init, List.Max** and **List.Show**. In addition, the **PersonRec** object has two further methods of its own: **Init** and **Show**. Although these appear to have the same names as two of the inherited methods, they are actually qualified by the object identifier, as comes out in their declarations:

```
procedure PersonRec.Init;
begin
  List.Init( Nums );
  Name:= 'Henry'
end; { PersonRec.Init }

procedure PersonRec.Show;
begin
  Write( Name, ' ' );
  List.Show
end; { PersonRec.Show }
```

Now look carefully at these two methods. Because **PersonRec** is a descendant type of **List** it can use **List's** methods **Init** and **Show**. When it does so it must of course use the qualifier **List**. It also add some extra characteristics of its own (to extend the inheritance metaphor). **PersonRec.Init** initialises the **Name** field of its object, while **PersonRec.Show** writes the **Name** field.

Obviously a variable of type **PersonRec** must be declared. Suppose **Student** is such a variable. Try out the following directives on the actors **Marks** and **Students** (remember **Marks** is an object of type **List**, so **Student** is a descendant of **Marks**):

```
Student.Init( 5 );               { initializes Name and inherited Member }
Marks.Init( 5 );                                 { initializes Member field }
```

```
Student.Show;                                    { writes Name and Member }
Writeln( Student.Max:10:0 );                          { Writes his top mark }
Marks:= Student;                                   { ancestor:= descendant }
Marks.Show;                                           { writes Member field }
```

The assignment above should raise some eyebrows:

```
Marks:= Student;
```

It completely breaks Turbo Pascal's hitherto strictly enforced typing rules! A variable of a descendant type may be assigned to a variable of an ancestor type (but not vice versa). Only the common fields are assigned, ie only the fields inherited from **Marks** (the **Member** field) are assigned. After the above code has executed **Marks** and **Student** should have the same values in their **Member** fields.

The third property of objects, **polymorphism**, is even more startling: it allows the processing of objects *whose type is not known at compilation*. This goes beyond the scope of this book. If your interest has been suitably aroused you will have to consult the Turbo Pascal 5.5 OOP guide, which has a very good illustration of objects in a graphics handling application, or the Turbo Vision Guide, which has over 400 pages of introductory material and tutorials.

Turbo vision

The major feature of the recently released Turbo Pascal version 6.0 is Turbo Vision. This is an event-driven toolbox of ready-made objects, such as overlapping windows, pull-down menus with hot keys, dialogue boxes, scroll bars, etc, which you can incorporate in your own programs by inheriting them (the version 6.0 Environment was in fact itself written with Turbo Vision!)

Needless to say, this is not for beginners, but more experienced programmers who get into Turbo Vision will find that it completely changes the way they write programs for other people to use.

SUMMARY

- A structured type is a type with components (of the same or different types)
- Records can have fields of different types.
- Files are logical or physical, disk or device, text or binary.
- Text files are accessed sequentially only from the beginning, and not for reading and writing at the same time.
- Binary files are accessed randomly at any position for reading and writing at the same time.
- Static variables have a fixed address on the stack and exist for the duration of a program.
- Dynamic variables are created from memory taken from the heap as and when they are needed during execution. Dynamic variables may be disposed of and their memory released during execution.
- Dynamic variables have no names, and are known only by the pointers which point to their addresses.
- Objects consist of data and methods (encapsulation), and may bequeath data and methods to descendants (inheritance). They may be processed as different types at different executions of the same compiled code (polymorphism).

EXERCISES

12.1 Write a procedure to reverse the case (ie uppercase to lowercase and vice versa) of a given text file (rewriting the file). Use sets of characters.

12.2 Languages exhibit a characteristic frequency distribution of single letters if a large enough sample of text is analysed. For example, in Act III of *Hamlet* the space has a frequency of 19.7%, the "e" 9.3%, the "o" 7.3%, while the "z" occurs only 14 times out of 35224 characters. (The space is important because it gives an indication of word length.) Write a program to determine the letter frequency of a sample of text in a text file. Assume that spaces only occur singly. Use sets.

12.3 As a project extend the RecordFile program in section 12.2 to write a student's marks once he has been found, and to ask for and implement changes in any of the marks.

13 Graphics

A computer screen is covered with small phosphorous dots called **pixels**, which can be made to light up, giving an image on the screen. The number of pixels available depends not so much on the physical monitor as on the particular graphics card (or device) installed in your computer. For example, the Colour Graphics Adapter (CGA) is able to display a grid of pixels 640 wide and 200 high, so we say its resolution is 640×200. The Hercules monochrome card, however, has a resolution of 720×348, while the IBM8514 card has a resolution of 1024×768. Then again some devices have a different resolution depending on whether or not you want more than two colours. For example, if you want a four colour display with the CGA card you only get 320×200 pixels in the grid.

So it's quite a jungle out there, especially if you want to write programs that other people can use on machines with different graphics devices. To address this problem, Borland (the company that has developed Turbo Pascal) has produced a system called the Borland Graphics Interface (BGI) which enables a program to detect at runtime which graphics card is installed, and to load the appropriate graphics driver.

13.1 GETTING STARTED

All the Turbo Pascal predeclared graphics constants, variables, procedures and functions are in the **Graph** unit, so this must always be referenced in a **uses** clause in any program (or unit) that uses graphics:

```
uses Graph;
```

Detection of the graphics device is done with the **DetectGraph** procedure:

```
var
  GrDriver, GrMode : integer;
begin
  GrDriver:= Detect;
  DetectGraph( GrDriver, GrMode );
  Writeln( GrDriver:4, GrMode:4 );
```

Detect is a predeclared constant in the **Graph** unit with the value zero. **DetectGraph** must be passed two integer **var** parameters. For autodetection, as it is called, the parameter **GrDriver** must be zero when **DetectGraph** is called. Since a **var** parameter is required, the constant **Detect** cannot be used as the actual parameter. The value returned in **GrDriver** by **DetectGraph** is a **driver code** indicating the graphics device, as shown in Table 13.1. These codes are actually constants defined in the **Graph** unit – they may be found in the GRAPH.DOC file on your Turbo Pascal disk. By the time you read this book there may be more – check the README file on your Turbo Pascal disk.

CGA	**= 1;**
MCGA	**= 2;**
EGA	**= 3;**
EGA64	**= 4;**
EGAMono	**= 5;**
IBM8514	**= 6;**
HercMono	**= 7;**
ATT400	**= 8;**
VGA	**= 9;**
PC3270	**= 10;**

Table 13.1 BGI Driver Codes

The parameter **GrMode** returned by **DetectGraph** gives the **mode code** for that particular device, which is the highest resolution possible. Codes available at the time of writing are shown in Table 13.2. These are also **Graph** unit constants.

DetectGraph doesn't initialise graphics. This is done by **InitGraph**:

```
GrDriver:= Detect;                                    { request autodetection }
InitGraph( GrDriver, GrMode, '\tp5' );
```

InitGraph actually calls **DetectGraph** – there is no need for you to do so unless you want to code different actions depending on which graphics driver is installed. Calling **InitGraph** with **GrDriver** set to **Detect** means that you are requesting autodetection. The values of **GrDriver** and **GrMode** returned by **InitGraph**'s call to **DetectGraph** are then used to load the appropriate driver. The graphics drivers are the files on your Turbo Pascal disk with the .BGI extensions. The third parameter of **InitGraph** must specify the path where the correct driver may be found (my drivers are in \TP5). This can be a string constant or variable. If its value is the null string the driver is expected to be in the current directory. In this way the driver is only loaded at runtime, so at compilation the type of graphics device need not be known.

At the time of writing the ATT400 and IBM 8514 cards are *not* autodetected. To use these cards you can override autodetection by passing **InitGraph** the values of their driver and mode codes, for example

```
GrDriver:= ATT400;
GrMode:= ATT400Hi;
InitGraph( GrDriver, GrMode, '' );                    { ATT card installed }
```

If you attempt autodetection on a machine with one of these cards **InitGraph** will probably load the CGA driver by default, so there won't be a runtime error.

If the BGI can't find its driver, or the machine doesn't have a graphics device, well and good. Calling **InitGraph** in such a situation will not cause a runtime error. But attempting to do any graphics will, with possible disastrous results. The function **GraphResult** returns an error code indicating what went wrong(zero if there was no error). This code is also returned by the **GrDriver** parameter of **InitGraph**.

```
CGAC0        = 0;   { 320x200 LightGreen, LightRed, Yellow; 1 page }
CGAC1        = 1;   { 320x200 LightCyan, LightMagenta, White; 1 page }
CGAC2        = 2;   { 320x200 Green, Red, Brown; 1 page }
CGAC3        = 3;   { 320x200 Cyan, Magenta, LightGray; 1 page }
CGAHi        = 4;   { 640x200 1 page }
MCGAC0       = 0;   { 320x200 LightGreen, LightRed, Yellow; 1 page }
MCGAC1       = 1;   { 320x200 LightCyan, LightMagenta, White; 1 page }
MCGAC2       = 2;   { 320x200 Green, Red, Brown; 1 page }
MCGAC3       = 3;   { 320x200 Cyan, Magenta, LightGray; 1 page }
MCGAMed      = 4;   { 640x200 1 page }
MCGAHi       = 5;   { 640x480 1 page }
EGALo        = 0;   { 640x200 16 color 4 page }
EGAHi        = 1;   { 640x350 16 color 2 page }
EGA64Lo      = 0;   { 640x200 16 color 1 page }
EGA64Hi      = 1;   { 640x350 4 color 1 page }
EGAMonoHi    = 3;   { 640x350 64K on card, 1 page; 256K on card, 2 page }
HercMonoHi   = 0;   { 720x348 2 page }
ATT400C0     = 0;   { 320x200 LightGreen, LightRed, Yellow; 1 page }
ATT400C1     = 1;   { 320x200 LightCyan, LightMagenta, White; 1 page }
ATT400C2     = 2;   { 320x200 Green, Red, Brown; 1 page }
ATT400C3     = 3;   { 320x200 Cyan, Magenta, LightGray; 1 page }
ATT400Med    = 4;   { 640x200 1 page }
ATT400Hi     = 5;   { 640x400 1 page }
VGALo        = 0;   { 640x200 16 color 4 page }
VGAMed       = 1;   { 640x350 16 color 2 page }
VGAHi        = 2;   { 640x480 16 color 1 page }
PC3270Hi     = 0;   { 720x350 1 page }
IBM8514LO    = 0;   { 640x480 256 colors }
IBM8514HI    = 1;   { 1024x768 256 colors }
```

Table 13.2 BGI Mode Codes

The most common errors have the following codes:

Code	*Meaning*
−1	No graphics detected.
−3	Graphics driver file can't be found.
−4	Invalid driver loaded.
−5	Insufficient memory to load the required driver.

GraphResult works like **IOResult**. Once called, it is reset to zero, so its value must be assigned to a variable if necessary. The following extract shows how to use it:

```
var
  GrErr, GrDriver, GrMode : integer;
begin
  GrDriver:= Detect;
  InitGraph( GrDriver, GrMode, '' );
  GrErr:= GraphResult;
  if GrErr = 0 then
  begin
    SetBkColor( Magenta );
    FillEllipse( 100, 100, 100, 50 );
    Readln
  end;
```

```
CloseGraph;
if GrErr <> 0 then
  Writeln( 'No graphics today - error code ', GrErr );
```

Note that **CloseGraph** *must* be used to return you to text mode. Strange things may happen if execution terminates with a call to **CloseGraph** because DOS doesn't like to be left hanging in graphics mode.

13.2 SCALING GRAPHICS OUTPUT

The position of a pixel on the graphics screen is given by two co-ordinates, *x* and *y*, where *x* is the vertical distance of the pixel from the top of the screen, and *y* is the horizontal distance from the *left* of the screen. By convention, pixel co-ordinates start at zero. So if your resolution is 640 × 200 the maximum values of *x* and *y* are 639 and 199 respectively. These co-ordinates are called **absolute** co-ordinates.

Two of the most basic procedures for drawing graphs are

Line(*x*1, *y*1, *x*2, *y*2 **)** { **integer arguments** }

which draws a line between the points (*x*1, *y*1) and (*x*2, *y*2)

and

PutPixel(*x*, *y*, *Colour* **)**

which draws the point (*x*, *y*) in the *Colour* specified (colour is discussed below in section 13.4). For example,

Line(0, 0, 200, 200)

(after a call to **InitGraph**) should draw a line from the top left corner of the screen no matter which graphics device you have. All pixel co-ordinates passed as parameters to **Graph** procedures and functions must be integers, otherwise a type mismatch compile error will be generated.

Where exactly the line ends is going to depend on the graphics card, and you might well think that to draw a line right across the screen involves knowing which graphics card is installed. However, the BGI is fortunately *device independent*, which means that you can use the whole screen *irrespective* of the graphics card. Otherwise the whole process of loading the graphics driver at runtime would be pointless.

There are two very important functions that help here: **GetMaxX** and **GetMaxY**. These return respectively the largest horizontal and vertical absolute co-ordinates available with the current graphics driver and mode. So

Line(0, 0, GetMaxX, GetMaxY);

will draw a line which covers the screen from top left to bottom right.

The procedure

Rectangle(*x*1, *y*1, *x*2, *y*2 **)** { **integer arguments** }

draws a rectangle with upper left corner at (*x*1, *y*1) and lower right corner at (*x*2, *y*2). See if you can draw a diagram like the one shown in Figure 13.1.

Drawing graphs of mathematical functions, as we did in Chapter 6, involves a little more work, in which **GetMaxX** and **GetMaxY** play a fundamental part. We wrote our own unit **GrScale** to transform our more convenient **problem** (or **world**) co-ordinates into the absolute screen co-ordinates required for the graphics card.

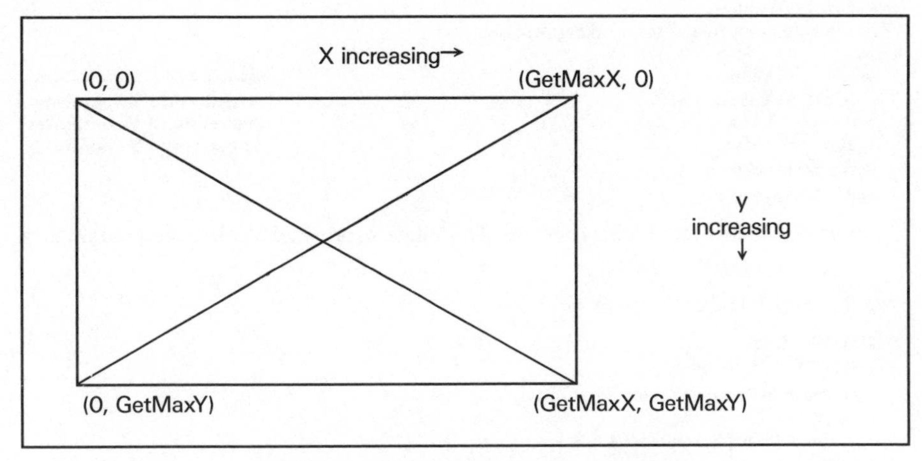

Figure 13.1 Absolute screen co-ordinates

The following is a more general unit, **MyGraphs**:

```
{------MyGraphs -----------------------------------------------------------------}
{                                                                                }
{  Procedures and functions in this unit assist in scaling the                   }
{  user's more convenient world co-ordinates into absolute                       }
{  screen co-ordinates.                                                          }
{--------------------------------------------------------------------------------}
  unit MyGraphs;

  interface
  uses Graph;
  var
    Left, Right, Top, Bottom: real;                         { world co-ordinates }
    function H( X: real): integer;
    function V( Y: real): integer;
    procedure ScLine( X1, Y1, X2, Y2 : real );
    procedure SetWindow( XMin, XMax, YMin, YMax: real );
  implementation
  function H;
  { Scales world X-coordinate (horizontal) into H absolute co-ordinate }
  var
    TempX : real;
  begin
    TempX:= GetMaxX * (X - Left) / (Right - Left);
    H:= Round( TempX )
  end; { H }
  function V;
  { Scales world Y-coordinate (vertical) into V absolute co-ordinate }
  { Vertical axis is inverted }
  var
    TempY : real;
  begin
    TempY:= GetMaxY * (Y - Top) / (Bottom - Top);
    V:= Round( TempY )
  end; { V }
  procedure ScLine;
  { World co-ordinate analogue of Line }
  begin
    Line( H( X1 ), V( Y1 ), H( X2 ), V( Y2 ) )
  end; { ScLine }
```

```
procedure SetWindow;
{ Passes world co-ordinates from calling program }
begin
  Left     := XMin;                              { smallest world X-coordinate }
    Right:= XMax;                                 { largest world X-coordinate }
  Bottom := YMin;                                { smallest world Y-coordinate }
    Top  := YMax                                  { largest world Y-coordinate }
  end; { SetWindow }
  end. { MyGraphs }
```

Before we discuss it let's see how it works. The following program uses it to draw the graph of

$$f(x) = 4\sin(x) + \cos(4x)$$

over the range 0 to 2π in steps of $\pi/40$:

```
program Draw;
uses Graph, MyGraphs;
  function F( X : real ): real;
  begin
    F:= 4 * Sin( X ) + Cos( 4 * X )
  end; { F }
var
  GrDriver,
  GrMode : integer;
  X, Xold : real;
  Y, Yold : real;
begin
  GrDriver:= Detect;
  InitGraph( GrDriver, GrMode, ' \ tp5' );
  SetWindow( 0, 8, -8, 8 );            { world co-ords X: 0 to 8, F: -8 to 8 }
  Xold:= 0;
  X:= 0;
  while X <= 2 * Pi do
  begin
    X:= X + Pi / 40;
    if X <= 2 * Pi then
      ScLine( Xold, F( Xold ), X, F( X ) );
    Xold:= X;
  end;
  Readln;
  CloseGraph
end.
```

The procedure **SetWindow** in the unit **MyGraphs** receives the ranges of the *world* co-ordinates from the calling program. **XMin** is the smallest x value, **XMax** the largest, etc. These are assigned to the local variables **Left, Right, Bottom** and **Top** for use by the rest of the unit.

The function **H** scales the horizontal world co-ordinate **X** into the horizontal absolute co-ordinate **H** using a linear transformation. You can easily derive it. We want to transform X to H using

$$H = aX + b \qquad (1)$$

which is the most general linear transformation. We can find a from the screen limits. When X = **Left**, H must be 0, so we substitute these values into Eqn (1):

$$0 = a\mathbf{Left} + b\,. \qquad (2)$$

And when X = **Right**, H must be **GetMaxX**:

$$\mathbf{GetMaxX} = a\mathbf{Right} + b\,. \qquad (3)$$

Solving Eqns (2) and (3) for a and b gives the required formula:

$$H = \mathbf{GetMaxX}(X - \mathbf{Left}) / (\mathbf{Right} - \mathbf{Left}).$$

You can check this formula by looking at the limits. When X = **Left**, $H = 0$ from the formula, which is correct, and similarly for X = **Right**.

A similar transformation is used to transform the vertical world co-ordinate **Y** into the absolute co-ordinate **V**, bearing in mind that the vertical axis must be inverted (world co-ordinates usually increase upwards).

The procedure **ScLine** simply draws a line between the world points (*x*1, *y*1) and (*x*2, *y*2) in the same way that **Line** does for absolute co-ordinates. You can add scaled versions of other graphics procedures and functions to **MyGraphs** as the need arises.

Note that **MyGraphs** does not call **InitGraph**, as **GrScale** did. It is better to do this from the calling program, now that you know how to do it, because you might want to use a different mode, or you might want to be able to specify a different path for the BGI driver.

13.3 SOME EXAMPLES

In this section, some further examples of graphics programs are given. A detailed discussion of the main functions and procedures in the **Graph** unit follows in the next section.

Tangents to a Curve

This program draws intersecting lines which approximate tangents to a curve. Its output is similar to that of the problem in Exercise 3.1.

```
program Tangents;
uses Graph, MyGraphs;
var
  GrDriver,
  GrMode : integer;
  Del,
  Inc,
  XMax,
  YMax    : real;
begin
  GrDriver:= Detect;
  InitGraph( GrDriver, GrMode, ' \tp5' );
  XMax:= 100;
  YMax:= 100;
  SetWindow( 0, XMax, 0, YMax );
  ScLine( 0, 0, XMax, 0 );                          { draw X-axis }
  ScLine( 0, 0, 0, YMax );                          { draw Y-axis }
  Del:= 5;
  Inc:= Del;

  while Inc <= XMax do
  begin
    ScLine( Inc, 0, 0, YMax - Inc );                { draw the lines }
    Inc:= Inc + Del
  end;

  Readln;
  CloseGraph
end.
```

Fourier approximation to a square wave

This program plots the Fourier approximation to a square wave using the formula quoted in Exercise 6.9. It has an infinite loop which allows you to specify different values of N (the number of terms in the Fourier series). Graphs are superimposed, so you can see the effect of increasing N. To stop the program, enter a value of 100 for N, or press **Ctrl-Break** twice. Note that text on the graphics screen looks different to the text you normally see on the screen.

The program uses two new procedures which must be added to the unit **MyGraphs**:

```
procedure ScLineTo( X, Y : real );
{ World co-ordinate analogue of LineTo }
begin
  LineTo( H( X ), V( Y ) )
end; { ScLineTo }

procedure ScMoveTo( X, Y : real );
```

```
{ World co-ordinate analogue of MoveTo }
begin
  MoveTo( H( X ), V( Y ) )
end; { ScMoveTo }
```

The complete Fourier approximation program is:

```
program DrawFourier;
uses Graph, MyGraphs;
function FrSqu( N: integer; T: real ): real;
           var
              K     :
                    word;
  Sum      : real;
begin
  Sum:= 0;
  for K:= 0 to N do
    Sum:= Sum + Sin( (2 * K + 1) * Pi * T ) / (2 * K + 1);
  FrSqu:= Sum * 4 / Pi
end; { FrSqu }

var
  GrDriver,
  GrMode,
  N        : integer;
  T        : real;
  NStr     : string;
  Pic      : pointer;
begin
  GrDriver:= Detect;
  InitGraph( GrDriver, GrMode, '\ tp5' );
  SetWindow( -2, 2, -2, 2 );
  GetMem( Pic, ImageSize( 0, 0, GetMaxX, GetMaxY ) );
  GetImage( 0, 0, GetMaxX, GetMaxY, Pic ^);                  { keep the image }
  repeat
    RestoreCrtMode;                                  { back to text for Readln }
    Write( 'Value of N? ' );
    Readln( N );
    SetGraphMode( GrMode );                                { back to graphics }
    SetGraphMode
    T:= -1;
    PutImage( 0, 0, Pic ^, 0 );                { put old image back on screen }
    OutText( 'Value of N: ' );
    Str( N, NStr );
    OutText( NStr );
    ScMoveTo( T, FrSqu( N, T ) );
    while T <= 1 do                          { draw the Fourier approximation }
    begin
      ScLineTo( T, FrSqu( N, T ) );
      T:= T + 0.05
    end;

    Readln;
    SetViewPort( 0, 0, 200, 15, False );                { clear part of screen }
    ClearViewPort;
    SetViewPort( 0, 0, GetMaxX, GetMaxY, False );
    GetImage( 0, 0, GetMaxX, GetMaxY, Pic ^);                      { keep image }
  until N = 100;

  CloseGraph
end.
```

Capacitor charge and discharge

This program plots the charge on a capacitor (C) connected in series with a battery (V) and a resistor (R) during successive periods of charging (switch closed) and discharging (switch open). While charging, the charge on the capacitor is given by

$$q(t) = (Q - CV)e^{-t/(RC)} + CV$$

and while discharging it is given by

$$q(t) = Qe^{-t/(RC)}.$$

In both cases, Q is the initial charge on the capacitor when the switch was last opened or closed, and t is the time elapsed since that moment. In the program, **T** represents this time, while **TotTim** is the total time that has elapsed.

```
program Cap;
uses Graph, MyGraphs;
const
  C       : real = 1;                                    { capacitance }
  Ch      : real = 0;                    { charge on capacitor at time T }
  Dt      : real = 0.1;                             { time increment }
  R       : real = 1;                                   { resistance }
  Steps   : word = 50;                 { no. of charge/discharge steps }
  TotTim  : real = 0;                            { total time elapsed }
  V       : real = 5;                                      { voltage }
var
  GrDriver,
  GrMode,
  I, J    : integer;                                       { counters }
  Q       : real;                                    { initial charge }
  T       : real;                              { time elapsed in cycle }
begin
  GrDriver:= Detect;
  InitGraph( GrDriver, GrMode, '\ tp5' );
  SetWindow( 0, 33, -10, 10 );
  ScMoveTo( TotTim, Ch );

  for J:= 1 to 3 do
  begin
    T:= 0;                                                { initialise }
    Q:= Ch;

    for I:= 0 to Steps do                                   { charging }
    begin
      T:= T + Dt;
      TotTim:= TotTim + Dt;
      Ch:= (Q - C * V) * Exp( - T / (R * C) ) + C * V;
      ScLineTo( TotTim, Ch )
    end;
          Q:= Ch;
          T:= 0;

          for I:= 0 to Steps do                          { discharging }
    begin
      T:= T + Dt;
      TotTim:= TotTim + Dt;
      Ch:= Q * Exp( - T / (R * C) );
      ScLineTo( TotTim, Ch )
    end

  end;

  Readln;
  CloseGraph
end.
```

Angle of launch for maximum range

This is an educational program of use to students learning Newtonian dynamics. The problem is to find, by trial and error, the launch angle for a projectile to give it the maximum horizontal range (see section 4.1 for the equations of motion). After each attempt, the trajectory of the projectile is left on the screen, together with the best angle used so far. Two **viewports** are used: one for the projectile, and one for the text. Note that one viewport can be cleared without affecting the other. If **Read** is used to read from the keyboard in graphics mode, the current pointer moves to the top left corner of the screen, irrespective of where it was when the **Read** was executed. The procedure **GrRead**, which is used in the maximum range program, tidies this up:

```
{------GrRead ----------------------------------------------------------------------}
{                                                                                  }
{  Gets legal numeric input from keyboard in graphics mode,                        }
{  with echo to screen.                                                            }
{ ---------------------------------------------------------------------------------}

  procedure GrRead( var X: real );
  const
    ChSet = [ '0'..'9', '.', '+', '-', 'E', 'e' ];
  var
    Code, I  : word;
    Ch       : char;
    InStr    : string;
  begin
    InStr:= '';
    I:= 0;
    repeat
      Ch:= ReadKey;
      if Ch <> #13 then                              { code for carriage return is #13 }
        begin
        if Ch In ChSet then
        begin
          I:= I + 1;
          Insert( Ch, InStr, I );
          OutText( Ch )
        end
        else
          Write( #7#7 )
        end
    until Ch = #13;
    Val( InStr, X, Code )
  end; { GrRead }
```

GrRead only accepts legal characters for numbers. If an illegal character is typed, the bell sounds and you can retype the character. There is no opportunity to change legal characters (ie the backspace is regarded as an illegal character). It is helpful to incorporate **GrRead** into the unit **MyGraphs**.

The program is as follows:

```
  program Range;
  uses Graph, MyGraphs;
  const
    AngMax      : real = 0;                      { angle for maximum range }
    Dt          : real = 0.1;                          { time increments }
    G           : real = 9.8;               { gravitational acceleration }
    U           : real = 70;                     { launch velocity (m/s) }
    XMax        : real = 0;                              { maximum range }
  var
    Ang         : real;                            { angle of projection }
    AngMaxStr   : string[10];          { string representation of AngMax }
    GrDriver,
    GrMode      : integer;
    T           : real;                                 { time in flight }
    X, Y        : real;                             { flight co-ordinates }
  begin
    GrDriver:= Detect;
    InitGraph( GrDriver, GrMode, '\ tp5' );
    SetWindow( 0, 500, 0, 300 );
    ScLine( 0, 0, 500, 0 );                                  { draw axes }
    ScLine( 0, 0, 0, 300 );

    repeat
      SetViewPort( GetMaxX div 2, 0, GetMaxX, 20, False );
```

```
    ClearViewPort;
    OutText( 'Best angle so far: ' );
    Str( AngMax:4:1, AngMaxStr );
      OutText( AngMaxStr );
      MoveTo( 0, 10 );
      OutText( 'Enter launch angle (0 to stop): ' );
      GrRead( Ang );
      SetViewPort( 0, 0, GetMaxX, GetMaxY, False);
      Ang:= Ang * Pi / 180;
      X:= 0;
      Y:= 0;
      T:= 0;
      ScMoveTo( X, Y );
      while Y >= 0 do
      begin
        ScLineTo( X, Y );
        T:= T + Dt;
        X:= U * Cos( Ang ) * T;
        Y:= U * Sin( Ang ) * T - G * T * T / 2
      end;
      if X > XMax then                                    { a new record }
      begin
        XMax:= X;
        AngMax:= Ang * 180 / Pi
      end
    until Ang = 0;
    CloseGraph
  end.
```

Fractals with Turtle graphics

The following unit, **Turtle**, simulates LOGO Turtle graphics. The turtle (which is not shown, although its path is drawn) can turn left or right a given number of degrees, and can move forward or back a given distance. It uses world co-ordinates (and the **MyGraphs** unit). Note that **Forward** is a reserved word and cannot be used as a procedure name. **Fwd** is used instead.

```
unit Turtle;
{ Uses world co-ordinate set in calling program }
interface
uses Graph, MyGraphs;
var A,                                          { angular heading in degrees }
    X, Y : real;                                           { current position }
procedure Back( D: real );
procedure ClearScreen;
procedure Fwd( D: real );
procedure Left( dA: real );
procedure Right( dA: real );
implementation
procedure Back;
begin
  Fwd( - D )
end; { Back }
procedure ClearScreen;
begin
  ClearViewPort;
  X:= 0;
  Y:= 0;
  A:= 90                                                     { heading up }
end; { ClearScreen }
procedure Fwd;
var
  dX, dY, NewX, NewY: real;
begin
```

```
  dX:= D * Cos( A * Pi / 180 );
  dY:= D * Sin( A * Pi / 180 );
  NewX:= X + dX;
  NewY:= Y + dY;
  ScLine( X, Y, NewX, NewY );
  X:= NewX;
  Y:= NewY
end; { Fwd }
procedure Left;
begin
  A:= A + dA
end; { Left }
procedure Right;
begin
  Left( - dA )
end; { Right }
end. { Turtle }
```

The following program uses **Turtle** to draw a tree using a recursively defined shape, which is an example of a **fractal**. (A fractal can be thought of as an object with *fractional* dimensions, for example 1.2, and which is characterised by infinite structure, often with self-replicating features.) The program draws a tree with a vertical stem of height **Leng**, which branches symmetrically, so that **Ang** is half the angle between the branches. Each branch is made a fraction **Frac** of the stem, and branches in the same way as the stem. New branches are always a fraction **Frac** of their parent branches. This pattern is repeated while the branches remain longer than two units. With a little thought you should be able to see how the recursive procedure **Tree** does this. Values of 50, 0.6 and 20 for **Leng, Frac** and **Ang** respectively give a fairly common or garden tree, while values of 60, 0.7 and 90, for example, give a slightly less usual looking tree. The program is as follows:

```
program GrowTree;
uses Graph, MyGraphs, Turtle;
var
  GrDriver, GrMode: integer;
  OldColor : word;
procedure Tree( Leng, Frac, Ang: real );
begin
  if Leng < 2 then
      Exit;
    Fwd( Leng );
    Left( Ang );
    Tree( Frac * Leng, Frac, Ang );
    Right( 2 * Ang );
    Tree( Frac * Leng, Frac, Ang );
    Left( Ang );
    Back( Leng )
end; { Tree }
begin
  GrDriver:= Detect;
  InitGraph( GrDriver, GrMode, '\ tp5' );
  SetWindow( -140, 140, -120, 120 );
  ClearScreen;                        { turtle at origin of world co-ordinates }
  OldColor:= GetColor;                       { record current drawing colour }
  SetColor( GetBkColor );                                { set drawing colour
                                                         to background colour }
  Back( 120 );                                         { plant it on the ground }
  SetColor( OldColor );               { re-instate the previous drawing colour }
  Tree( 50, 0.6, 20 );                                         { draw the tree }
  readln;
  CloseGraph
end.
```

The Julia set

The discovery of fractals in the past few years has led to a wealth of the most beautiful and fascinating pictures, as can be seen in Peitgen and Richter (1986). One such fractal is the **Julia set**. In this section we give a simple program for drawing the Julia set of the complex polynomial $z^2 - \mu$, where z is a complex variable, $z = x + iy$, and μ is a complex constant (parameter), $\mu = a + ib$.

A working definition of the Julia set of this family of polynomials is as follows. Take a region of the complex plane. For *every point* z_0 in this region calculate the **iterated function sequence** (IFS) of the polynomial:

$$z_1 = z_0^2 - \mu,$$
$$z_2 = z_1^2 - \mu,$$
$$z_3 = z_2^2 - \mu,$$
$$\dots,$$
$$z_n = z_{n-1}^2 - \mu$$

If an n can be found such that $z_n^2 > R$, where R is the radius of a (large) disk in the complex plane, z_0 is said to have *escaped*. The set of all points z_0 in the region of interest which do *not* escape is the Julia set of the polynomial.

The real and imaginary parts of the polynomial $z^2 - \mu$ are as follows:

$$\text{Re}(z) = x^2 - y^2 - a,$$
$$\text{Im}(z) = 2xy - b.$$

The program below draws the Julia set of $z^2 - 1.1$, so $a = 1.1$ and $b = 0$. Ideally R should be as large as possible, but we will take it as 4, since this gives quite a reasonable picture. You can experiment with larger values if you have the time! If z_0 has not escaped by the time n has reached the value of **MaxIts** (40), we will assume that it will never escape. The program checks each pixel in the world co-ordinate range $-2 \leq x \leq 2$, $-2 \leq y \leq 2$ to see if it escapes (applying the reverse of the transformation used in **MyGraphs** to change world co-ordinates to absolute co-ordinates). If the pixel escapes it is lit up. The Julia set is then the set of pixels shaded in the background colour. (Strictly speaking, the Julia set is the *boundary* of the region in the background colour, and the region itself is the *filled* Julia set.)

```
program Julia;
{ Draws the Julia set of the family: z * z - mu }
uses Graph, MyGraphs;
const
  MaxIts        : word = 40;                  { maximum no. of iterations }
  R             : real = 4;                                     { infinity }
var
  A, B,                                     { real and imaginary parts of mu }
  Xmin, Xmax, Ymin, Ymax : real;                { range of world co-ordinates }
  X, Y, X0, Y0, NewX, NewY : real;                      { world co-ordinates }
  Colour, GrDriver, GrMode : integer;                   { graphics variables }
  N : integer;                                                     { counter }
  Xp, Yp : integer;                                  { absolute co-ordinates }
begin
  Xmin:= -2;
  Xmax:= 2;
  Ymin:= -2;
  Ymax:= 2;
  A:= 1.1;
  B:= 0;
  GrDriver:= CGA;                                                 { CGA card }
  GrMode:= CGAC0;                                                { palette 0 }
  InitGraph( GrDriver, GrMode, '\ tp5' );
  for Xp:= 0 to GetMaxX do
    for Yp:= 0 to GetMaxY do
    begin
      X0:= (Xmax - Xmin) * Xp / GetMaxX + Xmin;
      Y0:= (Ymin - Ymax) * Yp / GetMaxY + Ymax;
      X:= X0;
```

```
      Y:= Y0;
      N:= 0;
      while (N < MaxIts) and (X * X + Y * Y <= R) do
      begin
        N:= N + 1;
        NewX:= X * X - Y * Y - A;
        NewY:= 2 * X * Y - B;
        X:= NewX;
        Y:= NewY
      end;
      if X * X + Y * Y > R then
      begin
        PutPixel( Xp, Yp, 1 )
      end
    end;
  Readln;
  CloseGraph
end.
```

You can approximate some of the beautiful colour pictures you may have seen of the Julia set by drawing an escaped pixel in a different colour, depending on how quickly it escapes:

```
      if X * X + Y * Y > R then
      begin
        N:= (N + 1) mod 4;
        PutPixel( Xp, Yp, N );
      end
```

(N + 1) mod 4 is just a matter of taste. **N mod 4** will give a different colouring.

Finally, you can speed up the drawing of this particular picture by a factor of four by observing that it has symmetry about both the x- and y-axes:

```
    for Xp:= 0 to GetMaxX div 2 do
      for Yp:= 0 to GetMaxY div 2 do
    ...
          if X * X + Y * Y > R then
            begin
              N:= (N + 1) mod 4;
              PutPixel( Xp, Yp, N );
              PutPixel( GetMaxX - Xp, Yp, N );
              PutPixel( Xp, GetMaxY - Yp, N );
              PutPixel( GetMaxX - Xp, GetMaxY - Yp, N );
          end
```

The boundary of the filled Julia set has the self-replicating property characteristic of fractals. Change the program (by adjusting **Xmin**, **Xmax**, etc.) to zoom in on one of the spires sticking out of the main body of the set. A little patience will be richly rewarded.

The Mandelbrot set

The **Mandelbrot set** was discovered by Benoit Mandelbrot, and has been described as the most complicated object known to man. It is related to the Julia set, and is drawn in much the same way, although it is more difficult to think about.

The Julia set above is for the polynomial $z^2 - \mu$ with $\mu = 1.1$. If you run the program for a different value of the parameter μ, the set will look different. The Mandelbrot set is concerned with μ, and is drawn in the *parameter* space of the polynomial. It is in fact the set of all values of μ for which the *origin* does not escape.

Recall that $\mu = a + ib$. For all possible values of a and b now (as opposed to x and y for the Julia set) we compute the IFS of $z^2 - \mu$ starting at $z = 0$ each time. If z_n *(the n-th iterate)* for a particular μ does not escape it belongs to the Mandelbrot set. The program is very similar to the one for the Julia set. Only the changes are shown here (highlighted):

```
    MaxIts      : word = 20;                     { maximum no. of iterations }
    R           : real = 10;                                      { infinity }
  ...
```

```
Xmin:= -0.5;                                        { range of A now }
   Xmax:= 1.5;
   Ymin:= -1;                                       { range of B now }
   Ymax:= 1;
...
      for Yp:= 0 to GetMaxY div 2 do
      begin
         A:= (Xmax - Xmin) * Xp / GetMaxX + Xmin;
         B:= (Ymin - Ymax) * Yp / GetMaxY + Ymax;
         X:= 0;
         Y:= 0;
...
           PutPixel( Xp, GetMaxY - Yp, 1 );
```

The Mandelbrot set of this function has symmetry about the *a* axis, and this is exploited to speed up the program. Take **MaxIts** = 20 and **R** = 10.

The Mandelbrot set is a fuzzy fractal. If you enlarge one of the little snowmen on its boundary (coastline) you will see a figure which is similar but not *identical* (zooming on the Julia set coastline reveals identical replicas of the Julia set). In fact the structures on the boundaries resemble Julia sets. It is as if the coastline of the Mandelbrot set is made by stitching together microscopic copies of the Julia sets which it represents.

Zooming in on the sea outside the Mandelbrot set may be rewarding too. You may find islands there that no-one else has ever seen.

13.4 BASIC GRAPHICS FEATURES

In this section we tidy up some of the graphics features that have been introduced in the examples above, and look at some new ones that are useful. All function and procedure parameters that refer to absolute co-ordinates are integers.

The current pointer

The current pointer (CP) is the graphics analogue of the text cursor, although it is never seen. A call to **InitGraph** positions it at (0, 0). The procedure

MoveTo(*x*, *y*)

moves the CP to the point (*x*, *y*), without drawing while it does so, whereas

LineTo(*x*, *y*)

draws a line *from* the CP to the point (*x*, *y*), while also moving the CP to that point.

Only commands that use the CP actually move it: **InitGraph***, **MoveTo**, **MoveRel**, **LineTo**, **LineRel**, **OutText**, **SetGraphMode***, **GraphDefaults***, **ClearDevice***, **SetViewPort***, and **ClearViewPort***. Procedures with asterisks (*) move the CP to (0, 0).

A hazy understanding of the CP soon causes unwanted lines on the screen! For example, a **LineTo** executed at the beginning of a graphics program will draw a line from (0, 0) to the CP, since **InitGraph** positions the CP at (0, 0).

Note that two of the procedures we have already seen, **Line** and **PutPixel**, do *not* move the current pointer.

MoveRel and **LineRel** move the CP a *relative* distance from its current position.

MoveRel(*dx*, *dy*) moves the CP a distance *dx* to the right from its current position and a distance *dy* down from its current position. So if it was at position (*x*, *y*) before the call to **MoveRel**, it moves to (*x*+*dx*, *y*+*dy*) after the call.

LineRel(*dx*, *dy*) draws a line from the CP to its new position defined by the relative increments *dx* and *dy*.

Relative viewports

A **viewport** is the graphics analogue of a text window. The current viewport defaults to the whole screen after a call to **InitGraph**. The procedure

SetViewPort(*x*1, *y*1, *x*2, *y*2, *Clip*)

where *Clip* is boolean, defines a smaller viewport, with its top left corner at (*x*1, *y*1) and its bottom right corner at (*x*2, *y*2). If *Clip* is true, all drawing in the new viewport is **clipped**, ie graphics images which go beyond its borders will *not* be drawn. If *Clip* is false, clipping does not take place.

The new viewport is not a minature of the whole screen, and subsequent drawing is relative to the new viewport, until the next call to **SetViewPort**. A numerical example might help. The two statements:

```
SetViewPort( 100, 50, 400, 100, True );
MoveTo( 10, 20 );
```

move the CP to the point with absolute co-ordinates (110, 70), ie (100+10, 50+20). The point (0, 0) is therefore at the top left corner of the *current* viewport, whether it is the default viewport, or one which has been set with **SetViewPort**.

ClearViewPort clears the current viewport (ie the rest of the screen is not cleared).

The functions **GetX** and **GetY** return the *x* and *y* co-ordinates of the CP *relative* to the current viewport. However, **GetMaxX** and **GetMaxY** always return *absolute* co-ordinates (ie relative to the *full* screen).

Co-ordinates passed to **SetViewPort** are absolute – otherwise you could never enlarge a viewport which is smaller than the full screen (could you?).

The procedure **GetViewSettings** returns the absolute co-ordinates of the top left and bottom right corners of the current viewport by means of a variable of the predeclared type **ViewPortType**:

```
ViewPortType = record
                 X1, Y1, X2, Y2 : word;
                 Clip           : boolean
               end;
```

X1, Y1, X2 and **Y2** will be set to 0, 0, **GetMaxX** and **GetMaxY** if the viewport is the full screen. This facility can be exploited to make the scaling in our unit **MyGraphs** relative to the current viewport. Introduce the following variable to **MyGraphs**' interface section:

```
var
  CurrentPort : ViewPortType;
```

Then introduce two new functions:

```
function XRange;
{ Calculates XRange for use in function H }
begin
  GetViewSettings( CurrentPort );
    with CurrentPort do
      XRange:= X2 - X1
end; { XRange }

function YRange;
{ Calculates YRange for use in function V }
begin
  GetViewSettings( CurrentPort );
    with CurrentPort do
      YRange:= Y2 - Y1
end; { YRange }
```

Finally, amend the scaling functions **H** and **V**:

```
TempX:= XRange * (X - Left) / (Right - Left);
TempY:= YRange * (Y - Top) / (Bottom - Top);
```

Scaled graphs may be drawn in several viewports, as long as **SetWindow** is called after each call to **SetViewPort**.

MyGraphs has undergone quite a few changes, so it is shown in full at the end of this chapter.

The following educational program demonstrates the use of different viewports to draw multiple straight line graphs:

```
program FriendlyLines;
{ Draws user friendly straight line graphs }
uses Crt, Graph, MyGraphs;
const
   Xmin        : real = -10;                    { world co-ordinate range }
   Xmax        : real = 10;
   Ymin        : real = -10;
   Ymax        : real = 10;
var
   Ch          : char;                                   { user option }
   GrDriver,
   GrMode      : integer;
   GrRight     : word;              { Right boundary of graph window }
   MenuBottom  : word;             { bottom boundary of menu window }
   X, M, C     : real;                             { data for the graph }

procedure GraphWindow; forward;
function Y( var X: real ): real; forward;

procedure Axes;
{ Draws axes in world co-ordinates and labels them }
var
   NStr : string;
begin
   ScLine( Xmin, 0, Xmax, 0 );
   ScLine( 0, Ymin, 0, Ymax );
   ScOutTextXY( 0.4, Ymax - 0.3, 'Y' );
   Str( Ymax:2:0, NStr );
   ScOutTextXY( -0.8, Ymax - 0.3, NStr );
   ScOutTextXY( Xmax - 0.5, 1, 'X' );
   Str( Ymax:2:0, NStr );
   ScOutTextXY( Xmax - 0.8, -0.4, NStr );
   Str( Ymin:2:0, NStr );
   ScOutTextXY( -1.2, Ymin + 1, NStr );
   Str( Xmin:2:0, NStr );
   ScOutTextXY( Xmin + 0.2, -0.4, NStr )
end; { Axes }
procedure Border;
{ Draws border around graph window }
begin
   ClearViewPort;
   ScLine( Xmin, Ymin, Xmax, Ymin );
   ScLine( Xmax, Ymin, Xmax, Ymax );
   ScLine( Xmax, Ymax, Xmin, Ymax );
   ScLine( Xmin, Ymax, Xmin, Ymin )
end; { Border }

procedure ClearGraph;
begin
   GraphWindow;                          { get the right viewport first }
   Border;
   Axes
end; { ClearGraph }

procedure DrawGraph;
{ Actually draws the graph }
begin
   GraphWindow;                        { must draw in the right window! }
   ScLine( Xmin, Y( Xmin ), Xmax, Y( Xmax ) )
end; { DrawGraph }
```

```
procedure GraphWindow;
{ Sets graph viewport }
begin
  SetViewPort( 0, 0, GrRight, GetMaxY, True )
end; { GraphWindow }
procedure Menu;
{ Co-ordinates relative to Menu window here }
begin
  SetViewPort( GrRight + 10, 0, GetMaxX, MenuBottom, True );
  OutText( 'Draws y = mx + c' );
  OutTextXY( 0, 20, 'OPTIONS are:' );
  OutTextXY( 0, 40, 'D: Draw graph' );
  OutTextXY( 0, 50, 'C: Clear window' );
  OutTextXY( 0, 60, 'Q: Quit' )
end; { Menu }
function Y;
{ The straight line itself }
begin
  Y:= M * X + C
end; { Y }
begin
  GrDriver:= cga;                                       { get into graphics }
  GrMode:= cgahi;
  InitGraph( GrDriver, GrMode, '\ tp5' );
  GrRight:= 3 * GetMaxX div 4;                          { some initialising now ... }
  MenuBottom:= 2 * GetMaxY div 5;
  GraphWindow;                                          { sets graph viewport }
  SetWindow( Xmin, Xmax, Ymin, Ymax );
  Border;                                               { set up graph and menu windows }
  Axes;
  Menu;
  repeat                                                { get option from user and act upon it }
    SetViewPort( GrRight + 10, MenuBottom + 5,
                 GetMaxX, GetMaxY, True );              { option window }
    ClearViewPort;
    OutText( 'Option? ' );
    Ch:= ReadKey;
    OutText( Ch );
    Ch:= UpCase( Ch );
    if Ch = 'D' then                                    { get values for M and C }
    begin
      MoveTo( 0, 20 );
      OutText( 'm? ' );
      GrRead( M );
      MoveTo( 0, 30 );
      OutText( 'c? ' );
      GrRead( C );
      DrawGraph
    end
    else if Ch = 'C' then
      ClearGraph
  until Ch = 'Q';
  CloseGraph
end.
```

Note that **SetWindow** only needs to be called once, because scaled drawing is done only in one viewport.

The aspect ratio

There is an old programmer's lament that goes, "Constants aren't and variables won't." The bane of computer graphics, in a nutshell, is that squares aren't. You may have noticed already that the statement

```
Rectangle( 0, 0, 100, 100 )
```

probably does not produce a square on your monitor, because most graphics cards do not display square pixels. This can be very irritating, but with the **GetAspectRatio** procedure and a little nifty arithmetic things can be squared up as it were. The statement

GetAspectRatio(*Xaspect*, *Yaspect* **)**

returns two word parameters whose ratio (ie *Xaspect / Yaspect*) is the ratio between the width and the height of the screen pixels in the current graphics mode. This ratio is called the **aspect ratio**, and is in fact used by the BGI to ensure that figures drawn by **Circle, Arc** and **PieSlice** are always displayed as circular regardless of which graphics device is installed.

The following statements will draw a (proper) square of width 100 pixels:

```
var
  Xasp, Yasp      : word;
...
 GetAspectRatio( Xasp, Yasp );
 Rectangle( 0, 0, 100, Round( Xasp / Yasp * 100 ) );
```

The parameters of **SetWindow** in the **MyGraphs** unit can be adjusted to take the aspect ratio into account. The following statements draw a proper square of length 5 world co-ordinate units in the current viewport (wherever it is). **Ymax** is adjusted so that a vertical unit in world co-ordinates has the same physical length as a horizontal unit.

```
var
  Xasp, Yasp      : word;
  Xmin, Xmax, Ymin, Ymax : real;
  CurrentPort     : ViewPortType;
...
  GetAspectRatio( Xasp, Yasp );
  Xmin:= 0;
  Xmax:= 10;
  Ymin:= 0;
  SetViewPort( ... )                                          { whatever }
  GetViewSettings( CurrentPort );
  with CurrentPort do
    Ymax:= (Yasp / Xasp) * (Y2 - Y1) / (X2 - X1) * Xmax;
  SetWindow( Xmin, Xmax, Ymin, Ymax );
  ScMoveTo( 0, 0 );
  ScLineTo( 0, 5 );
  ScLineTo( 5, 5 );
  ScLineTo( 5, 0 );
  ScLineTo( 0, 0 );
```

The physical dimensions of your monitor may be such that the aspect ratio returned by **GetAspectRatio** is not accurate enough. In this case you can fine-tune it yourself. It is best to set *Yaspect* at 10000, and to fiddle with *Xaspect* until you are satisfied (this will probably involve holding a ruler against your monitor). Once the ratio is correct the statement

SetAspectRatio(*Xaspect*, *Yaspect* **)**

will correct the values the BGI uses when it makes the automatic correction in **Circle, Arc** and **PieSlice**.

Text on the graphics screen

The procedure

OutTextXY(*x*, *y*, *TextString* **)**

draws the characters in *TextString* on the screen. The BGI provides a number of text styles (fonts), set by **SetTextStyle** and a number of output options (justify left or right, centre, rotate 90°, etc.) set by **SetTextJustify**. The size may be varied with **SetUserCharSize**. The default is that the first character in *TextString* is drawn so that its upper left corner is at position (*x*, *y*). **OutTextXY** never moves the CP.

You can consult the *Reference Guide* for details of all the options.

OutText(*TextString* **)** is similar, except that the text is positioned relative to the CP, according to the current justification settings. The CP is moved only if the text is horizontal and left justified.

Moving between the graphics and text screens

You can move between the graphics and text screens without calling the **InitGraph-CloseGraph** sequence each time, by using **RestoreCrtMode** and **SetGraphMode**:

```
var
  GrDriver, GrMode : integer;
begin
  GrDriver:= CGA;
  GrMode:= CGAhi;
  InitGraph( GrDriver, GrMode, '\ tp5' );
  OutText( 'Graphics mode ... ' );
  Readln;
  RestoreCrtMode;
  Writeln( 'Text now ... ' );
  Readln;
  SetGraphMode( GrMode );
  OutText( 'Graphics again ... ' );
  Readln;
  CloseGraph
```

Note that the contents of the graphics screen is lost after the call to **RestoreCrtMode**. The screen can be saved with **GetImage** and restored subsequently with **PutImage**, as in the Fourier approximation example above. These two procedures are discussed further below, in section 13.5.

Colour

Colour is rather confusing at first. Only some basics are given here. You should experiment on your own until you are satisfied that you know what's going on.

Black	**= 0;**
Blue	**= 1;**
Green	**= 2;**
Cyan	**= 3;**
Red	**= 4;**
Magenta	**= 5;**
Brown	**= 6;**
LightGray	**= 7;**
DarkGray	**= 8;**
LightBlue	**= 9;**
LightGreen	**= 10;**
LightCyan	**= 11;**
LightRed	**= 12;**
LightMagenta	**= 13;**
Yellow	**= 14;**
White	**= 15;**

Table 13.3 Standard colours

Your machine's colour capabilities depend on the graphics device installed. The concept central to the understanding of how colour graphics works is that of a **palette**. The palette is the selection of colours available in a particular mode. For example, in CGAC0 mode, the palette consists of four colours: the background colour (0), light green (1), light red (2) and yellow (3). The different palettes available are given in Table 13.2 (section 13.1). The background colour defaults to black, but may be changed by the statement

SetBkColor(*Colour* **)**

where *Colour* may be a word variable, a number, or one of the predeclared constants in Table 13.3. (Other colours are available on the IBM 8514 graphics device – see the *Reference Guide* or GRAPH.DOC on your Turbo Pascal disk.) All pixels not specifically set to some foreground colour are all set to the background colour. If the background colour is changed, all background pixels immediately change to that colour.

The colours in a palette are numbered from 0 upwards, *independently* of the predeclared constants in Table 13.3. The background colour is 0. **GetMaxColor** returns the number of colours supported in the current graphics mode. The foreground colour is selected from the palette with

SetColor(*Colour* **)**

Colour is the number of the colour in the current palette, which is not necessarily the value of the constant of the same name in Table 13.3. Drawing is done in this colour until the foreground colour is changed. For example, the statement

SetColor(2 **)**

in CGAC0 mode selects light red as the drawing colour, because it is the *second* foreground colour in that palette. **SetColor(LightRed)** will not work because the constant **LightRed** has the value 12 according to Table 13.3, and **CGAC0** mode only supports colours numbered up to 3.

SetColor(0) selects the background colour as the drawing colour. This is the standard way of rubbing something out:

```
SetColor( 2 );
Circle( 50, 50, 50 );                    { now you see it }
Readln;
SetColor( GetBkColor );
Circle( 50, 50, 50 );                    { now you don't }
Readln;
```

GetBkColor returns the current background colour (according to Table 13.3). If you want to draw in the background colour, it must be one of the colours in the palette.

GetColor returns the current drawing color in the palette, so if the mode is **CGAC0** and the current colour is light green, **GetColor** returns 1.

PutPixel(*x*, *y*, *Colour* **)** draws the pixel at (*x*, *y*) in the given palette colour.

GetPixel(*x*, *y* **)** returns the palette colour of the pixel at (*x*, *y*).

InitGraph always chooses the highest resolution for a particular device. If you want a lower resolution, or a different palette, **SetGraphmode(***GrMode***)** will select the mode *GrMode* (see Table 13.2) for the current driver.

Some experimentation may be necessary with the high resolution modes that support only two colours. **ATT400Hi** mode, for example (my computer has an ATT400 card), allows only black as the background colour. Any of the colours in Table 13.3 may be selected as the drawing colour, and this is done (you won't believe this) with the statement

SetBkColor(*Colour* **);**

I haven't been able to establish a satisfactory reason for this.

Palette colours can be changed on devices like the EGA which support 16 colours in the palette, with **SetPalette** and **SetAllPalette**. See the *Reference Guide* for details.

Printing the graphics screen

The graphics screen may be printed by pressing **Shift-PrtSc**, as long as the DOS program GRAPHICS.COM was run before your current session.

13.5 ANIMATION

Animation is the basis of computer games. The two examples in this section illustrate the general principles.

The first program shows a red steam engine puffing brown clouds of smoke as it moves along a green embankment against a blue background.

```
program Train;
uses Crt, Graph;
```

```
const
  dXword = 4;                                              { animation step-length }
    EngPts          = 27;
    NumPuff         : word = 5;                        { no. of puffs in smoke trail }
    PuffPts         = 21;
    Engine : array[1..EngPts] of PointType =
        ((X:0; Y:100), (X:5; Y:100), (X:5; Y:105), (X:13; Y:105),
         (X:13; Y:100), (X:15; Y:100), (X:15; Y:105), (X:16; Y:105),
         (X:16; Y:111), (X:15; Y:111), (X:15; Y:113), (X:13; Y:113),
         (X:13; Y:111), (X:8; Y:111), (X:8; Y:113), (X:6; Y:113),
         (X:6; Y:111), (X:3; Y:111), (X:3; Y:113), (X:1; Y:113),
         (X:1; Y:111), (X:0; Y:111), (X:0; Y:105), (X:3; Y:105),
         (X:3; Y:102), (X:0; Y:102), (X:0; Y:100 ));
    Puff            : array[1..PuffPts] of PointType =
        ((X:15; Y:94), (X:15; Y:93), (X:16; Y:93), (X:16; Y:92),
         (X:17; Y:92), (X:17; Y:91), (X:16; Y:91), (X:16; Y:90),
         (X:15; Y:90), (X:15; Y:89), (X:12; Y:89), (X:12; Y:90),
         (X:11; Y:90), (X:11; Y:91), (X:10; Y:91), (X:10; Y:92),
         (X:11; Y:92), (X:11; Y:93), (X:12; Y:93), (X:12; Y:94),
         (X:15; Y:94));
  var
    GrDriver, GrMode : integer;
    EnginePic : pointer;
    PuffPic   : pointer;
    X, Xold   : integer;
  begin
    GrDriver:= CGA;
    GrMode:= CGAC2;                                        { green, red, brown }
    InitGraph( GrDriver, GrMode, '\ tp5' );
    SetBkColor( Blue );
    SetColor( 1 );                                                  { green }
    SetLineStyle( SolidLn, 0, ThickWidth );
    Line( 0, 115, 319, 115 );                              { draw the railway line }
    SetLineStyle( SolidLn, 0, NormWidth );
    SetColor( 2 );                                                    { red }
    SetFillStyle( 1, 2 );
    FillPoly( EngPts, Engine );                                { draw the engine }
    GetMem( EnginePic, ImageSize( 0, 100, 16, 113 ) );
    GetImage( 0, 100, 16, 113, EnginePic ^ );                        { save it }
    SetColor( 3 );                                                  { brown }
    SetFillStyle( 1, 3 );
    FillPoly( PuffPts, Puff );                              { draw a puff of smoke }
    GetMem( PuffPic, ImageSize( 10, 89, 17, 94 ) );
    GetImage( 10, 89, 17, 94, PuffPic ^);                            { save it }
    X:= dX;                        { now send it along the line leaving a trail of smoke }
    while X < 300 do
    begin
      PutImage( X-dX, 100, EnginePic^, XORPut );              { rub out old image }
      PutImage( X, 100, EnginePic^, XORPut );                   { draw new one }
      if X mod (4 * dX) = 0 then                             { puff every 4th step }
      begin
        Delay( 400 );                                    { 400 millisecond delay }
        PutImage( X+10, 89, PuffPic^, XORPut );
        Xold:= X + 10 - 4 * NumPuff * dX;
        if Xold >= 0 then
          PutImage( Xold, 89, PuffPic^, XORPut );
                                                                { rub out last puff }
        Sound( 100 );
        Delay( 200 );
        NoSound
      end;
       X:= X + dX
    end;
    Delay( 1000 );
```

```
 Sound( 200 );
 Delay( 1000 );
 NoSound;
    Readln;
    FreeMem( EnginePic, ImageSize( 0, 100, 16, 113 ) );
    FreeMem( PuffPic, ImageSize( 10, 89, 17, 94 ) );
    CloseGraph
  end.
```

The basic shape of the engine is a **polygon** – a figure composed only of straight lines. The procedure

DrawPoly(*Points*, *PointSet*)

draws a polygon of *Points* vertices. The co-ordinates of the vertices must be stored in *PointSet*, which must be an array of the predeclared type **PointType**:

```
type
  PointType = record
                X, Y : integer
              end;
```

In the program the engine has **EngPts** (27) vertices, the co-ordinates of which are assigned to the constant array **Engine**. Note that the first and last points must be the same to make the polygon close up.

The procedure actually used is **FillPoly**, which is similar to **DrawPoly**, except that the polygon is shaded. The design and colour of the shading is set by **SetFillStyle**:

SetFillStyle(*Pattern*, *Colour*)

Pattern is a word parameter. Values from 0 to 11 give predeclared **fill patterns**; higher values may be used for your own patterns. Details are in the *Reference Guide* and Appendix B.

The basis of animation is to save an image, rub it out, draw it nearby, rub it out, and so on. This is done with **GetImage** and **PutImage**.

GetImage(*x*1, *y*1, *x*2, *y*2, *BitMap*)

stores the image on the rectangular region of the screen bounded by the points (*x*1, *y*1) and (*x*2, *y*2) in the variable *BitMap*, which is an **untyped** parameter (its starting address and size is passed to the procedure). *BitMap* must be large enough to hold the image. It is usually most convenient for *BitMap* to be a dynamic variable (**EnginePic^** and **PuffPic^** above), because the image can take up a lot of memory. The amount of memory required by an image in the rectangular region bounded by (*x*1, *y*1) and (*x*2, *y*2) is returned by the function

ImageSize(*x*1, *y*1, *x*2, *y*2)

Sufficient memory can be allocated to the dynamic variable with

GetMem(Pointer, Size)

The memory is released by

FreeMem(*Pointer*, *Size*)

Size must be the exact amount of space allocated by **GetMem**.

The image saved by **GetImage** in *BitMap* is drawn on the screen by

PutImage(*x*1, *y*1, *BitMap*, *BitBlt*)

The upper left corner of the image will be at the point (*x*1, *y*1). *BitMap* is an untyped parameter containing the bit image. *BitBlt* is a word parameter which specifies how the pixels in the image are to interact with the pixels currently on the screen in the image area. It is pronounced "bit blit" which is a mnemonic for the instruction "bit block transfer" on an old type of minicomputer. The value of *BitBlt* used here is the predeclared constant **XORPut** (=1), which **XOR**s each bit on the screen with the corresponding bit in the image. The effect of this is that if an image is superimposed on itself the resultant image is set to the background colour, whereas if the image is placed anywhere else, the resultant is the same as the superimposed image. This is ideal for animation. An image can be drawn by **XOR**ing it, rubbed out by **XOR**ing it at the same place, and then moved by **XOR**ing it at a new position.

Other predeclared values for *BitBlt* are **CopyPut, OrPut, AndPut** and **NotPut**. You can discover their meanings by experimenting, or by looking in the *Reference Guide*.

The second example of animation shows how the cursor movement keys can be used to change the direction of a moving image. A small box moves according to which of **Up-, Down-, Left-** or **Right-arrow** has most recently been pressed. Pressing any other cursor movement key makes the box stop. The program stops when **Enter** is pressed.

```
program MoveBox;
uses Crt, Graph;
const
  Wait = 5;                                    { milliseconds between moves }
var
  GrDriver, GrMode, W, H, dX, X, dY, Y : integer;
  IStr: string;
  Pic : pointer;
  Ch : char;
begin
  GrDriver:= CGA;
  GrMode:= CGAC0;
  InitGraph( GrDriver, GrMode, '\ tp5' );
  X:= 0;
  Y:= GetMaxY div 2;
  W:= 2;
  H:= 2;
  Rectangle( X, Y, X+W, Y+H );
  SetFillStyle( 1, GetColor );
  FloodFill( X+1, Y+1, GetColor );
  GetMem( Pic, ImageSize( X, Y, X+W, Y+H ) );
  GetImage( X, Y, X+W, Y+H, Pic );
  PutImage( X, Y, Pic^, XORPut );
  dX:= 1;
  dY:= 0;
  repeat
    repeat
      X:= X + dX;
      Y:= Y + dY;
      PutImage( X, Y, Pic^, XORPut );
      Delay( Wait );
      PutImage( X, Y, Pic^, XORPut )
    until KeyPressed;
    Ch:= ReadKey;
    Ch:= ReadKey;
    dX:= 0;
    dY:= 0;
    case Ord( Ch ) of
      72: dY:= -1;                                  { Up arrow }
      80: dY:= 1;                                   { Down arrow }
      75: dX:= -1;                                  { Left arrow }
      77: dX:= 1                                    { Right arrow }
    end; { case }
  until Ord( Ch ) = 13;
  CloseGraph
end.
```

Note that *two* calls to **ReadKey** are needed to get the **extended key codes** for the cursor keys, because these keys cannot be represented by the standard (single character) ASCII codes (see Appendix C).

13.6 SAVINGS A GRAPHICS IMAGE TO DISK

GetImage and **PutImage** may be used with **BlockWrite** and **BlockRead** to save and read a graphics image to and from disk:

```
program SaveGraph;
uses Graph;
var
  F           : file;
  GrDriver,
  GrMode      : integer;
  Pic         : pointer;
  PicSize     : word;
begin
  GrDriver:= Detect;
  InitGraph( GrDriver, GrMode, '\ tp5' );
  Circle( 50, 50, 50 );
  PicSize:= ImageSize( 0, 0, GetMaxX, GetMaxY );
  Assign( F, 'PIC.' );
  Rewrite( F, PicSize );
  GetMem( Pic, PicSize );
  GetImage( 0, 0, GetMaxX, GetMaxY, Pic^ );
  Readln;
  BlockWrite( F, Pic^, 1 );
  ClearViewPort;
  Readln;
  FreeMem( Pic, PicSize );                              { just to make sure }
  GetMem( Pic, PicSize );
  Reset( F, PicSize );
  BlockRead( F, Pic^, 1 );
  PutImage( 0, 0, Pic^, XORPut );
  Readln;
  CloseGraph
end.
```

This is an alternative method to the static variable one given at the end of section 12.3.

13.7 OTHER GRAPHICS GOODIES

Arc(*x*, *y*, *StAngle*, *EndAngle*, *Radius*) draws a circular arc centred at (*x*, *y*), from *StAngle* to *EndAngle*. The angle is measured counterclockwise, with 0° at 3 o'clock.

Circle(*x*, *y*, *Radius*) draws a circle centred at (*x*, *y*) with the given radius.

Ellipse(*x*, *y*, *StAngle*, *EndAngle*, *XRadius*, *YRadius*) draws an elliptical arc. The parameters have the same meaning as in **Arc**. *XRadius* and *YRadius* are the horizontal and vertical axes.

FillEllipse(*x*, *y*, *XRadius*, *YRadius*) draws a filled ellipse in the current fill pattern and colour.

FloodFill(*x*, *y*, *Border*) floods a region bounded by the colour *Border* and enclosing the point (*x*, *y*) with the current fill pattern.

SetLineStyle may be used to change the style of line drawn. See the *Reference Guide* for details.

The EGA (256K), VGA and Hercules graphics cards support multiple graphics pages. A graphics image may be drawn off-screen with **SetActivePage** and then quickly brought on-screen by changing the visual graphics page with **SetVisualPage**.

13.8 THE MYGRAPHS UNIT

The complete listing of the unit **MyGraphs**, which transforms world co-ordinates to absolute co-ordinates, is given here:

```
{------MyGraphs-------------------------------------------------------------}
{                                                                           }
{  Procedures and functions in this unit, except for GrRead,                }
{  assist in scaling the user's more convenient world co-ordinates          }
{  into absolute screen co-ordinates.                                       }
{  GrRead gets keyboard input in graphics mode and echoes to                }
{  screen.                                                                  }
{---------------------------------------------------------------------------}
```

```
unit MyGraphs;

interface
uses Crt, Graph;
var
  Left, Right, Top, Bottom : real;                    { world co-ordinates }
  CurrentPort              : ViewPortType;

procedure GrRead( var X: real );
function H( X: real): integer;
procedure ScLine( X1, Y1, X2, Y2 : real );
procedure ScLineTo( X, Y : real );
procedure ScMoveTo( X, Y : real );
procedure ScOutTextXY( X, Y : real; TextString: string );
procedure SetWindow( XMin, XMax, YMin, YMax: real );
function V( Y: real): integer;
function XRange: integer;
function YRange: integer;

implementation

procedure GrRead;
{ Gets legal numeric input from keyboard in graphics mode,        }
{ with echo to screen.                                             }
const
  ChSet = [ '0'..'9', '.', '+', '-', 'E', 'e' ];
var
  Code, I : word;
  Ch      : char;
  InStr   : string;
begin
  InStr:= '';
  I:= 0;
  repeat
    Ch:= ReadKey;
    if Ch <> #13 then                    { code for carriage return is #13 }
      begin
      if Ch In ChSet then
      begin
        I:= I + 1;
        Insert( Ch, InStr, I );
        OutText( Ch )
      end
      else
        Write( #7#7 )
      end
  until Ch = #13;
  Val( InStr, X, Code )
end; { GrRead }

function H;
{ Scales world X-coordinate into H absolute co-ordinate }
var
  TempX : real;
begin
  TempX:= XRange * (X - Left) / (Right - Left);
  H:= Round( TempX )
end; { H }

procedure ScLine;
{ World co-ordinate analogue of Line }
begin
  Line( H( X1 ), V( Y1 ), H( X2 ), V( Y2 ) )
end; { ScLine }

procedure ScLineTo;
{ World co-ordinate analogue of LineTo }
begin
  LineTo( H( X ), V( Y ) )
```

```
end; { ScLineTo }

procedure ScMoveTo;
{ World co-ordinate analogue of MoveTo }
  begin
    MoveTo( H( X ), V( Y ) )
  end; { ScMoveTo }

  procedure ScOutTextXY;
  { World co-ordinate analogue of OutTextXY }
  begin
    OutTextXY( H( X ), V( Y ), TextString )
  end; { ScOutTextXY }

  procedure SetWindow;
  { Passes world co-ordinates from calling program }
  begin
    Left    := XMin;                    { smallest world X-coordinate }
    Right   := XMax;                    { largest world X-coordinate }
    Bottom  := YMin;                    { smallest world Y-coordinate }
    Top     := YMax                     { largest world Y-coordinate }
  end; { SetWindow }

  function V;
  { Scales world Y-coordinate into V absolute co-ordinate }
  { Vertical axis is inverted }
  var
    TempY : real;
  begin
    TempY:= YRange * (Y - Top) / (Bottom - Top);
    V:= Round( TempY )
  end; { V }

  function XRange;
  { Calculates XRange for use in function H }
  begin
    GetViewSettings( CurrentPort );
      with CurrentPort do
        XRange:= X2 - X1
  end; { XRange }

  function YRange;
  { Calculates YRange for use in function V }
  begin
    GetViewSettings( CurrentPort );
      with CurrentPort do
        YRange:= Y2 - Y1
  end; { YRange }

  end. { MyGraphs }
```

SUMMARY

- The Borland Graphics Interface (BGI) can automatically detect most graphics devices.
- Absolute co-ordinates are the co-ordinates of a pixel on the screen, and must be passed as integer parameters to all standard functions and procedures.
- The unit **MyGraphs** developed in this chapter is useful for transforming world (problem) co-ordinates into absolute co-ordinates.
- Different viewports may be opened in different parts of the screen. Text and graphics output may be sent to the viewports.
- Pixel co-ordinates in the current viewport are relative to the top left corner of the viewport.
- A graphics image may be saved in a disk file, to be read and viewed again later.

EXERCISES

13.1 Rework Exercise 6.6 with graphics output.

13.2 The Spiral of Archimedes may be represented in polar co-ordinates by the equation

$$r = at,$$

where r is the distance along a ray from the origin making an angle t radians with the x-axis, and a is some constant. (The shells of a class of animals called nummulites grow in this way.) Write a program to draw the spiral for some values of a. (If a point has polar co-ordinates (r, θ), its cartesian co-ordinates are $x = r\cos(\theta)$, $y = r\sin(\theta)$.)

13.3 Another type of spiral is the logarithmic spiral, which describes the growth of shells of animals like the periwinkle and the nautilis. Its equation is

$$r = aq^t,$$

where r and t are as in Exercise 13.2 and $a > 0$, $q > 1$. Write a program to draw this spiral.

13.4 The arrangement of seeds in a sunflower head (and other flowers, like daisies) follows a fixed mathematical pattern. The nth seed is at position

$$r = \sqrt{n},$$

with angular co-ordinate $\pi dn/180$ radians, where d is the constant angle of divergence (in degrees) between any two successive seeds, ie between the nth and $(n+1)$th seeds. A perfect sunflower head is generated by $d = 137.51°$. Write a program to plot the seeds (either use a point for each seed, or construct a picture to represent each seed). A remarkable feature of this is that the angle d must be exact to get proper sunflowers. Experiment with some different values, for example 137.45° (spokes, fairly far out), 137.65° (spokes all the way), 137.92° (Catherine wheels).

13.5 The equation of an ellipse in polar co-ordinates is given by

$$r = a(1 - e^2) / [1 - e\cos(\theta)],$$

where a is the semi-major axis and e is the eccentricity, if one focus is at the origin, and the semi-major axis lies on the x-axis.

Halley's Comet, which visited us recently, moves in an elliptical orbit about the sun (at one focus) with a semi-major axis of 17.9 A.U. (A.U. stands for Astronomical Unit, which is the mean distance of the Earth from the Sun: 149.6 million km.) The eccentricity of the orbit is 0.967276. Write a program which draws the orbit of Halley's Comet and the Earth (assumed circular).

13.6 A rather beautiful fractal picture can be drawn by plotting the points (x_k, y_k) generated by the following difference equations

$$x_{k+1} = y_k[1 + \sin(0.7x_k)] - 1.2|x_k|^{0.5},$$

$$y_{k+1} = 0.21 - x_k,$$

starting with $x_0 = y_0 = 0$. Write a program to draw the picture (plot individual points; do not join them).

13.7 Extend the block animation program in section 13.5 to move the block diagonally as well, in response to the **Home, End, PgUp** and **PgDn** keys.

13.8 Have a look at the Julia sets of $z^2 - \mu$, for $\mu = 1.25$, and $\mu = -0.27334 + 0.007421i$. You may need to use a slightly smaller region than the one in the program above for the best effect.

Zoom in on some parts of the coastline of the Mandelbrot set, for example the region $0.04 \leq a \leq 0.06$, $0.98 \leq b \leq 1$, where $\mu = a + ib$.

14 Simulation

The remaining chapters of this book will introduce very little new Turbo Pascal syntax, but will rather apply what we have already learnt to problem solving in a number of interesting areas.

An extremely powerful application of modern computers is in **simulation**. A simulation is a **computer experiment** which mirrors some aspect of the real world that appears to be based on random processes, or is too complicated to understand properly. (Whether events can be really random is actually a philosophical or theological question.) Some examples are: radio-active decay, bacteria division and traffic flow. The essence of a simulation program is that the programmer is unable to predict beforehand exactly what the outcome of the program will be, which is true to the event being simulated. For example, when you spin a coin, you do not know exactly what the result will be.

Random events are easily simulated in Turbo Pascal with the standard function **Random**, which generates a uniformly distributed **pseudo-random number** in the range 0 ≤ **Random** < 1 (a computer cannot generate truly random numbers, but they can be practically unpredictable), for example:

```
for I:= 1 to 10 do
  Writeln( Random );
```

Output:

```
2.3283064365E-10
3.1379939523E-02
8.6104846722E-01
2.0258096512E-01
2.7292126720E-01
6.7165441858E-01
3.1869127112E-01
1.6179546528E-01
3.7223835872E-01
4.2567376746E-01
```

14.1 SPINNING A FAIR COIN

If a fair (unbiased) coin is spun, the probability of getting heads or tails is 0.5 (50%). Since the value of **Random** is equally likely to be anywhere in the interval [0; 1), we can call it heads if **Random** is less than 0.5, and tails otherwise. The following program simulates an experiment in which a fair coin is spun 50 times:

```
for I:= 1 to 50 do
  if Random < 0.5 then
    Write( 'H' )
  else
    Write( 'T' );
```

The results appear to be completely random. The acid test is that there is no way someone could detect, by examining them, whether those results came from the simulation or from a real experiment. However, if we re-run the program, we get exactly the same sequence of H and T, which is *not* true to life, as every gambler knows! This is because the random number sequence always starts in the same place (this makes it easier to debug simulation programs). To seed

Random at a different starting point each time the program runs, insert the statement **Randomize** at the beginning of the program. Each run of the program will then produce different output, as the following two samples show:

```
HHHTHHTHTTTHTTTTHHTTTHTTHHHHTHHHHHHHHTHHHHTHTHHTHHH
HHTTHHHTHHHTTTTHHHTHHHTHTTTHTTTTHTHHHTHHHTHTHHTH
```

Obviously, if you run this program you are most unlikely to get exactly the same results as these!

14.2 ROLLING A FAIR DIE

If a fair die (plural dice) is rolled, the number uppermost is equally likely to be any integer from 1 to 6. This program simulates 20 rolls of a die. The output from two successive runs is shown:

```
Randomize;
for I:= 1 to 20 do
  Write( Trunc( 6 * Random + 1 ):3 );
```

Output:

```
5 4 4 5 2 4 5 3 5 3 4 4 4 4 2 5 6 2 2 1
2 6 1 4 4 2 4 6 4 1 2 3 4 2 5 6 5 6 6 1
```

Since **Random** is a decimal number in the [0; 1), **6 * Random** will be in the range [0; 6), and **(6 * Random + 1)** will be in the range [1; 7), ie between 1.000000 and 6.999999. Discarding the decimal part of this will therefore give an integer in the required range. Once again, **Randomize** ensures that the two sequences are different.

We can do some statistics on our simulated experiment, just as if it were a real one. For example, we could estimate the mean of the number on the uppermost face of the die when it is rolled 100 times, say, and also the probability of getting a six. The output from two successive runs is shown:

```
Randomize;
Mean:= 0;
Num6:= 0;
Throws:= 100;

for I:= 1 to Throws do
begin
  N:= Trunc( 6 * Random + 1 );
  Mean:= Mean + N;
  if N = 6 then
    Num6:= Num6 + 1
end;

Writeln( 'Mean:            ', Mean / Throws :6:2 );
Writeln( 'Chances of a 6: ', Num6 / Throws :6:2 );
...

Mean:            3.38
Chances of a 6:  0.19

Mean:            3.46
Chances of a 6:  0.20
```

Re-run the program increasing the value of **Throws** each time, and observe what happens to the mean and the chances of getting a six.

14.3 BACTERIA DIVISION

If a fair coin is spun, or a fair die is rolled, the different events (getting heads, or a six) happen with equal likelihood. Suppose, however, that a certain type of bacteria divides (into two) in a given time interval with a probability of 0.75 (75%), and that if it does not divide, it dies. Since **Random** is equally likely to be anywhere between 0 and 1, the chances of it being less than 0.75 are 75 per cent. We can therefore simulate this situation as follows:

```
Randomize;
R = Random;
if R < 0.75 then
  Writeln( 'I am now we' );
```

```
if R >= 0.75 then
Writeln( 'I am no more' );
```

Can you see that the following would be wrong:

```
if Random < 0.75 then
  Writeln( 'I am now we' );
if Random >= 0.75 then
Writeln( 'I am no more' );
```

The principle is that **Random** should be called only once for each event being simulated. The single event here is whether or not the bacterium divides.

14.4 A RANDOM WALK

A drunken sailor has to negotiate a jetty toward his ship. The jetty is 50 paces long and 20 wide. A mate places him in the middle of the jetty at the quay-end, and points him toward the ship. Suppose at every step he has a 60 per cent chance of lurching toward the ship, but a 20 per cent chance of lurching to the left or right (he manages always to be facing the ship). If he reaches the shipend of the jetty, he is hauled aboard by waiting mates.

The problem is to simulate his progress along the jetty, and to estimate his chances of getting to the ship without falling into the sea. To do this correctly, we must simulate one **walk** along the jetty, find out whether or not he reaches the ship, and then repeat this simulation 100 times, say. The proportion of simulations that end with the sailor safely in the ship will be an estimate of his chances of making it to the ship. For a given walk we assume that if he has not either reached the ship or fallen into the sea after, say, 10000 steps, he dies of thirst on the jetty.

To represent the jetty, we set up co-ordinates with the x-axis running along the middle of the jetty with the origin at the quayend. x and y are measured in steps. The sailor starts his walk at the origin each time. The structure plan, program and output from two successive runs are as follows:

```
1.  Initialise variables
2.  Repeat 100 simulated walks down the jetty
    2.1.  Start at the quay-end of the jetty
    2.2.  While still on the jetty and still alive repeat:
          2.2.1.  Get a random number R for the next step
          2.2.2.  If R < 0.6 then
                  2.2.2.1.  Move forward (to the ship)
                            Otherwise if R < 0.8 then
                  2.2.2.2.  Move port
                            Otherwise
                  2.2.2.3.  Move starboard
    2.3.  If he got to the ship then
          2.3.1.  Count that walk as a success
3.  Compute and write estimated probability of reaching the ship.
```

```
program DrunkenSailor;
const
  Safe    : word = 0;                  { number of times he makes it }
  Sims    : word = 100;                       { number of simulations }
  Steps   : word = 0;          { number of steps taken on a given walk }
var
  Prob    : real;                    { probability of reaching ship }
  R       : real;                                   { random number }
  Walks   : word;                                         { counter }
  X, Y    : integer;                             { position on jetty }
begin
  Randomize;

  for Walks:= 1 to Sims do
  begin
    Steps:= 0;                                    { each new walk ... }
    X:= 0;                                { ... starts at the origin }
    Y:= 0;
```

```
{ continue walking until he arrives, falls off or dies }
  while (X <= 50) and (Abs( Y ) <= 10) and (Steps < 10000) do
  begin
    Steps:= Steps + 1;                          { that's another step }
      R:= Random;                         { random number for that step }
      if R < 0.6 then                          { which way did he go? }
        X:= X + 1                                { maybe forward ... }
      else if R < 0.8 then
        Y:= Y + 1                                 { maybe to port ... }
      else
        Y:= Y - 1                                { maybe to starboard }
    end;

    if X > 50 then
      Safe:= Safe + 1                           { he actually made it! }
  end;

  Prob:= 100 * Safe / Sims;
  Writeln( 'Probability of reaching ship: ', Prob: 6:1, '%' )
end.

Probability of reaching ship:    93.0%
Probability of reaching ship:    89.0%
```

14.5 DEALING A BRIDGE HAND

Simulation is the basis of many computer games. The program in this section simulates a deal of 13 playing cards from a pack of 52. Note that apart from **Randomize**, the only executable statements in the main program are four procedure calls.

The names of the four suits are assigned to components 0 to 3 of the constant string array **Suit**, and the 13 face values are assigned to components 0 to 12 of the constant string array **Face**.

A hand of 13 cards is dealt by the procedure **Deal**. To deal a card, a random integer in the range 0 to 51 is generated, ie the 52 cards are represented uniquely by the numbers 0 to 51. The main problem is that a given card may only be dealt once. To ensure this, a local array **List** is set up. All its elements are initially zero (meaning no cards have been dealt yet). The function **RanInt** generates a random integer and assigns it to **I**. **List[I]** is checked. If it is still zero, that card has not yet been dealt, so **I** is put into the next element of **Hand**, and **List[I]** is set to 1, indicating that card **I** has now been dealt. If **List[I]** already has the value 1 when **I** comes up, it means that card **I** has already been dealt, so another random integer is generated. This process is repeated 13 times, until the array **Hand** contains 13 unique numbers in the range 0 to 51. This part of the problem may be structure planned as follows:

Repeat 13 times:
1. Get a random number
2. Convert it to an integer **I** in the range 0 to 51
3. While **List[I]** <> 0 repeat:
   3.1. Get another random integer **I**
4. Set **List[I]** to 1
5. Assign **I** to the next element of **Hand**.

BubbleDown sorts the first **N** elements of its array parameter **X** into descending order. It is used to sort the elements of **Hand** into order, rather like a player sorts his cards after the deal.

Show displays the sorted hand. Each element of **Hand** is subjected to integer division by 13. The quotient **S** will be in the range 0 to 3 (won't it?) and gives the suit. The remainder **F**, computed in the next line of **Show**, will be in the range 0 to 12, and gives the face value. For example, the number 49 on division by 13 gives a quotient of 3 (Spades) and a remainder of 10 (Queen), as shown in the first line of output after the program, which is as follows:

```
program BridgeHand;
uses Crt;
const
  Suit     : array[0..3] of string =
             ('Clubs', 'Diamonds', 'Hearts', 'Spades' );
  Face     : array[0..12] of string =
             ('Two', 'Three', 'Four', 'Five', 'Six', 'Seven', 'Eight',
              'Nine', 'Ten', 'Jack', 'Queen', 'King', 'Ace');
type
  HandType = array[1..13] of byte;
var
  Hand : HandType;
procedure BubbleDown( var X : HandType; N : word );
{ sorts first N elements of X into descending order }
var
  J, K    : word;
  Sorted  : boolean;
  Temp    : byte;
begin
  K:= 0;

  repeat
    Sorted:= True;
    K:= K + 1;
    for J:= 1 to N-K do
      if X[J] < X[J + 1] then
      begin
        Temp:= X[J];
        X[J]:= X[J + 1];
        X[J + 1]:= Temp;
        Sorted:= False
      end
    until Sorted

end; { BubbleDown }

procedure Deal( var Hand : HandType );
{ deals 13 cards from a shuffled pack }
var
  I, Card : byte;
  List    : array[0..51] of byte;                    { the check list }

  function RanInt: word;
  { generates a random integer in the range 0 to 51 }
  begin
    RanInt:= Trunc( 52 * Random )
  end; { RanInt }

begin
  FillChar( List, SizeOf( List ), 0 );                     { zeros all }
  for Card:= 1 to 13 do                                { get 13 of them }
  begin
    I:= RanInt;

    while List[I] <> 0 do                             { already dealt ... }
      I:= RanInt;                                     { ... so try again }

    List[I]:= 1;                                             { tick it off }
    Hand[ Card ]:= I
  end

end; { Deal }

procedure Show( Hand : HandType );
{ displays the hand }
var
  Card, F, S : byte;
begin
  ClrScr;

  for Card:= 1 to 13 do
```

```
begin
  S:= Hand[ Card ] div 13;
  F:= Hand[ Card ] mod 13;
  Write( Face[ F ], ' of ', Suit[ S ] );
    GoToXY( 20, WhereY );
    Writeln( Hand[ Card ]:8, S:8, F:8 )
  end
end; { Show }

begin
  Randomize;
  Deal( Hand );
  BubbleDown( Hand, 13 );
  Show( Hand )
end.
```

A different hand will be dealt every time the program is run. Here is a sample hand (the headings for the last three columns have been inserted into the text for clarity):

	Hand	*Suit*	*Face*
Queen of Spades	49	3	10
Three of Spades	40	3	1
Ace of Hearts	38	2	12
Ten of Hearts	34	2	8
Five of Hearts	29	2	3
Three of Hearts	27	2	1
King of Diamonds	24	1	11
Four of Diamonds	15	1	2
Two of Diamonds	13	1	0
King of Clubs	11	0	11
Queen of Clubs	10	0	10
Ten of Clubs	8	0	8
Four of Clubs	2	0	2

You may feel that the method of shuffling the cards with the **while-do** loop in **Deal** is inefficient, because as more cards are dealt, so the number of calls to **Random** goes up. **Deal** may be changed as follows. It now shuffles all 52 cards in the pack, by starting with a sorted pack, and swopping them at random, rather like a Bubble Sort. (I am indebted to one of my 1984 first-year students, S.D.H. Elliott, for this suggestion.)

```
procedure Deal( var Hand : HandType );
{ shuffles the whole pack now }
var
  I, Card, Temp : byte;
  List          : array[0..51] of byte;                { the check list }
function RanInt: word;
{ generates a random integer in the range 1 to 52 now }
begin
  RanInt:= Trunc( 52 * Random ) + 1
end; { RanInt }
begin
  for Card:= 1 to 52 do
    Hand[ Card ]:= Card - 1;                           { pack sorted at first }
  for Card:= 1 to 52 do
  begin
    I:= RanInt;
    Temp:= Hand[ Card ];
    Hand[ Card ]:= Hand[ I ];
    Hand[ I ]:= Temp
  end
end; { Deal }
```

Note that **RanInt** is now in the range 1 to 52 since it represents the *position* of a card rather than the card itself. The only other change required is that **Hand** must have 52 elements. With a few more amendments (like copying the appropriate elements of **Hand** into another array), all four hands can be displayed. You may like to compare the computing time for the two methods by coding a counter to record the number of calls to **Random**.

14.6 TRAFFIC FLOW

A major application of simulation is in modelling the traffic flow in large cities, so as to be able to try out different traffic light patterns on the computer before inflicting them on the real traffic (this has been done on a large scale in Leeds in the UK, for example). In this example we look at a very small part of this problem: how to simulate the flow of a single line of traffic through one set of traffic lights. We make the following assumptions (you can make additional or different ones if like):

1. Traffic travels straight, without turning.
2. The probability of a car arriving at the lights in any one second is independent of what happened during the previous second. This is called a **Poisson process**. This probability (call it p) may be estimated by watching cars at the intersection and monitoring their arrival pattern. In this simulation we take $p = 0.3$ (this is entirely arbitrary).
3. When the lights are green, assume the cars move through at a steady rate of, say, eight every ten seconds.
4. In the simulation, we will take the basic time interval to be ten seconds, so we want a display showing the length of the queue of traffic (if any) at the lights every ten seconds.
5. We will set the lights red or green for variable multiples of ten seconds.

For the sample run below the lights are red for 40 seconds (**Red:= 4**), green for 20 seconds (**Green:= 2**). The simulation runs for 480 seconds (**T:= 48**).

```
program Traffic;
uses Crt;
const
   Cars : integer = 0;                        { no cars in queue to start with }
   GreenTimer : word = 0;                     { counter for green lights }
   Lights      : char = 'R';                  { lights red to start with }
   P           : real = 0.3;                  { probability a car arrives in any second }
   RedTimer    : word = 0;                    { counter for red lights }
var
   Green       : word;                        { period lights are green }
   I           : word;                        { car counter }
   Red         : word;                        { period lights are red }
   Sec         : word;                        { counter }
   Sim         : word;                        { simulation counter }
   T           : word;                        { period of simulation }

procedure ShowQueue; forward;

procedure Go;
{ Lights are green here }
begin
   GreenTimer:= GreenTimer + 1;               { advance timer }
   Cars:= Cars - 8;                           { let 8 cars through }
   if Cars < 0 then                           { may have been less than 8! }
     Cars:= 0;
   ShowQueue;                                 { display traffic queue }
   if GreenTimer = Green then
   begin
     Lights:= 'R';                            { change lights ... }
  GreenTimer:= 0                              { ... and reset timer }
   end
end; { Go }

procedure ShowQueue;
{ display the queue of cars }
begin
   Write( Sim:3 );
   Write( Lights:2, '      ' );
```

```
  for I:= 1 to Cars do
    Write( '*' );
  Writeln
end; { ShowQueue }

procedure Stop;
{ Lights are red here }
begin
  RedTimer:= RedTimer + 1;                          { advance timer }
  ShowQueue;                                { display traffic queue }
  if RedTimer = Red then
  begin
    Lights:= 'G';                                  { change lights ... }
    RedTimer:= 0;                               { ... and reset timer }
  end
end; { Stop }

begin
  ClrScr;
  Randomize;
  Red:= 4;
  Green:= 2;
  T:= 48;

  for Sim:= 1 to T do                    { run for T 10-sec intervals }
  begin
    for Sec:= 1 to 10 do
      if Random < P then
        Cars:= Cars + 1;                         { another car arrives }
      if Lights = 'G' then
        Go
      else
        Stop
  end

end.
```

```
 1 R   *
 2 R   **
 3 R   ****
 4 R   ********
 5 G   ***
 6 G
 7 R   **
 8 R   *******
 9 R   ************
10 R   ***************
11 G   ********
12 G   ****
13 R   *****
14 R   ******
15 R   *******
16 R   **********
17 G   ******
18 G
19 R   *
20 R   ******
21 R   **********
22 R   ***************
23 G   *********
24 G   ****
25 R   *****
26 R   ********
27 R   ***********
28 R   ************
29 G   *******
30 G   ***
31 R   ****
```

```
32 R   *****
33 R   ********
34 R   ***********
35 G   *****
36 G
37 R   *****
38 R   **********
39 R   **************
40 R   ****************
41 G   ***********
42 G   ******
43 R   ***********
44 R   ***************
45 R   *********************
46 R   *************************
47 G   ***********************
48 G   ******************
```

From this particular run it seems that a traffic jam is building up, although more and longer runs are needed to see if this is really so. In that case, one can experiment with different periods for red and green lights in order to get an acceptable traffic pattern before setting the real lights to that cycle (try it). This is the great value of this sort of simulation. Of course, we can get closer to reality by considering two-way traffic, and allowing cars to turn in both directions, and occasionally to break down, but this program gives the basic ideas.

14.7 QUEUES

The traffic flow simulation in the previous sections looks at the queue of traffic from the point of view of the traffic authorities (How long is the queue after a certain time?), and not from the point of view of an individual driver (How long have *I* been in the queue?). In this section we look at how to simulate a simple first-in-first-out **(FIFO)** queue, from the *second* point of view. There are now *two* random processes involved: the arrival of users, and the service of users, both of which we assume to be **Poisson** distributed. These processes may be represented by two random variables: the **inter-arrival time** (*IAT*) between users joining the end of the queue, and the **service time** (*ST*) for the user at the head of the queue. Let us suppose that these random variables are distributed as follows (for example, based on a survey in a Post Office):

IAT (*secs*)	*Probability (frequency)*	*Probability (cumulative)*
10	0.10	0.10
15	0.25	0.35
20	0.30	0.65
25	0.25	0.90
30	0.10	1.00

ST (*secs*)	*Probability (frequency)*	*Probability (cumulative)*
5	0.08	0.08
10	0.14	0.22
15	0.18	0.40
20	0.24	0.64
25	0.22	0.86
30	0.14	1.00

We also need to define the following terms:

A: clock time of arrival;
E: clock time of entry into service;
L: clock time of leaving service ($L = E + ST$);
T: user's time in system ($T = L - A$);
W: user's waiting time ($W = E - A$).

The aim of the simulation is to estimate a user's mean time in the system, and mean waiting time, to see if these are acceptable. If they are not, attempts can be made to improve the service. The structure plan is as follows:

1. Repeat for each user:
   1.1. Generate *IAT* according to Poisson distribution
   1.2. Update arrival time
   1.3. Determine when user enters service as follows:
   If he arrives after previous user has left then
   1.3.1. He enters service immediately
   Otherwise
   1.3.2. He enters service when previous user leaves
   1.4. Generate *ST* according to Poisson distribution
   1.5. Determine when he leaves service
   1.6. Add wait time and time in service to running total
2. Compute mean wait time and mean time in system for all users.

An interesting problem is to determine the length of the queue the moment after each user joins it. To do this we need to record all the leave times in an array, and use a term *H* which identifies the user at the head of the queue. The following section should be added to the structure plan:

   1.7. While arrival time ≥ *H*'s leave time repeat:
   1.7.1. Increase *H* by 1
   1.8. Determine length of queue between *H* and current user.

The program below simulates the service of 50 users, and writes out the variables defined above for each user. A sample run is shown as well:

```
program Fifo;
uses Crt;
const
  Arr        : real = 0;                    { clock time of arrival }
  Head       : word = 0;                    { user at head of queue }
  MeanTIS    : real = 0;                    { mean user time in system }
  MeanWait   : real = 0;                    { mean user wait time }
  Num               = 50;                   { number of users }
var
  Ent        : real;                        { clock time of entry into service }
  IAT        : real;                        { inter-arrival time }
  Leave      : array[ 0..Num ] of real;
                                            { clock time of leaving service }
  Leng       : word;                        { length of queue }
  R          : real;                        { random number }
  ST         : real;                        { service time }
  TIS        : real;                        { time in system }
  User       : word;                        { user number }
  Wait       : real;                        { user wait time }
begin
  Randomize;
  Leave[0]:= 0;
  ClrScr;
  HighVideo;
  Write( '    USER     IAT     ARR     ENT     ST' );
  Writeln( '    LEAVE     WAIT     TIS     LEN' );
  NormVideo;
  Writeln;

  for User:= 1 to Num do
  begin
    R:= Random;                             { generate inter-arrival time }

    if R < 0.1 then
    IAT:= 10
  else if R < 0.35 then
```

```
      IAT:= 15
    else if R < 0.65 then
      IAT:= 20
    else if R < 0.90 then
      IAT:= 25
    else
      IAT:= 30;
    Arr:= Arr + IAT;
    if Arr >= Leave[ User - 1 ] then                  { find when service entered }
        Ent:= Arr
      else
        Ent:= Leave[ User - 1 ];
      R:= Random;                    { now generate service time independently }
      if R < 0.08 then
        ST:= 5
      else if R < 0.22 then
        ST:= 10
    else if R < 0.40 then
      ST:= 15
    else if R < 0.64 then
        ST:= 20
      else if R < 0.86 then
        ST:= 25
      else
        ST:= 30;
      Leave[ User ]:= Ent + ST;
      Wait:= Ent - Arr;
      TIS:= Leave[ User ] - Arr;
      MeanTIS:= MeanTIS + TIS;
      MeanWait:= MeanWait + Wait;
      while Arr >= Leave[ Head ] do               { determine length of queue }
        Head:= Head + 1;
      Leng:= User - Head + 1;
      Write( User:7, IAT:7:0, Arr:7:0, Ent:7:0, ST:7:0 );
      Writeln( Leave[ User ]:7:0, Wait:7:0, TIS:7:0, Leng:7 )
      end;
   Writeln;
   MeanTIS:= MeanTIS / Num;
   MeanWait:= MeanWait / Num;
   Writeln( 'Mean wait time:          ', MeanWait:5:1, ' secs' );
   Writeln( 'Mean time in system: ', MeanTIS:6:2, ' secs' )
 end.
```

Sample output:

USER	IAT	ARR	ENT	ST	LEAVE	WAIT	TIS	LEN
1	10	10	10	15	25	0	15	1
2	20	30	30	10	40	0	10	1
3	20	50	50	25	75	0	25	1
4	25	75	75	25	100	0	25	1
5	20	95	100	20	120	5	25	2
6	25	120	120	25	145	0	25	1
7	10	130	145	15	160	15	30	2
8	25	155	160	25	185	5	30	2
9	20	175	185	20	205	10	30	2
10	30	205	205	30	235	0	30	1
11	20	225	235	25	260	10	35	2
12	20	245	260	25	285	15	40	2
13	15	260	285	25	310	25	50	2
14	10	270	310	20	330	40	60	3
15	20	290	330	30	360	40	70	3
16	20	310	360	20	380	50	70	3
17	20	330	380	20	400	50	70	3

18	20	350	400	20	420	50	70	4
19	20	370	420	15	435	50	65	4
20	20	390	435	15	450	45	60	4
21	15	405	450	30	480	45	75	4
22	20	425	480	20	500	55	75	4
23	20	445	500	20	520	55	75	4
24	20	465	520	25	545	55	80	4
25	20	485	545	15	560	60	75	4
26	20	505	560	15	575	55	70	4
27	15	520	575	15	590	55	70	4
28	10	530	590	25	615	60	85	5
29	15	545	615	5	620	70	75	5
30	30	575	620	25	645	45	70	4
31	20	595	645	20	665	50	70	4
32	30	625	665	20	685	40	60	3
33	30	655	685	15	700	30	45	3
34	10	665	700	25	725	35	60	3
35	15	680	725	20	745	45	65	4
36	25	705	745	15	760	40	55	3
37	20	725	760	20	780	35	55	3
38	20	745	780	25	805	35	60	3
39	20	765	805	10	815	40	50	3
40	15	780	815	15	830	35	50	3
41	20	800	830	25	855	30	55	4
42	25	825	855	15	870	30	45	3
43	30	855	870	25	895	15	40	2
44	15	870	895	20	915	25	45	2
45	20	890	915	5	920	25	30	3
46	15	905	920	30	950	15	45	3
47	10	915	950	25	975	35	60	3
48	25	940	975	30	1005	35	65	3
49	25	965	1005	20	1025	40	60	3
50	10	975	1025	25	1050	50	75	3

Mean wait time: **33.0 secs**
Mean time in system: **53.50 secs**

One way of improving service could be to guarantee service in 25 seconds or under. This could be implemented, for example, by having a probability of 0.36 for a service time of 25, and removing the service time of 30. This has a noticeable effect on the means (try it).

14.8 TABLES TEST

In this section we see how random numbers may be used to program a simple tables test. Two random integers in the range 1 to 12 are generated and the user is asked to enter their product. The program tells the user if the answer is right or wrong, and keeps a score.

A two-dimensional version of the check list in the card dealing simulation above is used to ensure that a correctly answered question is never repeated. When the product of **R1** and **R2** is correctly given, the components **Check[R1, R2]** and **Check[R2, R1]** of the two-dimensional array **Check** are changed from zero (their initial value) to 1 (since 3 × 7 = 7 × 3). When the next **R1** and **R2** are generated, the product of these two elements is computed. If it is 1, that question has been asked, and a new pair is generated. (Two-dimensional arrays are discussed in Chapter 15.)

```
program Tables;
{ Generates QNum ''times tables'' questions. Questions are not           }
{ repeated if correctly answered.                                        }

uses Crt;
const
  Finish    : boolean = false;                          { finish flag }
  QNum      : word    = 10;                     { number of questions }
var
  Ans       : word;                                    { right answer }
```

```
   Check      : array[1..12, 1..12] of byte;                { check table }
   Hz         : word;                                 { frequency counter }
   LineNo     : byte;                                { screen line number }
   Name       : string;                                     { user's name }
   Num        : real;                                   { question number }
   Response   : char;                                          { Y or N }
   R1, R2     : byte;                                    { random numbers }
   Right      : word;                                      { number right }

function RanInt( N: byte ): byte;
{ generates random integer in range 2..N }
begin
   RanInt:= Trunc( (N - 1) * Random + 2 )
end; { RanInt }

begin
   Randomize;
   FillChar( Check, SizeOf( Check ), 0 );
   Write( 'Hi there. What is your name? ' );
   Readln( Name );
   Writeln;
repeat
   ClrScr;
   Writeln( 'Tables Test for ', Name );
   Writeln;
   Right:= 0;
   Num:= 1;

   while Num <= QNum do
   begin
      R1:= RanInt( 12 );
      R2:= RanInt( 12 );

      while Check[ R1, R2 ] * Check[ R2, R1 ] = 1 do
      begin
         R1:= RanInt( 12 );                                   { try again }
      R2:= ranInt( 12 )
      end;

      Write( Num:3:0, R1:6, 'x', R2, ' = ' );
      LineNo:= WhereY;
      Readln( Ans );
      GoToXY( 24, LineNo );
      if Ans = R1 * R2 then
      begin
         Check[ R1, R2 ]:= 1;                    { so we don't use them again }
         Check[ R2, R1 ]:= 1;
         Right:= Right + 1;
         Writeln( #7, 'Correct!' )
      end
      else
         begin
            Sound( 100 );
            Delay( 1000 );
            NoSound;
            Write( 'Oh, ', Name, ', no! The right answer is ' );
            Writeln( R1 * R2 )
         end;
      Num:= Num + 1
   end;
   Writeln;
   Writeln( Name, ', your score was ', Right, '/', QNum );
      Writeln;
   if Right = QNum then
```

```
begin
  for Hz:= 400 to 800 do
  begin
      Sound ( Hz );
      Delay ( 10)
    end;
    NoSound;
    TextBackground ( 1 );
    HighVideo;
    Write ( 'Well done, ' );
    TextColor( 14 + 128 );
    Write( Name );
      TextBackground( 0 );
      TextColor( 7 );
      NornVideo;
      Writeln;
      Writeln;
    end;
    Write( 'Do you want another test? (y/n): ' );
    Response:= ReadKey;
    Writeln( Response ) = 'N' then
      Finish:= true
  until Finish
end.
```

SUMMARY

- A simulation is a computer program which mimics a real-life situation which is apparently based on chance.
- The pseudo-random number generator **Random** returns a uniformly distributed random number in the range [0; 1), and is the basis of the simulations discussed in this chapter.
- **Random** will generate a different random number sequence every time it is called if the statement **Randomize** procedes the first call to **Random**.
- Every independent event being simulated requires a separate random number.

EXERCISES

14.1 In a game of Bingo the numbers 1 to 99 are drawn at random from a bag. Write a program to simulate the draw of the numbers (each number can be drawn only once), writing the numbers as they are drawn ten to a line.

14.2 Random can be used to estimate π as follows (such a method is called a Monte Carlo method). Write a program which generates random points in a square of length 2, say, and which counts what proportion of these points falls inside the circle of unit radius that fits exactly into the square. This proportion will be the ratio of the area of the circle to that of the square. Hence estimate π. (This is not a very efficient method, as you will see from the number of points required to get even a rough approximation.)

14.3 The aim of this exercise is to simulate bacteria growth. Suppose that a certain type of bacteria divides or dies according to the following assumptions:

a) during a fixed time interval, called a generation, a single bacterium divides into two identical replicas with probability p;

b) if it does not divide during that interval, it dies (ie ceases to be, shuffles off this mortal coil);

c) the offspring (called daughters) will divide or die during the next generation, independently of the past history (there may well be no offspring, in which case the colony becomes extinct).

Start with a single individual and write a program which simulates a number of generations. Take $p = 0.75$. The number of generations which you can simulate will depend on your computer system. Carry out a large number (for example 100) of such simulations. The probability of ultimate extinction, $p(E)$, may be estimated as the proportion of simulations that end in extinction. You can also estimate the mean size of the nth generation from a large number of simulations (the theoretical mean is $(2p)^n$).

Statistical theory asserts that the expected value of the extinction probability $p(E)$ is whichever is the smaller of 1, and $(1-p)/p$. So for $p = 0.75$, $p(E)$ is expected to be 1/3. But for $p \leq 0.5$, $p(E)$ is expected to be 1, which means that extinction is certain (a rather unexpected result). You can use your program to test this theory by running it for different values of p, and estimating $p(E)$ in each case.

14.4 Dribblefire Jets Inc. make two types of aeroplane, the two-engined DFII, and the four-engined DFIV. The engines are terrible and fail with probability 0.5 on a standard flight (the engines fail independently of each other). The manufacturers claim that the planes can fly if at least half of their engines are working, ie the DFII will crash only if both its engines fail, while the DFIV will crash if all four, or if any three engines fail.

You have been commissioned by the Civil Aviation Board to ascertain which of the two models is less likely to crash. Since parachutes are expensive, the cheapest (and safest!) way to do this is to simulate a large number of flights of each model. For example, two calls of **Random** could represent one standard DFII flight: if both random numbers are less that 0.5, that flight crashes, otherwise it doesn't. Write a program which simulates a large number of flights of both models, and estimates the probability of a crash in each case. If you can run enough simulations, you may get a surprising result. (Incidentally, the probability of n engines failing on a given flight is given by the binomial distribution, but you do not need to use this fact in the simulation.)

14.5 Two players, A and B, play a game called Eights. They take it in turns to choose a number 1, 2 or 3, which may not be the same as the last number chosen (so if A starts with 2, B may only choose 1 or 3 at the next move). A starts, and may choose any of the three numbers for the first move. After each move, the number chosen is added to a common running total. If the total reaches 8 exactly, the player whose turn it was wins the game. If a player causes the total to go over 8, the other player wins. For example, suppose A starts with 1 (total 1), B chooses 2 (total 3), A chooses 1 (total 4) and B chooses 2 (total 6). A would like to play 2 now, to win, but he can't because B cunningly played it on the last move, so A chooses 1 (total 7). This is even smarter, because B is forced to play 2 or 3, making the total go over 8 and thereby losing.

Write a program to simulate each player's chances of winning, if they always play at random.

15 Matrices and their Applications

In this chapter we look at how to write programs to solve problems involving matrices, with examples from such areas as linear algebra, networks, population dynamics, surveying and Markov processes.

The applications introduced here follow on from Chapter 9, where arrays with only one index (subscript) were discussed (such arrays are also called **vectors**). In this chapter we deal with arrays having more than one index, or **multi-dimensional** arrays. Although the number of dimensions is unlimited, we will discuss only two-dimensional arrays here, since these occur most often. An array with two indices can represent a **table** of numbers, since one index (usually the first) can label the *rows* in the table, while the second index labels the *columns*. This is also the convention adopted for matrices. Tables and matrices look exactly the same, but since matrices are used in mathematical applications, we will deal with them separately.

15.1 TABLES: A CONCRETE EXAMPLE

A ready-mix concrete company has three factories (S1, S2 and S3) which must supply three building sites (D1, D2 and D3). The costs of transporting a load of concrete from any factory to any site are given by the following cost table:

	D1	D2	D3
S1	3	12	10
S2	17	18	35
S3	7	10	24

The factories can supply 4, 12 and 8 loads per day respectively, and the sites require 10, 9 and 5 loads per day respectively. The real problem is to find the cheapest way to satisfy the demands at the sites, but we are not considering that here.

Suppose the factory manager proposes the following transportation scheme (each entry represents the number of loads of concrete to be transported along that particular route):

	D1	D2	D3
S1	4	0	0
S2	6	6	0
S3	0	3	5

This sort of scheme is called a solution to the transportation problem. The cost table (and the solution) can then be represented by tables C and X, say, where c_{ij} is the entry in row i and column j of the cost table, with a similar convention for **X**.

To compute the cost of the above solution, each entry in the solution table must be multiplied by the corresponding entry in the cost table (this operation is not to be confused with matrix multiplication, which is discussed in the next section). The following program will do what is required:

```
type
  Mat = array[ 1..3, 1..3 ] of real;
const
  C        : Mat = ((3, 12, 10), (17, 18, 35), (7, 10, 24));
  X        : Mat = ((4, 0, 0), (6, 6, 0), (0, 3, 5));
  TotCost : real = 0;
var
  I, J : byte;
begin
  for I:= 1 to 3 do
    for J:= 1 to 3 do
      TotCost:= TotCost + C[ I,J ] * X[ I,J ];
  Writeln( 'Total cost: ', TotCost:6:2 );
```

Each table is of type **Mat**, which is a **multidimensional array**. Syntactically, you can also code this as an array whose component type is also an array:

```
Mat = array[ 1..3 ] of array[ 1..3 ] of real;
```

Note how an array-type constant is set up. The constants of each dimension are enclosed in separate sets of parentheses, separated by commas. The innermost constants correspond to the rightmost dimension. Basically, in the case of tables, this means that the rows of the table appear in groups in the innermost parentheses. This is equivalent to the following assignments of the components of **C** and **X**:

C	X
C[1,1]:= 3	X[1,1]:= 4
C[1,2]:= 12	X[1,2]:= 0
C[1,3]:= 10	X[1,3]:= 0
C[2,1]:= 17	X[2,1]:= 6
C[2,2]:= 18	X[2,2]:= 6
C[2,3]:= 35	X[2,3]:= 0
C[3,1]:= 7	X[3,1]:= 0
C[3,2]:= 10	X[3,2]:= 3
C[3,3]:= 24	X[3,3]:= 5

The order of assignment of components of an array-type constant is called **odometer** order because the last index moves most rapidly.

Arrays can be assigned in their entirety, as long as they are assignment compatible. So if **Y** is also of type **Mat**, the assignment

```
Y:= C;
```

is valid.

15.2 MATRICES

A **matrix** is a two-dimensional array (ie a table) which may be used in a wide variety of representations. For example, a distance array representing the lengths of direct connections in a network is a matrix. We will deal mainly with square matrices in this chapter (ie matrices having the same number of rows as columns), although in principle a matrix can have any number of rows or columns. A matrix with only one column is also called a **vector**.

A matrix is usually denoted by a bold capital letter, for example A, and each entry, or element, of the matrix is denoted by the small letter of the same name followed by two subscripts, the first indicating the row of the element, and the second indicating the column. So a general element of the matrix A is called a_{ij}, meaning it may be found in row i and column j. If A has three rows and columns (3×3 for short) it will look like this in general:

$$\begin{bmatrix} a_{11} & a_{12} & a_{13} \\ a_{21} & a_{22} & a_{23} \\ a_{31} & a_{32} & a_{33} \end{bmatrix}.$$

If, for example,

$$A = \begin{bmatrix} 6 & 2 & 0 \\ -1 & 4 & 7 \\ 5 & 1 & 13 \end{bmatrix},$$

then $a_{21} = -1$, $a_{23} = 7$, $a_{31} = 5$, and so on.

Reading and writing matrices: the MyMats unit

Arrays unfortunately cannot be read and written directly in Turbo Pascal, as they can in languages such as True BASIC, and so each component must be explicitly handled in a **for** loop. For example, if **X** is a matrix with *n* rows and *m* columns, the following code will write the components of **X** one row at a time:

```
for I:= 1 to N do
begin
  for J:= 1 to M do
    Write( X[ I,J ] );
  Writeln
end
```

Reading is similar. These two operations are included in the unit MyMats below as two procedures **MatRead** and **MatWrite**, which require a matrix to be passed as a parameter. This is turn requires a prior type definition. Turbo Pascal does not allow arrays with a *variable* number of components in each dimension to be passed as parameters (as do FORTRAN and True BASIC, for example). The maximum size of the matrix must therefore be declared in the unit, or in some other unit which is used both by **MyMats** and the calling program. The alternative is not to have the procedures in a unit (which necessarily must be precompiled, hence the need for the maximum number of components), but to include them in the calling program at compilation with the {**$I**} compiler directive (see Appendix E). The matrix type definition can then appear in the calling program, and can be changed from run to run.

In **MyMats** a (6 × 6) matrix type is defined, as this is the largest matrix needed in this chapter. **MatWrite** passes the format for the **Write** as two parameters, **W** and **D**:

```
Write( X[ I,J ]:W:D );
```

MatRead reads from a text file on disk; the name of the file is passed as a parameter. Examples are given below. The unit is as follows:

```
unit MyMats;
{ Matrix handling utilities }
interface
type
  Mat = array[ 1..6, 1..6 ] of real;                    { formal parameter type }
procedure MatRead( var X: Mat; N, M: byte; DskName: string );
procedure MatWrite( var X: Mat; N, M, W, D: byte );
```

```
implementation
{------MatRead------------------------------------------------------------------}
{                                                                               }
{ Reads an NxM matrix row by row from the text file saved under                 }
{ DskName.                                                                      }
{-------------------------------------------------------------------------------}
procedure MatRead;
var
  F : text;
  I, J : byte;
begin
  Assign( F, DskName );
  Reset( F );
    for I:= 1 to N do
    for J:= 1 to M do
      Read( F, X[ I,J ] );
    Close( F )
  end; { MatRead }

  {------MatWrite-------------------------------------------------------------}
  {                                                                           }
  {    Writes an NxM matrix row by row in W:D format
  {---------------------------------------------------------------------------}
  procedure MatWrite;
  var
    I, J : byte;
  begin
    for I:= 1 to N do
    begin
      for J:= 1 to M do
        Write( X[ I,J ]:W:D );
      Writeln
    end
  end; { MatWrite }

  end. { MyMats }
```

Matrix multiplication

Various mathematical operations are defined on matrices. Probably the most important one is **matrix multiplication**. It is used widely in such areas as network theory, solution of linear systems of equations, transformation of co-ordinate systems, and population modelling. The rules for multiplying matrices look a little weird at first, but will be justified by the applications that follow.

When two matrices **A** and **B** are multiplied together, their product is a third matrix **C**. The operation is written as

$$\mathbf{C} = \mathbf{AB} ,$$

and the general element c_{ij} of **C** is formed by taking the scalar product of the *i*th row of **A** with the *j*th column of **B**. It follows that **A** and **B** can only be successfully multiplied (in that order) if the number of columns in **A** is the same as the number of rows in **B**.

Definition

If **A** is a $(n \times m)$ matrix and **B** is a $(m \times p)$ matrix, their product **C** will be a $(n \times p)$ matrix such that the general element c_{ij} of **C** is given by

$$c_{ij} = \sum_{k=1}^{m} a_{ik} b_{kj} .$$

Note that in general **AB** is not equal to **BA** (matrix multiplication is not commutative).

Examples:

$$\begin{bmatrix} 1 & 2 \\ 3 & 4 \end{bmatrix} \times \begin{bmatrix} 5 & 6 \\ 0 & -1 \end{bmatrix} = \begin{bmatrix} 5 & 4 \\ 15 & 14 \end{bmatrix};$$

$$\begin{bmatrix} 1 & 2 \\ 3 & 4 \end{bmatrix} \times \begin{bmatrix} 2 \\ 3 \end{bmatrix} = \begin{bmatrix} 8 \\ 18 \end{bmatrix}.$$

The procedure **MatMult** below multiplies two matrices together. If your area of programming is in the mathematical sciences or engineering, it is part of your education to be able to code such a procedure! **A** is $(n \times m)$ and **B** is $(m \times p)$. The product **C** is $(n \times p)$. You can include **MatMult** in the unit **MyMats** if you insert the line

```
procedure MatMult( var A, B, C: Mat; N, M, P : byte );
```

in the interface section, and the procedure itself in the implementation section:

```
{------MatMult-----------------------------------------------------------------------------------}
{                                                                                              }
{ Multiplies matrix A (N x M) by B (M x P) and stores product in                               }
{ C (N x P)                                                                                    }
{----------------------------------------------------------------------------------------------}

procedure MatMult;
var
  I, J, K : byte;
begin
  for I:= 1 to N do
    for J:= 1 to P do
    begin
      C[ I,J ]:= 0;
      for K:= 1 to M do
        C[ I,J ]:= C[ I,J ] + A[ I,K ] * B[ K,J ]
    end
end; { MatMult }
```

The following program uses all three procedures in the MyMats unit to read two (2×2) matrices **X** and **Y** from the text files MAT1 and MAT2 respectively, and to write their product Z:

```
program Mult;
uses MyMats;
  var
  X, Y, Z : Mat;
begin
  MatRead( X, 2, 2, 'mat1.' );
  MatRead( Y, 2, 2, 'mat2.' );
  MatMult( X, Y, Z, 2, 2, 2 );
  MatWrite( Z, 2, 2, 4, 0 );
  readln
end.
```

Try it out on the two examples of matrix multiplication above (the vectors are (2×1), ie they have 2 rows and 1 column).

If it's more convenient, you can adjust **MatRead** to read the number of components in each dimension from the disk. This information would then have to appear in the first line of the file.

15.3 NETWORKS

In our first application of matrix multiplication we consider a problem which at first glance seems to have nothing to do with it.

A spy ring

Suppose five spies in an espionage ring have the code names Alex, Boris, Cyril, Denisov and Eric (whom we can label A, B, C, D and E respectively). The hallmark of a good spy network is that each agent is not able to contact all the others. The arrangement for this particular group is:

Alex can contact only Cyril;
Boris can contact only Alex or Eric;
Denisov can contact only Cyril;
Eric can contact only Cyril or Denisov.

(Cyril can't contact anyone in the ring: he takes information out of the ring to the spymaster. Similarly, Boris brings information in from the spymaster: no-one in the ring can contact him.) The need for good spies to know a bit of matrix theory becomes apparent when we spot that the possible paths of communication between the spies can be represented by a (5 × 5) matrix, with the rows and columns representing the transmitting and receiving agents respectively, thus:

	A	B	C	D	E
A	0	0	1	0	0
B	1	0	0	0	1
C	0	0	0	0	0
D	0	0	1	0	0
E	0	0	1	1	0

We will call this matrix **A**. It clearly represents a **directed network** with the spies at the **nodes**, and with **arcs** all of length 1, where a network is a collection of points, called nodes, joined by lines, called arcs. In a directed network, movement is only possible along the arcs in one direction (see Figure 15.1).

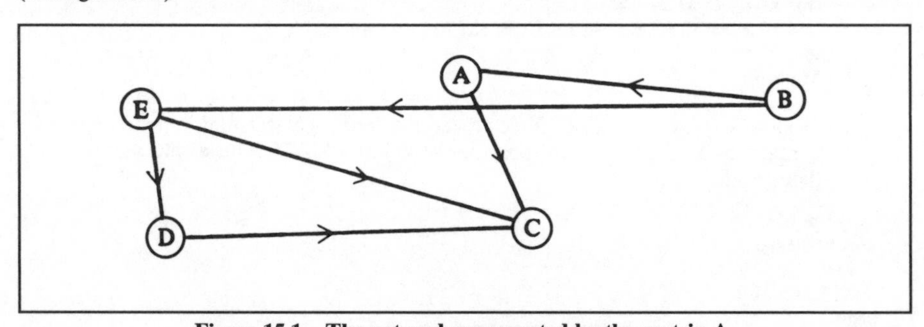

Figure 15.1 The network represented by the matrix A

The matrix **A** may also be thought of as an **adjacency** matrix, with a 1 in row *i* and column *j* if there is an arc from node *i* to node *j*, or a 0 in that position if there is no arc between those two nodes. The diagonal elements of **A** (ie a_{11}, a_{22}, etc.) are all zero because good spies do not talk to themselves (since they might then talk in their sleep and give themselves away).

Now let's multiply this matrix **A** by itself and see what happens. We note before we start on this awesome task that each 1 in **A** represents a single path of length *one* arc in the network (path here means a direct link between two agents). Well, if we do the multiplication, we get

$$\begin{bmatrix} 0 & 0 & 1 & 0 & 0 \\ 1- & 0- & 0- & 0- & 1 \\ 0 & 0 & 0 & 0 & 0 \\ 0 & 0 & 1 & 0 & 0 \\ 0 & 0 & 1 & 1 & 0 \end{bmatrix} \times \begin{bmatrix} 0 & 0 & 1 & 0 & 0 \\ 1 & 0 & 0 & 0 & 1 \\ 0 & 0 & 0 & 0 & 0 \\ 0 & 0 & 1 & 0 & 0 \\ 0 & 0 & 1 & 1 & 0 \end{bmatrix}$$

$$= \begin{bmatrix} 0 & 0 & 0 & 0 & 0 \\ 0 & 0 & 2 & 1 & 0 \\ 0 & 0 & 0 & 0 & 0 \\ 0 & 0 & 0 & 0 & 0 \\ 0 & 0 & 1 & 0 & 0 \end{bmatrix} \text{, which is called } \mathbf{A}^2.$$

Row 2 and column 3 have been highlighted in the two versions of **A** above to help interpret $\mathbf{A}^2$ (which is defined as the matrix **A** multiplied by itself). The element 2 in $\mathbf{A}^2$ (row 2, column 3) results when row 2 of **A** is multiplied term by term with column 3, and the products added. This gives us the scalar product

$$1 \times 1 + 0 \times 0 + 0 \times 0 + 0 \times 1 + 1 \times 1 = 2.$$

The first non-zero term arises because there is a path from node 2 to node 1, which we will denote by (2-1), followed by a path (1-3), giving a composite path (2-1-3) of length 2 (ie from Boris to Cyril via Alex). The second non-zero term arises because there is a path (2-5) followed by a path (5-3), giving a second composite path (2-5-3) of length 2 (ie from Boris to Cyril again, but via Eric this time). It is clear therefore that the entries in $\mathbf{A}^2$ represent the number of paths of length 2 between the various nodes in the network (on the strict understanding that all arcs are of length 1). There are therefore only four paths of length 2: two from Boris to Cyril, as we have seen, one from Boris to Denisov, and one from Eric to Cyril (a path of length 2 in the spy context means one intermediary).

Having got so much interesting information from $\mathbf{A}^2$, the obvious thing to do now is to multiply the matrix $\mathbf{A}^2$ by **A** again, to form the third power of **A**. If you do this correctly, you will get for your trouble the rather dull matrix

$$\text{A3} = \begin{bmatrix} 0 & 0 & 0 & 0 & 0 \\ 0 & 0 & 1 & 0 & 0 \\ 0 & 0 & 0 & 0 & 0 \\ 0 & 0 & 0 & 0 & 0 \\ 0 & 0 & 0 & 0 & 0 \end{bmatrix}$$

The single 1 in $\mathbf{A}^3$ tells us that there is only one path of length *three* in the network (ie with *two* intermediaries) and that it is from Boris to Cyril. Drawing the network, or alternatively examining the appropriate row and column in $\mathbf{A}^2$ and **A** that give rise to this single entry in $\mathbf{A}^3$, reveals that the actual route is Boris-Eric-Denisov-Cyril.

If we now compute $\mathbf{A}^4$, we will find that every element is zero (such a matrix is called the null matrix), signifying that there are no paths of length 4 in the network, which can be verified by inspection. All higher powers of **A** will also obviously be null, since if there are no paths of length 4, there can hardly be any that are longer!

In general, then, the element in row *i* and column *j* of the *k*th power of an adjacency matrix is equal to the number of paths consisting of *k* arcs linking nodes *i* and *j*.

Coming back to our spy network, since the elements of **A** are the number of paths of length 1, and the elements of $\mathbf{A}^2$ are the number of paths of length 2, etc., then clearly the sum of all these powers of **A** will tell us how many paths of any length there are altogether between the various nodes. We can therefore define a reachability matrix **R** for this (5×5) network:

$$\mathbf{R} = \mathbf{A} + \mathbf{A}^2 + \mathbf{A}^3 + \mathbf{A}^4 .$$

R is also a (5×5) matrix, and its elements give the total number of paths of communication between the agents. Doing the calculation gives us

$$R = \begin{bmatrix} 0 & 0 & 1 & 0 & 0 \\ 1 & 0 & 3 & 1 & 1 \\ 0 & 0 & 0 & 0 & 0 \\ 0 & 0 & 1 & 0 & 0 \\ 0 & 0 & 2 & 1 & 0 \end{bmatrix} .$$

So we can read off from the reachability matrix **R** the fact that there are, for example, three different paths between Boris and Cyril, but only two between Eric and Cyril (the actual lengths of these paths will have been calculated in finding the powers of **A**). The name reachability is used because the non-zero elements of **R** indicate who may contact whom, directly or indirectly, or for a general distance network, which nodes can be reached from each node.

The reachability matrix

In general, the **reachability** matrix **R** of a $(n \times n)$ network may be defined as the sum of the first $(n-1)$ powers of its associated adjacency matrix **A**. You may be wondering why we can stop at the $(n-1)$th power of **A**. The elements of $\mathbf{A}^{(n-1)}$ will be the number of paths that have $(n-1)$ arcs, ie that connect *n* nodes (since each arc connects two nodes). Since there are no further nodes that can be reached, it is not necessary to raise **A** to the *n*th power.

However, $\mathbf{A}^n$ does reveal an interesting property of networks, which you may have already guessed, and which we will look at in the next section.

The procedure **Reachable** below computes the reachability matrix **R** for any network given the adjacency matrix **A**, ie it computes

$$\mathbf{R} = \mathbf{A} + \mathbf{A}^2 + \mathbf{A}^3 + \dots + \mathbf{A}^{(n-1)} ,$$

where **A** is $(n \times n)$. It uses the arrays **B, C** and **D** to store products and sums. A procedure **MatSum** to add two compatible matrices first needs to be included in the unit **MyMats**. Add the line

```
procedure MatSum( var A, B, C: Mat; N, M: byte );
```

to the interface section, and the following to the implementation section:

```
{------MatSum--------------------------------------------------------------------------------------------}
{                                                                                                      }
{ Adds the NxM matrices A and B storing sum in C.                                                      }
{------------------------------------------------------------------------------------------------------}
```

```
procedure MatSum;
var
  I, J : byte;
  begin
    for I:= 1 to N do
      for J:= 1 to M do
        C[ I,J ]:= A[ I,J ] + B[ I,J ]
  end; { MatSum }
```

The complete program to compute a reachability matrix is then as follows:

```
program Reach;
uses MyMats;
const
  N = 5;
var
  A, R : Mat;

procedure Reachable( Var R: Mat; A: Mat; N: byte );
{ Computes the reachability matrix R of the NxN adjacency                    }
{ matrix A.                                                                  }
var
  I: byte;
  B, C, D : Mat;
begin
  B:= A;                                                    { first power of A }
  R:= A;                                                     { first term of R }

  for I:= 1 to N-2 do
  begin
    MatMult( A, B, C, N, N, N );                         { next power of A in C }
    B:= C;                                            { increasing powers of A }
    MatSum( B, R, D, N, N );

                                              { sum of increasing powers of A in D }
    R:= D                                                           { update R }
  end
end; { Reachable }

begin
  MatRead( A, N, N, 'REACH.' );
  Reachable( R, A, N );
  MatWrite( R, N, N, 4, 0 );
  readln
end.
```

It may help to go through **Reachable** by hand for $n = 5$ to see how it works. Keep track of the contents of **B, C, D** and **R** in terms of the adjacency matrix **A**.

Cycles

If any elements of $\mathbf{A}^n$, where **A** is the adjacency matrix of a network with n nodes, are non-zero, what does this imply? Such a non-zero element means a path of length n, ie a path linking $(n+1)$ nodes. Since the network has only n nodes, it must therefore have a cycle (a path which passes through a particular set of nodes indefinitely). So we have a neat test for cycling in a network: if $\mathbf{A}^n$ is null, there are no cycles; if it is not null, there are cycles.

Indeed, since we need to compute all the intermediate powers of **A** in order to get $\mathbf{A}^n$, we can spot cycles that do not involve all the nodes before we have got $\mathbf{A}^n$. If any smaller power of **A** has at least one non-zero entry on its main diagonal, the network will have at least one cycle, since a path that starts and ends at the same node must be cyclic. So we can extend the test for cycling to the following:

IF any of the matrices $\mathbf{A}^2$, $\mathbf{A}^3$, ..., $\mathbf{A}^{(n-1)}$ has a non-zero entry anywhere on a main diagonal,

OR $\mathbf{A}^n$ has a non-zero entry anywhere,

THEN the network has at least one cycle, defined by the positions of the non-zero entries,

ELSE it has no cycles.

Postscript

If **A** has no rows that are full of zeros (ie each node has an exit), or no columns full of zeros (ie each node can be reached), then there must be a cycle (if not, there may still be one, but we can't be sure).

15.4 LESLIE MATRICES: POPULATION GROWTH

Another very interesting and useful application of matrices is in population dynamics, but we will need to do some preliminary work before we can see where the matrices come in.

In this section we are going to see how to model a population of rabbits. The approach we are going to take requires that we divide the rabbit population up into a number of age classes, where the members of each age class are one time unit older than the members of the previous class, the time unit being whatever is convenient for the population being studied (days, months, etc.).

If X_i is the size of the ith age class, we define a **survival factor** P_i as the proportion of the ith class that survive to the $(i+1)$th age class (ie the proportion that graduate) and F_i as the **mean fertility** of the ith class, ie the mean number of newborn individuals expected to be produced during one time interval by each member of the ith class at the beginning of the interval (only females count in biological modelling, since there are always enough males to go round!).

Suppose for our modified rabbit model we have three age classes, with X_1, X_2 and X_3 members respectively. We will call them young, middle-aged and old-aged for convenience. (We could easily have had more age classes: see the example at the end of this section.) We will take our time unit as one month, so X_1 are the number that were born during the current month, and which will be considered as youngsters at the end of the month. X_2 are the number of middle-aged rabbits at the end of the month, and X_3 the number of oldsters. Suppose the youngsters cannot reproduce, so that $F_1 = 0$. The fertility rate for middle-aged rabbits is 9, so $F_2 = 9$, while that of oldsters is 12, so $F_3 = 12$. The probability of survival from youth to middle-age is one third, so $P_1 = 1/3$, while no less than half the middle-aged rabbits live to become oldsters, so $P_2 = 0.5$. With this information we can quite easily compute the changing population structure month by month, as long as we have the population breakdown to start with. First we calculate how many babies are born in the current month. Let's call this number **New** for the moment, and not X_1 yet:

```
New:= F2 * X2 + F3 * X3;                                        (1)
```

At the end of the current month, some lucky middle-aged rabbits get promoted to oldsters, so the new value for X_3 will be given by

```
X3:= P2 * X2;                                                   (2)
```

Similarly, some youngsters will get to experience the delights of middle-age:

```
X2:= P1 * X1;                                                   (3)
```

Finally, now that we have used the current value of X_1, we can update it:

```
X1:= New;                                                       (4)
```

Note that we took care to compute the new arrivals in equation (1) from the values of X_2 and X_3 *before* they were updated in equations (2) and (3). This effectively implies that the gestation period is one month. Also it would be incorrect to use X_1 on the lefthand side of equation (1) because then we would be using the wrong value of X_1 in equation (3).

We are assuming for the sake of illustration that all old-aged rabbits die at the end of the month.

This can be corrected in two ways. The members of the third age class could be defined as those rabbits which are three months *and* older at the end of the current month, in which case we would need to introduce a P_3, being the probability that an oldster does not die that month. The example of the American robin at the end of this section uses this device. Alternatively, one can simply have more age classes, although this will require more biological data. When this type of model was tried out on elephants in the Kruger National Park, in South Africa, it was found that 60 age classes were needed, with a time unit of one year, since very few elephants live beyond the age of 60 years.

If we have some values of X_1, X_2 and X_3 to start with, we can write a program that uses the above scheme to update the age classes month by month, for as long as we like, and so project the rabbit population into the future. In the program below, we use the fertility rates and survival probabilitites as above. We start the model with one old rabbit, and no others, so $X_1 = X_2 = 0$, and $X_3 = 1$. The output after the program gives the population structure and the total population over a period of 24 months.

```
program Rabbits;
uses Crt;
var
  F           : text;
  F2, F3      : real;                      { fertility rates }
  New         : real;    { newborn rabbits in current month }
  P1, P2      : real;                { survival probabilities }
  T           : word;                                 { time }
  Total       : real;              { total rabbit population }
  X1, X2, X3  : real;                          { age classes }
begin
  Assign( F, 'RABBITS.' );
  Reset( F );
  Read( F, X1, X2, X3, F2, F3, P1, P2 );
  Total:= X1 + X2 + X3;
  T:= 0;
  ClrScr;
  Writeln( 'Month', 'Young':14, 'Middle':14, 'Old':14, 'Total':14 );
  Writeln;
  Writeln( T:5, X1:14:1, X2:14:1, X3:14:1, Total:14:1 );

  for T:= 1 to 24 do
  begin
    New:= F2 * X2 + F3 * X3;
    X3:= P2 * X2;
    X2:= P1 * X1;
    X1:= New;
    Total:= X1 + X2 + X3;
    Writeln( T:5, X1:14:1, X2:14:1, X3:14:1, Total:14:1 )
  end;

  Readln
end.
```

Output:

Month	Young	Middle	Old	Total
0	0.0	0.0	1.0	1.0
1	12.0	0.0	0.0	12.0
2	0.0	4.0	0.0	4.0
3	36.0	0.0	2.0	38.0
4	24.0	12.0	0.0	36.0
5	108.0	8.0	6.0	122.0
6	144.0	36.0	4.0	184.0
7	372.0	48.0	18.0	438.0
8	648.0	124.0	24.0	796.0
9	1404.0	216.0	62.0	1682.0

10	**2688.0**	**468.0**	**108.0**	**3264.0**
11	**5508.0**	**896.0**	**234.0**	**6638.0**
12	**10871.9**	**1836.0**	**448.0**	**13155.9**
13	**21899.9**	**3624.0**	**918.0**	**26441.9**
14	**43631.7**	**7300.0**	**1812.0**	**52743.7**
15	**87443.5**	**14543.9**	**3650.0**	**105637.3**
16	**174694.8**	**29147.8**	**7272.0**	**211114.6**
17	**349593.5**	**58231.6**	**14573.9**	**422398.9**
18	**698970.7**	**116531.1**	**29115.8**	**844617.5**
19	**1398168.8**	**232990.0**	**58265.5**	**1689424.3**
20	**2796096.3**	**466055.8**	**116495.0**	**3378647.1**
21	**5592442.1**	**932031.2**	**233027.9**	**6757501.1**
22	**11184615.2**	**1864145.5**	**466015.6**	**13514776.3**
23	**22369496.4**	**3728201.3**	**932072.7**	**27029770.5**
24	**44738685.0**	**7456491.4**	**1864100.7**	**54059277.0**

Fractional rabbits should be kept, and not rounded (and certainly not truncated). They occur because the fertility rates and survival probabilities are averages.

If you look carefully at the output you may spot that after some months the total population doubles every month. But what you probably won't spot is that the numbers in the three age classes tend to a limiting ratio of 24:4:1. This can be demonstrated very clearly if you run the model with an initial population structure having this limiting ratio. We will come back to this intriguing result at the end of this section.

Well, what has all this got to do with matrices? Everything, as we shall see in a moment. If we denote the current month by t, and next month by $(t+1)$, we can refer to this month's youngsters as $X_1(t)$, and to next month's as $X_1(t+1)$, and similarly for the other two age classes. The scheme of equations (1) to (4) for updating the population can then be written as three equations:

$$X_1(t+1) = F_2X_2(t) + F_3X_3(t)$$
$$X_2(t+1) = P_1X_1(t)$$
$$X_3(t+1) = P_2X_2(t)$$

The obvious thing to do now is to define a population vector $\mathbf{X}(t)$, with three components, $X_1(t)$, $X_2(t)$, and $X_3(t)$, representing the three age classes of the rabbit population in month t. The above three equations specify how to get from $\mathbf{X}(t)$ to $\mathbf{X}(t+1)$, and using this vector, with a matrix for the coefficients on the right-hand side, we can easily rewrite the equations as

$$\begin{bmatrix} X_1 \\ X_2 \\ X_3 \end{bmatrix}_{t+1} = \begin{bmatrix} 0 & F_2 & F_3 \\ P_1 & 0 & 0 \\ 0 & P_2 & 0 \end{bmatrix} \times \begin{bmatrix} X_1 \\ X_2 \\ X_3 \end{bmatrix}_{t}$$

where the subscript at the bottom of the vectors indicates the month. We can write this even more concisely as the matrix equation

$$\mathbf{X}(t+1) = \mathbf{L}\,\mathbf{X}(t)\,, \tag{5}$$

where L is the matrix

$$\begin{bmatrix} 0 & 9 & 12 \\ 1/3 & 0 & 0 \\ 0 & 1/2 & 0 \end{bmatrix}$$

in this particular case. **L** is called a **Leslie Matrix**. A population model can always be written in the form of equation (5) if the concepts of age classes, fertility, and survival factors, as outlined above, are used.

Now that we have established a matrix representation for our model, we can easily write a program using matrix multiplication and repeated application of equation (5):

$$\mathbf{X}(t+2) = \mathbf{L}\,\mathbf{X}(t+1),$$
$$\mathbf{X}(t+3) = \mathbf{L}\,\mathbf{X}(t+2), \text{ etc.}$$

However, we only need one vector **X** in the program, because after each matrix multiplication we can assign the product back to **X**. The following program will produce the same output as the previous one, but it is more general, and can be easily extended to handle more age classes. Note that a (3 × 1) array **X** could be used for the population vector in place of the (6 × 6) array defined by the type **Mat**, in order to save space. **MatMult** would then have to be rewritten, since both the operands in the matrix multiplication are assumed to be of type **Mat**.

```
program LeslieRabbits;
uses Crt, MyMats;
const
  N = 3;                                        { number of age classes }
var
  L    : Mat;                                         { Leslie Matrix }
  X    : Mat;                                     { population vector }
  D    : Mat;                             { dummy for multiplication }
  T    : word;                                                { time }
function PopTot( X: Mat; N: byte ): real;
var
  I    : byte;
  Sum  : real;
begin
  Sum:= 0;
  for I:= 1 to N do
    Sum:= Sum + X[ I,1 ];                          { first column only }
  PopTot:= Sum
end; { PopTot }
begin
  MatRead( L, N, N, 'LESLIE.');
  MatRead( X, N, 1, 'INITIAL.' );
  T:= 0;
  ClrScr;
  Writeln( 'Month', 'Young':14, 'Middle':14, 'Old':14, 'Total':14 );
  Writeln;
  Writeln( T:5, X[ 1,1 ]:14:1, X[ 2,1 ]:14:1, X[ 3,1 ]:14:1,   PopTot( X, 3 ):14:1 );
  for T:= 1 to 24 do
  begin
    MatMult( L, X, D, N, N, N );
    X:= D;
    Writeln( T:5, X[ 1,1 ]:14:1, X[ 2,1 ]:14:1, X[ 3,1 ]:14:1,   PopTot( X, 3 ):14:1 )
  end
end.
```

We have already observed that after sufficient time has elapsed, the total population doubles every month. This factor is called the **growth factor**, and is a property of the particular Leslie matrix being used (for those who know about such things, it's the **dominant eigenvalue** of the matrix). The growth factor is 2 in this example, but if the values in the Leslie matrix are changed, the long-term growth factor changes too (try it and see).

We have also noted that the values of the three age classes reach a limiting ratio of 24:4:1. This limiting ratio is called the **stable age distribution** of the population, and again it is a property of the Leslie matrix (in fact, it is the **eigenvector** belonging to the dominant eigenvalue of the matrix). Different population matrices lead to different stable age distributions.

The interesting point about all this is that *any* given Leslie matrix always eventually gets a population into the *same* stable age distribution, which increases eventually by the *same* growth factor each month, *no matter what the initial population breakdown is*. For example, if you run the above model with any other initial population, it will always get into a stable age distribution of 24:4:1 with a growth factor of 2 (try it and see).

15.5 MARKOV CHAINS

Often a process that we wish to model may be represented by a number of possible **discrete** (ie discontinuous) states that describe the outcome of the process. For example, if we are spinning a coin, then the outcome is adequately represented by the two states heads and tails (and nothing in between). If the process is random, as it is with spinning coins, there is a certain probability of being in any of the states at a given moment, and also a probability of changing from one state to another. If the probability of moving from one state to another depends on the present state, and not on any previous state, the process is called a **Markov chain**. The progress of the drunk sailor in Chapter 14 is an example of a Markov chain. A variation on this example is given below. Markov chains are used widely in such diverse fields as biology and business decision making, to name just two areas. We will give two simple examples to illustrate the concept.

Weather prediction

The first example concerns weather prediction. Suppose the weather in a certain area on a given day may be in one of three states: rainy, fair or snowy. We can represent these states by a three-component vector $\mathbf{X}(t)$, where $X_1(t)$, $X_2(t)$, and $X_3(t)$ are the probabilities of the weather being rainy, fair or snowy on day t. Obviously, the components of $\mathbf{X}(t)$ must sum to 1, since the weather can be in no other state. After observing the weather pattern for many days, it seems that if it is rainy today, it will be the same tomorrow half of the time, and equally likely to be fair or snowy the rest of the time. If it is fair today, the weather tomorrow is equally likely to be rainy or snowy (two fair days in a row are unheard of). If it is snowy today, it will be the same tomorrow half of the time, and equally likely to be rainy or fair the rest of the time.

In the last three sentences, we have stated the **transition probabilities** of moving from any one state today to any other state tomorrow. These probabilities are best expressed in the form of a **transition probability matrix, P,** where **P** is given by

		TODAY		
		Rainy	*Fair*	*Snowy*
TOMORROW	*Rainy*	0.5	0.5	0.25
	Fair	0.25	0.0	0.25
	Snowy	0.25	0.5	0.5

Note that the columns of **P** add up to 1. What is the weather likely to do tomorrow? The chances of it being rainy tomorrow are 0.5 if it rained or was fair today, and 0.25 if it snowed today (top row of **P**). Thus, if time t is today, the probability of it being rainy tomorrow, represented by $X_1(t+1)$, is given by

$$X_1(t+1) = 0.5X_1(t) + 0.5X_2(t) + 0.25X_3(t)\,. \tag{1}$$

Similarly, the chances of it being fair or snowy tomorrow are given by equations (2) and (3):

$$X_2(t+1) = 0.25X_1(t) + 0.25X_3(t)\,, \tag{2}$$

$$X_3(t+1) = 0.25X_1(t) + 0.5X_2(\mathrm{t}) + 0.5X_3(\mathrm{t})\,. \tag{3}$$

We can write equations (1) to (3) in matrix form, as we did with the rabbit model:

$$\begin{bmatrix} X_1 \\ X_2 \\ X_3 \end{bmatrix}_{t+1} = \begin{bmatrix} 0.5 & 0.5 & 0.25 \\ 0.25 & 0.0 & 0.25 \\ 0.25 & 0.5 & 0.5 \end{bmatrix} \times \begin{bmatrix} X_1 \\ X_2 \\ X_3 \end{bmatrix}_{t}$$

or more concisely,

$$\mathbf{X}(t+1) = \mathbf{P}\,\mathbf{X}(\mathrm{t})\,. \tag{4}$$

By applying equation (4) repeatedly, we can find the long range weather prospects, provided we know the state of the weather on a given day. Suppose it is rainy today. Then $X_1(0) = 1$, since it is certain, while $X_2(0) = X_3(0) = 0$. Using these starting values, we can generate the probability states of the weather for as long as we like.

The computing is almost identical to that required in the previous section for generating the rabbit population over a number of months. In fact, the same program can be used, with only minor formatting changes. Starting with a rainy day at time $t = 0$, the program gives the following output for the next week:

DAY	RAINY	FAIR	SNOWY
0	1.0000	0.0000	0.0000
1	0.5000	0.2500	0.2500
2	0.4375	0.1875	0.3750
3	0.4063	0.2031	0.3906
4	0.4023	0.1992	0.3984
5	0.4004	0.2002	0.3994
6	0.4001	0.2000	0.3999
7	0.4000	0.2000	0.4000

We see from the output that the probabilities converge to the **limiting probabilities** 0.4, 0.2, 0.4. In fact, they converge to the *same* limit for a given transition matrix **P**, whatever the initial state happens to be (try this out with different initial states). The limiting probabilities in this example mean that in the long run it rains 40 per cent of the time, snows 40 per cent of the time, and is fair for the rest of the time (one day in five).

A random walk

The second example is a variation on the random walk problem of Chapter 14. A street has six intersections. A drunk man wanders down the street. His home is at intersection 1, and his favourite bar at intersection 6. At each intersection other than his home or the bar he moves in the direction of the bar with probability 2/3, and in the direction of his home with probability 1/3. He never wanders down a side street. If he reaches his home or the bar, he disappears into them, never to re-appear (when he disappears we say in Markov jargon that he has been absorbed).

We would like to know: what are the chances of him ending up at home or in the bar, if he starts at a given corner (other than home or the bar, obviously)? He can clearly be in one of six states, with respect to his random walk, which can be labelled by the intersection number, where state 1 means *Home* and state 6 means *Bar*. We can express this Markov process by the following transition matrix:

		Present State (corner)					
		Home	2	3	4	5	*Bar*
	Home	1	1/3	0	0	0	0
	2	0	0	1/3	0	0	0
Next State	3	0	2/3	0	1/3	0	0
(Corner)	4	0	0	2/3	0	1/3	0
	5	0	0	0	2/3	0	0
	Bar	0	0	0	0	2/3	1

The entries for *Home-Home* and *Bar-Bar* are both 1 because he stays put there with certainty.

We can compute the probability states in the same way as we did for the weather in the land of Oz, forming the new state vector from the old one each time:

$$\mathbf{X}(t+1) = \mathbf{P}\,\mathbf{X}(t)\,.$$

If we suppose the man starts at intersection 2, the initial probabilities will be (0; 1; 0; 0; 0; 0). Using this starting vector, we generate the following states in the future:

TIME	HOME	2	3	4	4	BAR
0	0.0000	1.0000	0.0000	0.0000	0.0000	0.0000
1	0.3333	0.0000	0.6667	0.0000	0.0000	0.0000
2	0.3333	0.2222	0.0000	0.4444	0.0000	0.0000
3	0.4074	0.0000	0.2963	0.0000	0.2963	0.0000
4	0.4074	0.0988	0.0000	0.2963	0.0000	0.1975
5	0.4403	0.0000	0.1646	0.0000	0.1975	0.1975
6	0.4403	0.0549	0.0000	0.1756	0.0000	0.3292
7	0.4586	0.0000	0.0951	0.0000	0.1171	0.3292
8	0.4586	0.0317	0.0000	0.1024	0.0000	0.4073
9	0.4692	0.0000	0.0553	0.0000	0.0683	0.4073
10	0.4692	0.0184	0.0000	0.0596	0.0000	0.4528
11	0.4753	0.0000	0.0322	0.0000	0.0397	0.4528
12	0.4753	0.0107	0.0000	0.0347	0.0000	0.4793
13	0.4789	0.0000	0.0187	0.0000	0.0231	0.4793
14	0.4789	0.0062	0.0000	0.0202	0.0000	0.4947
15	0.4810	0.0000	0.0109	0.0000	0.0135	0.4947
...						
30	0.4838	0.0001	0.0000	0.0003	0.0000	0.5158
...						
40	0.4839	0.0000	0.0000	0.0000	0.0000	0.5161
...						
50	0.4839	0.0000	0.0000	0.0000	0.0000	0.5161

By running the program for long enough, we soon find the limiting probabilities: he ends up at home about 48 per cent of the time, and at the bar about 52 per cent of the time. Perhaps this is a little surprising; from the transition probabilities, we might have expected him to get to the bar rather more easily. It just goes to show that you should never trust your intuition when it comes to statistics!

Note that the Markov chain approach is *not* a simulation: one gets the *theoretical* probabilities each time (this can all be done mathematically, without a computer). But it is interesting to confirm the limiting probabilities by simulating the drunk's progress, using a random number generator (see Exercise 15.3 below).

15.6 SOLUTION OF LINEAR EQUATIONS BY GAUSS REDUCTION

A problem that often arises in scientific applications is the solution of a system of linear equations, for example,

$$\begin{aligned} 2x - y + z &= 4 \\ x + y + z &= 3 \\ 3x - y - z &= 1\,. \end{aligned}$$

One method of solution is by **Gauss reduction**, which we discuss here. Write the coefficients of the lefthand side as a matrix, with the righthand side constants as a vector on the righthand side of the matrix, separated by a vertical line, thus:

$$\left[\begin{array}{ccc|c} 2 & -1 & 1 & 4 \\ 1 & 1 & 1 & 3 \\ 3 & -1 & -1 & 1 \end{array}\right]$$

This is simply shorthand for the original set, and is sometimes called the **augmented matrix** of the system. As long as we perform only *row* operations on the numbers, we can omit the symbols x, y, and z each time. We will still refer to the coefficient array as the matrix **A**.

We start with the first row (R1), and call it the **pivot row**. We call the element a_{11} (= 2) the **pivot element**. Divide the whole pivot row by the pivot element, so the augmented array now looks like this:

$$\left[\begin{array}{ccc|c} 1 & -1/2 & 1/2 & 2 \\ 1 & 1 & 1 & 3 \\ 3 & -1 & -1 & 1 \end{array}\right]$$

Rows R2 and R3 are now called **target rows**. The object is to get zeros in all the target rows below (and above, if necessary) the pivot element. Take the target row R2. Replace each element in the row by itself minus the corresponding element in the pivot row. The array now looks like this:

$$\left[\begin{array}{ccc|c} 1 & -1/2 & 1/2 & 2 \\ 0 & 3/2 & 1/2 & 1 \\ 3 & -1 & -1 & 1 \end{array}\right]$$

Now take the target row R3. To reduce a_{31} to zero with an operation involving the pivot row requires replacing the target row by itself minus the pivot row multiplied by a_{31} (bearing in mind for the subsequent computer solution that this operation can change the value of a_{31} itself!):

$$\left[\begin{array}{ccc|c} 1 & -1/2 & 1/2 & 2 \\ 0 & 3/2 & 1/2 & 1 \\ 0 & 1/2 & -5/2 & -5 \end{array}\right]$$

We now designate R2 as the pivot row, and the new a_{22} as the pivot element. The whole procedure is repeated, except that the target rows are now R1 and R3, and the object is to get zeros in these two rows above and below the pivot element. The result is:

$$\left[\begin{array}{ccc|c} 1 & 0 & 2/3 & 7/3 \\ 0 & 1 & 1/3 & 2/3 \\ 0 & 0 & -8/3 & -16/3 \end{array}\right]$$

Now take R3 as the pivot row, with the new a_{33} as the pivot element, and R1 and R2 as target rows. After repeating similar operations on them, the array finally looks like this:

$$\left[\begin{array}{ccc|c} 1 & 0 & 0 & 1 \\ 0 & 1 & 0 & 0 \\ 0 & 0 & 1 & 2 \end{array}\right]$$

Since we have retained the mathematical integrity of the system of equations by performing operations on the rows only, this is equivalent to

$$\begin{aligned} x + 0y + 0z &= 1 \\ 0x + y + 0z &= 0 \\ 0x + 0y + z &= 2\,. \end{aligned}$$

The solution may therefore be read off as $x = 1, y = 0, z = 2$.

The procedure **Gauss** below performs a Gauss reduction on a system of five or fewer equations. The augmented array **A** is passed as a parameter. On entry, its rightmost column should contain the righthand side constants of the equations. On return, the rightmost column will contain the solution. For larger systems, the arrays in the type definition **Mat** in the unit **MyMats** should be enlarged.

```
program Solver;
uses MyMats;
const
  N = 3;          { number of equations }
var
  A: Mat;         { augmented matrix }

{------Gauss-------------------------------------------------------------------}
{                                                                              }
{ Performs a Gauss reduction on the N equations in the augmented               }
{ matrix A. The solution will be in the last column on return.                 }
{ For systems with more than 5 equations redefine type Mat in                  }
{ MyMats.                                                                      }
{------------------------------------------------------------------------------}

procedure Gauss( var A: Mat; N: byte );
var
  J, PivRow, TarRow : byte;
  PivElt, TarElt : real;
  begin
  { Make each row the pivot row in turn, and divide each element              }
  { in the pivot row by the pivot element.                                    }
  for PivRow:= 1 to N do
  begin
    PivElt:= A[ PivRow, PivRow ];
    for J:= 1 to N+1 do
      A[ PivRow, J ]:= A[ PivRow, J ] / PivElt;
    { Then replace all other rows (target rows) by target row                }
    { minus pivot row minus pivot row times element in target row            }
    { and pivot column.                                                      }
    for TarRow:= 1 to N do
      if TarRow <> PivRow then
      begin
        TarElt:= A[ TarRow, PivRow ];
        for J:= 1 to N+1 do
          A[ TarRow, J ]:= A[ TarRow, J ] - A[ PivRow, J ]  * TarElt
    end
  end
end; { Gauss }
begin
  MatRead( A, N, N+1, 'GAUSS.' );
  Gauss( A, N );
  MatWrite( A, N, N+1, 4, 0 );                    { solution is in last column }
end.
```

Unfortunately, things can go wrong with our procedure:

1. The pivot element could be zero. This happens quite easily when the coefficients are all integers. However, rows of the array can be interchanged (see Exercise 15.4) without changing the system of equations. So a non-zero pivot element can often be found in this way (but see the next two cases).
2. A row of zeros could appear right across the array (in which case a non-zero pivot element cannot be found). In this case the system of equations is indeterminate and the solution can only be determined down to as many arbitrary constants as there are rows of zeros.
3. A row of the array could be filled with zeros, except for the extreme righthand element. In this case the equations are inconsistent, which means there are no solutions.

It is a nice programming project to extend the above subroutine to deal with these three cases.

Gauss reduction can also be used to invert a matrix. Suppose we want to invert the matrix

$$\mathbf{A} = \begin{bmatrix} 2 & 2 & 2 \\ 3 & 2 & 2 \\ 3 & 2 & 3 \end{bmatrix}$$

Construct the augmented array **A**|**I**, ie

$$\left[\begin{array}{ccc|ccc} 2 & 2 & 2 & 1 & 0 & 0 \\ 3 & 2 & 2 & 0 & 1 & 0 \\ 3 & 2 & 3 & 0 & 0 & 1 \end{array}\right]$$

where **I** is the identity matrix, and perform a Gauss reduction until the identity matrix has appeared to the left of the vertical line, so that the augmented array finally looks as follows:

$$\left[\begin{array}{ccc|ccc} 1 & 0 & 0 & -1 & 1 & 0 \\ 0 & 1 & 0 & 3/2 & 0 & -1 \\ 0 & 0 & 1 & 0 & -1 & 1 \end{array}\right]$$

The entity to the right of the line is the inverse of **A**. If **A** is not invertible, the process breaks down and a row of zeros appears.

To use the above program to invert a matrix, simply change the three occurrences of **N+1** to **N+N** (this is the number of columns in the augmented matrix).

15.7 VOLUME OF EXCAVATION

A problem that arises in the building industry is the calculation of the volume of earth to be excavated from a site. We assume that the excavation is to have a rectangular level base and vertical sides. The area to be excavated is surveyed, and the heights of the ground above the excavation base are found, say, on a 10 metre square grid. So part of a plan of such an excavation could look something like this:

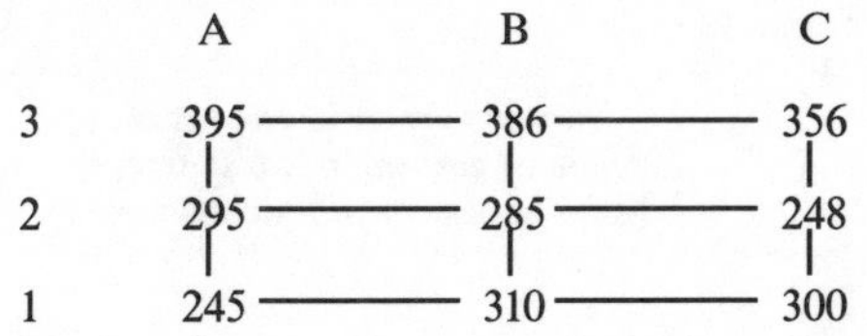

	A	B	C
3	395	386	356
2	295	285	248
1	245	310	300

The numbers are the heights above the excavation base in centimetres. Consider the square bounded by A3, B3, A2 and B2. The volume of the vertical square prism excavated beneath it is the horizontal plan area times the average height of the corners above the base, ie

Volume $= 10 \times 10 \times (3.95 + 3.86 + 2.85 + 2.95) / 4$ cubic metres.

We could do this for every vertical square prism to be excavated and add up all the volumes so calculated. However, an easier way presents itself if we spot that some corner heights are used in four squares, some in two squares, and some in only one, as shown below:

Grid point	*Corner height*	*Number of squares* (n) *corner appears in*	n × *corner ht*
A3	3.95	1	3.95
B3	3.86	2	7.72
C3	3.56	1	3.56
A2	2.95	2	5.90
B2	2.85	4	11.40
C2	2.48	2	4.96
A1	2.45	1	2.45
B1	3.10	2	6.20
C1	3.00	1	3.00
		TOTAL:	49.14

From this table, the volume excavated may then be calculated as

$$10 \times 10 \times 49.14 / 4 = 1228.5 \text{ cubic metres.}$$

In general, the corner heights may be represented by a matrix **H**, say, where a particular height is given by h_{ij}, and where i and j label the rows and columns of the grid. Suppose there are m rows and n columns in the grid. The contributions of the heights to the total volume are as follows:

Corners in 1 square: $h_{11} + h_{1n} + h_{m1} + h_{mn}$

Corners in 2 squares: $2\sum_{i=2}^{m-1}(h_{i1} + h_{in}) + 2\sum_{j=2}^{n-1}(h_{1j} + h_{mj})$

Corners in 4 squares: $4\sum_{i=2}^{m-1}\sum_{j=2}^{n-1} h_{ij}$.

This sort of calculation is what computers were made for. The next program computes the volume of excavation under a ($m \times n$) grid:

```
program Dig;
uses MyMats;
const
  M = 3;                                          { no. of rows in grid }
  N = 3;                                          { no. of columns in grid }
var
  H : Mat;                                        { heights above level base }

function VolEx( var H: Mat; M, N: byte ): real;
{ Computes volume of excavation under grid heights H }
const
  V1     : real = 0;                              { sum of corners in one square }
  V2     : real = 0;                              { sum of corners in two squares }
  V4     : real = 0;                              { sum of corners in four squares }
var
  I, J   : byte;
begin
  V1:= H[ 1,1 ] + H[ 1,N ] + H[ M,1 ] + H[ M,N ];

  for I:= 2 to M-1 do
    V2:= V2 + 2 * (H[ I,1 ] + H[ I,N ] );

  for J:= 2 to N-1 do
    V2:= V2 + 2 * (H[ 1,J ] + H[ M,J ] );

  for I:= 2 to M-1 do
    for J:= 2 to N-1 do
      V4:= V4 + 4 * H[ I,J ];
```

```
VolEx:= 100 * (V1 + V2 + V4) / 4                                { total volume }
end; { VolEx }
begin
  MatRead( H, M, N, 'VOLUME.' );                    { data in disk file 'VOLUME.' }
  Writeln( 'Volume excavated:', VolEx( H, M, N ):8:1,   ' cubic metres' )
end.
```

15.8 AREA OF A SITE

A frequent problem in land surveying is the calculation of the area of a plot of ground. Assuming the sides of the plot to be straight, this amounts to finding the area of an irregular polygon, ie an n-sided figure with straight sides. The algorithm outlined here uses the **determinant** of a matrix to compute this area.

Consider the (3×3) matrix

$$\mathbf{A} = \begin{bmatrix} a_{11} & a_{12} & a_{13} \\ a_{21} & a_{22} & a_{23} \\ a_{31} & a_{32} & a_{33} \end{bmatrix} .$$

Its determinant, Det($\mathbf{A}$), is defined as

$$\text{Det}(\mathbf{A}) = a_{11}(a_{22}a_{33} - a_{23}a_{32}) + a_{12}(a_{23}a_{31} - a_{21}a_{33}) + a_{13}(a_{21}a_{32} - a_{22}a_{31}) .$$

Now consider the triangle in the example below:

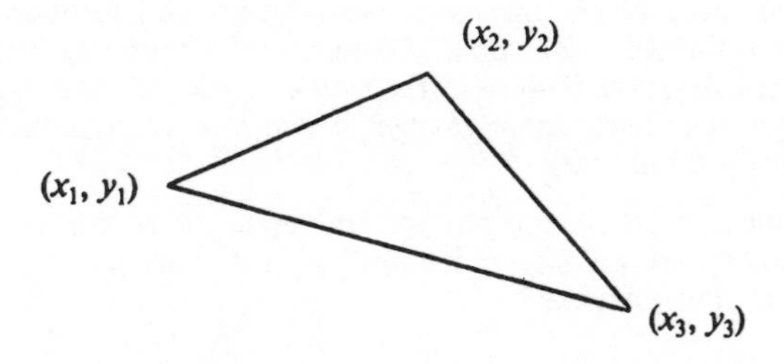

If the positions of its vertices are represented by Cartesian co-ordinates in the usual way, the area of the triangle may be given as

$$\text{Area} = 0.5 \times \text{Det} \begin{bmatrix} 1 & 1 & 1 \\ y_1 & y_2 & y_3 \\ x_1 & x_2 & x_3 \end{bmatrix}$$

(this is not difficult to prove: drop perpendiculars from the vertices to the x-axis and use the areas of the resulting trapezia in the figure to find the area of the triangle).

The point about this is that a polygon with n vertices may be broken up into $(n-2)$ triangles sharing a common vertex by drawing lines from the common vertex to each other vertex in turn, as shown in Figure 15.2.

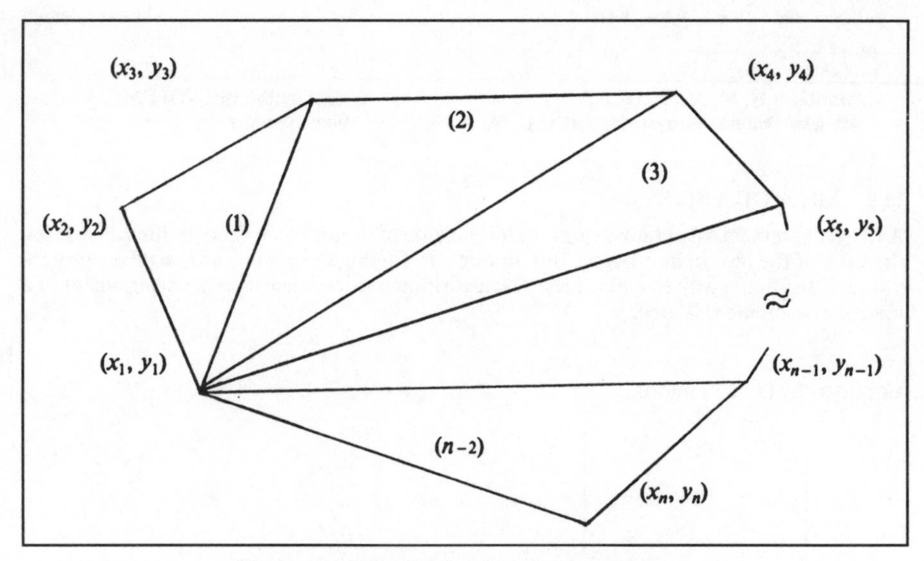

Figure 15.2 Triangle showing a common vertex

The area of the ith triangle (numbered from the left) in the composite figure is thus

$$0.5 \times \text{Det} \begin{bmatrix} 1 & 1 & 1 \\ y_1 & y_{i+1} & y_{i+2} \\ x_1 & x_{i+1} & x_{i+2} \end{bmatrix} \qquad (*)$$

as can easily be seen by writing out the expression for the case of a six-sided polygon, for example. The area of the n-sided polygon thus formed is the sum of the areas (*) for i running from 1 to $(n-2)$. The formula works, by the way, even if some of the interior angles of the polygon are reflex. This is because the sign of a determinant changes if two rows or columns are interchanged (puzzle that one out if you want to!).

The program that follows computes the area of any polygon with up to 100 vertices, where the only condition on the data is that the co-ordinates of the vertices must be given in order as one moves around the figure in a clockwise sense.

```
program Site;
const
  Area : real = 0;
  MaxPts = 100;
type
  ArrType = array[ 1..3, 1..3 ] of real;
var
  A       : ArrType;
  F       : text;
  I       : word;                              { counter }
  N       : word;                              { number of vertices }
  X, Y    : array[ 1..MaxPts ] of real;

function Det3( var A: ArrType ): real;
{ Determinant of the 3x3 matrix A }
begin
  Det3:=      A[1,1] * (A[2,2] * A[3,3]  -  A[2,3] * A[3,2])
            + A[1,2] * (A[2,3] * A[3,1]  -  A[2,1] * A[3,3])
            + A[1,3] * (A[2,1] * A[3,2]  -  A[2,2] * A[3,1])
```

```
end; { Det3 }

begin
Assign( F, 'SITE.' );
Reset( F );
Read( F, N );                                   { number of vertices }
for I:= 1 to N do
  Read( F, X[I], Y[I] );                        { co-ordinates of vertices }
  A[1,1]:= 1;
  A[1,2]:= 1;
  A[1,3]:= 1;
  A[2,1]:= X[1];
  A[3,1]:= Y[1];
  for I:= 1 to N-2 do
  begin
    A[2,2]:= Y[I+1];
    A[3,2]:= X[I+1];
    A[2,3]:= Y[I+2];
    A[3,3]:= X[I+2];
    Area:= Area + 0.5 * Det3( A )
  end;
  Writeln( Area:8:2 )
end.
```

Try it out on the following data, which are the coordinates of the vertices of a seven-sided figure with one reflex angle, with an area of 4 units: (0, 0), (−1, 1), (0, 2), (1, 2), (1, 1), (2, 1), (2, 0). The text file SITE above should look something like this:

```
7
0 0 -1 1 0 2 1 2 1 1 2 1 2 0
```

The sample is for a seven-sided figure with one reflex angle, the area of which is 4.

15.9 ROTATION OF A COORDINATE SYSTEM

When a Cartesian coordinate system is rotated counterclockwise through an angle a the new coordinates (x', y') of a point in the rotated system are given by

$$x' = x\cos(a) + y\sin(a)$$
$$y' = -x\sin(a) + y\cos(a)$$

where (x, y) are its coordinates before rotation. In section 8.1 we saw how to compute the new coordinates using a function. This transformation may also be done with matrix multiplication (in fact, this is one of the reasons why matrix multiplication was invented):

$$\mathbf{X}' = \mathbf{A}\,\mathbf{X}$$

$$\text{where } \mathbf{A} = \begin{bmatrix} \cos(a) & \sin(a) \\ -\sin(a) & \cos(a) \end{bmatrix}$$

$$\text{and } \mathbf{X} = \begin{bmatrix} x \\ y \end{bmatrix}, \quad \mathbf{X}' = \begin{bmatrix} x' \\ y' \end{bmatrix}.$$

The program below writes out the new coordinates of a set of points after a rotation specified by the user:

```
program Rot;
uses MyMats;
var
  Ang        : real;
  R, X, XD   : Mat;
begin
  Write( 'Angle of rotation (degrees): ' );
```

```
  Readln( Ang );
  Ang:= Ang * Pi / 180;
  R[ 1,1 ]:= Cos( Ang );
  R[ 1,2 ]:= Sin( Ang );
  R[ 2,1 ]:= - R[ 1,2 ];
  R[ 2,2 ]:= R[ 1,1 ];
  repeat
    Readln( X[ 1,1 ], X[ 2,1 ] );                    { coords in old system }
      MatMult( R, X, XD, 2, 2, 1 );                          { rotate }
      Writeln( XD[ 1,1 ]:6:2, XD[ 2,1 ]:6:2 )              { new coords }
    until Eof                                      { Ctrl-Z-Enter to end }
  end.
```

Try it out on some points which lie on the *x*-axis, for example (1, 0) transforms to (0, -1) after a rotation of 90 degrees.

15.10 THE MYMATS UNIT

For the record, the **MyMats** matrix handling unit is as follows:

```
unit MyMats;
interface
type
                  Mat = array[ 1..6, 1..6 ] of real;       { formal parameter type }
procedure MatMult( var A, B, C: Mat; N, M, P: byte );
procedure MatRead( var X: Mat; N, M: byte; DskName: string );
procedure MatSum( var A, B, C: Mat; N, M: byte );
procedure MatWrite( var X: Mat; N, M, W, D: byte );
implementation
{------MatMult-----------------------------------------------------------------------}
{                                                                                  }
{ Multiplies matrix A (N x M) by B (M x P) and stores product in                   }
{ C (N x P)                                                                        }
{----------------------------------------------------------------------------------}
procedure MatMult;
var
  I, J, K : byte;
begin
  for I:= 1 to N do
    for J:= 1 to P do
    begin
      C[ I,J ]:= 0;
      for K:= 1 to M do
        C[ I,J ]:= C[ I,J ] + A[ I,K ] * B[ K,J ]
    end
end; { MatMult }
{------MatRead-----------------------------------------------------------------------}
{                                                                                  }
{ Reads an NxM matrix row by row from the text file saved under                    }
{ DskName.                                                                         }
{----------------------------------------------------------------------------------}
procedure MatRead;
var
  F : text;
  I, J : byte;

begin
  Assign( F, DskName );
  Reset( F );
  for I:= 1 to N do
    for J:= 1 to M do
      Read( F, X[I, J] );
```

```
  Close( F )
end; { MatRead }

{------MatSum------------------------------------------------------------------}
{                                                                              }
{ Adds the NxM matrices A and B storing sum in C.                              }
  {---------------------------------------------------------------------------}
  procedure MatSum;
  var
    I, J : byte;
  begin
    for I:= 1 to N do
      for J:= 1 to M do
        C[ I,J ]:= A[ I,J ] + B[ I,J ]
  end; { MatSum }

  {------MatWrite-------------------------------------------------------------}
  {                                                                           }
  { Writes an NxM matrix row by row in W:D format.                            }
  {---------------------------------------------------------------------------}

  procedure MatWrite;
  var
    I, J : byte;
  begin
    for I:= 1 to N do
    begin
      for J:= 1 to M do
        Write( X[I, J]:W:D );
      Writeln
    end
  end; { MatWrite }

  end. { MyMats }
```

SUMMARY

- A table or matrix may be represented in Turbo Pascal by a two-dimensional array.
- The user-defined unit **MyMats** has various matrix handling utilities: read, write, multiplication and addition.

EXERCISES

In these exercises, take type Mat as something like:

Mat = array[1..6, 1..6] of real;

15.1 Write a procedure Trans(var A: Mat; N, M: byte) which replaces the $(n \times m)$ matrix A by its own transpose. (A transpose of an $(n \times m)$ matrix is an $(m \times n)$ matrix with the rows and columns of the original matrix interchanged, ie a_{ij} is replaced by a_{ji}.)

15.2 Compute the limiting probabilities for the drunk in section 15.5 when he starts at each of the remaining intersections in turn, and confirm that the closer he starts to the bar, the more likely he is to end up there.

15.3 Write a program to *simulate* the drunk's progress down the street. Start him at a given intersection, and generate a random number to decide whether he moves toward the bar or home, according to the probabilities in the transition matrix. For each simulated random walk, record whether he ends up at home or in the bar. Repeat a large number of times. The proportion of walks that end up in either place should approach the limiting probabilities computed using the Markov model in Exercise 15.2. Hint: if the random number is less than 2/3 he moves toward the bar (unless he is already at home or the bar, in which case that random walk ends), otherwise he moves toward home.

15.4 Write a procedure RowSwop(var A: Mat; I, J, M: byte) to interchange rows I and J of an ($n \times m$) matrix A.

15.5 Write a procedure

Sum(A: Mat; var Row, Col: real; I, J, N, M: byte)

to find the sums (Row and Col) of the Ith row and Jth column respectively of the ($n \times m$) matrix A.

15.6 Write a procedure

MaxElt(A: Mat; var Max: real; var RowMax, ColMax: byte; N, M: byte)

to return the largest element Max of an ($n \times m$) matrix A, and the row (RowMax) and column (ColMax) in which it occurs.

15.7 Write a procedure to invert a square matrix by Gauss reduction. It should have a parameter which is set to 0 on entry, and which should be changed to 1 on return if the inverse cannot be found.

15.8 The following system, suggested by T.S. Wilson, illustrates nicely the problem of ill-conditioning mentioned in Exercise 7.3:

$$
\begin{aligned}
10x + 7y + 8z + 7w &= 32 \\
7x + 5y + 6z + 5w &= 23 \\
8x + 6y + 10z + 9w &= 33 \\
7x + 5y + 9z + 10w &= 31 \,.
\end{aligned}
$$

Use the Gauss reduction program in this chapter to show that the solution is $x = y = z = w = 1$. Then change the righthand side constants to 32.01, 22.99, 32.99 and 31.01 (a change of about 1 in 3000) and find the new solution. Finally, change the righthand side constants to 32.1, 22.9, 32.9 and 31.1 and observe what effect this has on the solution.

16 Introduction to Numerical Methods

A major scientific use of modern digital computers is in finding numerical solutions to mathematical problems which have no analytical solutions, ie solutions which may be written down in terms of polynomials and the known mathematical functions such as logarithms, sines, exponentials, etc. In this chapter we look briefly at three areas where **numerical methods** have been highly developed: solving equations, evaluating integrals and derivatives, and solving differential equations.

16.1 EQUATIONS

In this section we consider how to solve equations in one unknown numerically. The general way of expressing the problem is to say that we want to solve the equation

$$f(x) = 0\,,$$

ie we want to find the value(s) of x that make the lefthand side vanish, where $f(x)$ is any given function. Such a value of x is called a root of the equation. There are mathematical solutions for a very small class of functions f. For example, if $f(x)$ is a polynomial of order two (ie a quadratic equation), there is a well-known formula for the solution. But there is no general method for finding an analytical solution for any given $f(x)$.

Newton's method

This is perhaps the easiest numerical method to implement for solving equations. The basic idea is as follows: given some initial guess at the root x_0, the method makes use of the first derivative $f'(x_0)$ to improve the guess by computing x_1, which in general is closer to the root that the first guess. The process is continued until the required accuracy is reached. Figure 16.1 illustrates Newton's method geometrically.

From the figure we see that

$$f'(x_k) = [f(x_k) - 0]/(x_k - x_{k+1})\,.$$

Solving for x_{k+1} gives

$$x_{k+1} = x_k - f(x_k)/f'(x_k)\,. \qquad (1)$$

Equation (1) is **Newton's algorithm**. It is implemented as follows:

1. Read in a starting value x, and required accuracy (e)
2. While $|f(x)| \geq e$ repeat up to 20 times, say:
   2.1 Replace x by $x - f(x)/f'(x)$
   2.2 Write x and $f(x)$
3. Stop.

It is necessary to limit step 2 since the process may not converge (see below).

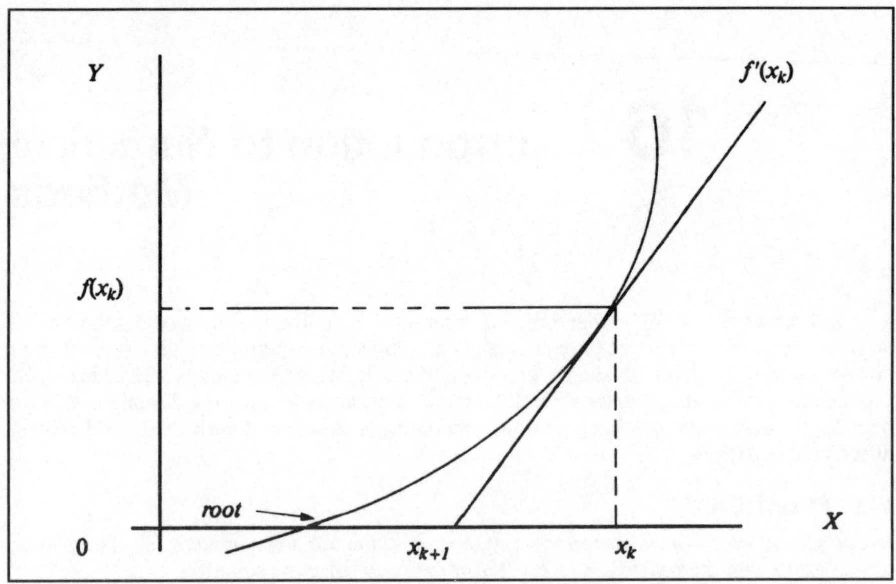

Figure 16.1 Graphical Derivation of Newton's Method.

A program using Newton's method to solve the equation

$$x^3 + x - 3 = 0$$

starting with $x = 2$, is given in section 8.1. From the output shown there we can see that the process converges rapidly. The method is so simple that it can even be implemented on a calculator without much effort.

As an exercise, try running the program with different starting values of x to see whether the algorithm always converges.

Also try finding a non-zero root of

$$2x = \tan(x)$$

using Newton's method (there is no **Tan** standard function – use **Sin(X)/Cos(X)**). You might have some trouble with this one. For example, the following output results if we start the process with $x = 2$:

x	$f(x)$
3.638682	**6.7348E+00**
-5.905311	**-1.2208E+01**
8.585583	**1.8285E+01**
84.579658	**1.6941E+02**
...	

The estimates of the root are clearly diverging. In fact the method has jumped past a number of roots, as can be seen by sketching the graph carefully. This highlights the only serious problem that arises with Newton's method: it only converges to a root if the starting guess is close enough. Since "close enough" depends on $f(x)$ and on the root, one can obviously get into difficulties here. The only remedy is some intelligent trial-and-error work on the initial guess.

Newton's method may also fail if $f(x)$ is very flat near a root, since the algorithm requires division by $f'(x)$, which can get very small in this case. This can easily result in an overflow error. If the method fails to find a root, the Bisection method, discussed below, should be used.

Newton's method may be built in (hardwired) to calculators to evaluate reciprocals and nth roots, for example. To find the reciprocal of a number A amounts to solving the equation

$$f(x) = 1/x - A = 0\,.$$

Applying equation (1) to this form of $f(x)$ gives, after a little algebra,

$$x_{k+1} = x_k(2 - Ax_k).$$

Note that this requires no divisions: it was used on old-fashioned computers with no division facility.

The hire purchase rip-off

When an item is bought on so-called hire purchase, the interest is calculated in advance in one lump sum, which is added to the capital amount, the sum being equally divided over the repayment period. The buyer, however, is often under the impression that the interest is calculated on a reducing balance. For example, suppose the cash price of the item is \$10000, and equal monthly payments must be made over a period of three years. If the quoted hire purchase interest rate is 25%, the payments are calculated by adding three times 25% of \$10000 to \$10000, and dividing the sum by 36, giving repayments of \$486 per month. The effect of this is that the total interest charges over the three-year period amount to \$7500. It is extremely interesting, and revealing, to work out what effective nominal annual interest rate, compounded monthly on a reducing balance, would result in the same monthly repayments.

When a loan of amount A is repaid over a period of k years, with a nominal annual interest of r on the reducing balance, the payments P made n times a year are given by

$$P = (r/n)A(1 + r/n)^{nk}/[(1 + r/n)^{nk} - 1].$$

Our problem amounts to solving this equation for the unknown effective interest rate r, when $A = 10000$, $P = 486$, $k = 3$ and $n = 12$. It is convenient to change the unknown to x, where

$$x = 1 + r/n\,.$$

If we re-arrange the expression for P, and define $f(x)$ as

$$f(x) = Ax^{nk+1} - (A + P)x^{nk} + P\,,$$

then we have to solve the equation

$$f(x) = 0\,,$$

which must be done with Newton's method. This requires the first derivative of $f(x)$, *viz.*

$$f'(x) = (nk + 1)Ax^{nk} - nk(A + P)x^{nk-1}\,.$$

As an exercise, program Newton's method to solve this problem. Remember that the interest rate r is given by

$$r = n(x-1).$$

You will find that the effective annual interest rate is no less than 40.8 per cent!

The bisection method

Consider again the problem of solving the equation

$$f(x) = x^3 + x - 3 = 0.$$

We attempt to find by inspection, or trial-and-error, two values of x, call them x_L and x_R, such that $f(x_L)$ and $f(x_R)$ have different signs, ie $f(x_L)f(x_R) < 0$. If we can find two such values, the implication is that the root lies somewhere in the interval between them, since $f(x)$ changes sign on this interval (see Figure 16.2). In this example, $x_L = 1$ and $x_R = 2$ will do, since $f(1) = -1$ and $f(2) = 7$. In the Bisection method, we estimate the root by x_M, where x_M is the midpoint (hence the name **bisection**) of the interval $[x_L; x_R]$, ie

$$x_M = (x_L + x_R)/2 \qquad (2)$$

Then if $f(x_M)$ has the same sign as $f(x_L)$, as drawn in the figure, the root clearly lies betwen x_M and x_R. We must then redefine the lefthand end of the interval as having the value of x_M, ie we let the new value of x_L be x_M. Otherwise, if $f(x_M)$ and $f(x_L)$ have different signs, we let the new value of x_R be x_M, since the root must lie between x_L and x_M in that case. Having redefined x_L or x_R as the case may be, we bisect the new interval again according to equation (2) and repeat the process until the distance between x_L and x_R is as small as we please.

The neat thing about this method is that we can calculate before starting how many bisections are needed to obtain a certain accuracy, given initial values of x_L and x_R. (With Newton's method, we can never be sure exactly how many iterations will be needed.) Suppose we start with $x_L = a$, and $x_R = b$. After the first bisection the worst possible error (E_1) in x_M is

$$E_1 = |a - b|/2 ,$$

since we are estimating the root as being at the midpoint of the interval $[a; b]$. The worst that can happen is that the root is actually at x_L or x_R, in which case the error is E_1. After the second bisection, the error E_2 will obviously be half of E_1, ie

$$E_2 = |a - b|/4 = |a - b|/2^2 .$$

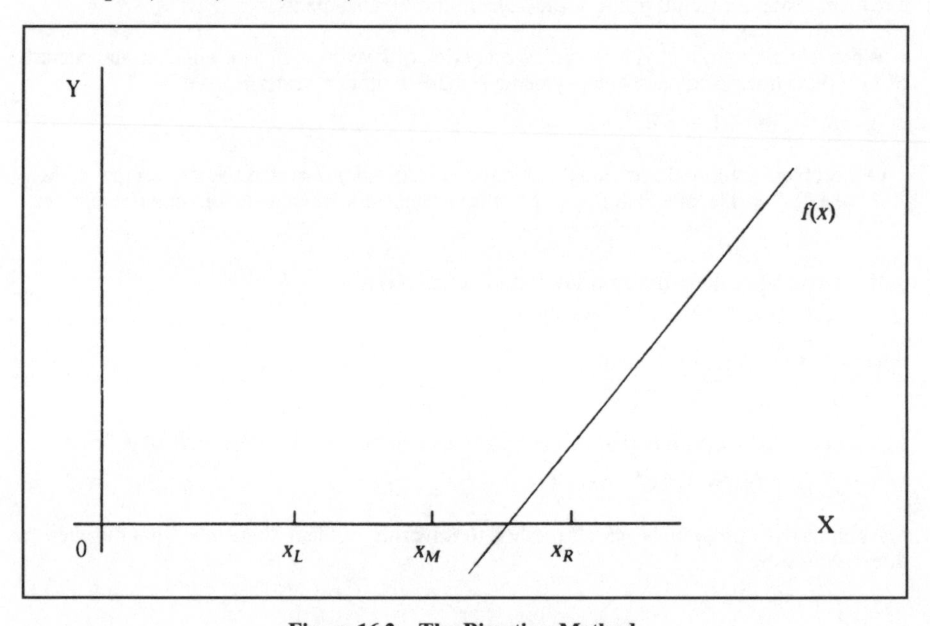

Figure 16.2 The Bisection Method

Carrying on like this, after n bisections the worst possible error E_n is given by

$$E_n = |a - b|/2^n.$$

If we want to be sure that this is less than some specified error E, we must see to it that n satisfies the inequality

$$|a - b|/2^n < E,$$

ie $\quad 2^n > |a - b|/E,$

ie $\quad n \log(2) > \log(|a - b|/E),$

ie $\quad n > \log(|a - b|/E)/\log(2) \qquad (3)$

Since n is the number of bisections, it must be an integer. The smallest integer n that exceeds the righthand side of inequality (3) will do as the maximum number of bisections required to guarantee the given accuracy E.

The following scheme may be used to program the Bisection method. It will work for any function $f(x)$ that changes sign (in either direction) between the two values a and b, which must be found beforehand by the user.

1. Read a, b and E
2. Initialise x_L and x_R
3. Compute maximum bisections n from inequality (3)
4. Repeat n times:
   4.1. Compute x_M according to equation. (2)
   4.2. If $f(x_L)f(x_M) > 0$ then
      4.2.1. Let $x_L = x_M$ otherwise
      4.2.2. Let $x_R = x_M$
5. Write root x_M
6. Stop.

We have assumed that the procedure will not find the root exactly because of the minute chances of the equality comparison being true. But if you are skeptical, you can replace step 4 in the plan with a **while-do** loop!

An advantage of the Bisection method is that it is guaranteed to find you a root if you can find two starting values for x_L and x_R between which the function will change sign. You can also compute in advance the number of bisections needed to attain a given accuracy. Its disadvantage is that it is an inefficient method, in that successive bisections do not necessarily move closer to the root, as often happens with Newton's method. In fact, it is interesting to compare the two methods on the same function to see how many more steps the Bisection method requires than Newton's method. For example, to solve the equation stated above,

$$x^3 + x - 3 = 0,$$

the Bisection method takes 21 steps to reach the same accuracy as Newton's in five steps.

16.2 INTEGRATION

Although most respectable mathematical functions can be differentiated analytically, the same cannot unfortunately be said for integration. There are no general rules for integrating, as there are for differentiating. (This is an interesting fact of mathematical life which you may wish to ponder!) For example, the indefinite integral of a function as simple as

$$e^{-x^2}$$

cannot be found mathematically. We therefore need a numerical method for evaluating integrals.

This is actually quite easy to do, and depends on the well-known fact that the definite integral of a function $f(x)$ between the limits $x = a$ and $x = b$ is equal to the area under $f(x)$ bounded by the x-axis and the two lines $x = a$ and $x = b$. So all numerical methods for integrating simply involve more or less ingenious ways of estimating the area under $f(x)$.

One rough and ready, yet perfectly valid, way of doing this is by drawing the curve of $f(x)$ on squared graph paper (the smaller the squares the better) and counting the number of squares that fall under the curve. The only problem is what to do when the graph cuts across a square: do you count the square, or not, or how much of it do you count? The method that we will consider below, called the Trapezoidal (or Trapezium) Rule, effectively approximates $f(x)$ by a straight line across each square that it crosses, for the compelling reason that every schoolchild knows how to calculate the area of the resulting shape, which is a series of trapezia.

The Trapezoidal Rule

Before we derive the rule, a little notation will make the problem clearer. We want to integrate $f(x)$ with respect to x between the limits $x = a$ and $x = b$. We divide the area under $f(x)$ up into a lot of vertical panels of equal width h (called the panel-width, or step-length, or grid-size). One such panel is shown in Figure 16.3. If there are n such panels, then clearly

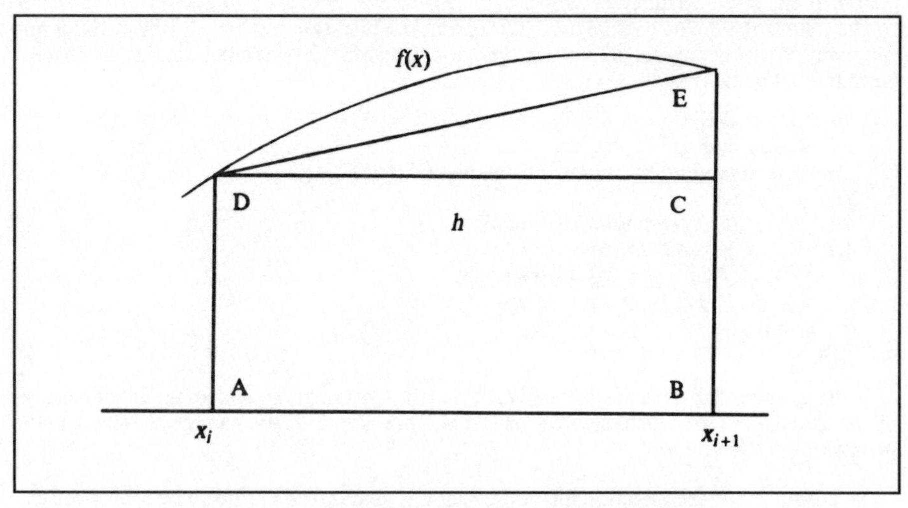

Figure 16.3 A Typical Panel for the Trapezoidal Rule.

$$h = (b - a)/n, \text{ so that } n = (b - a)/h. \quad (4)$$

The vertical edges of the panels will meet the x-axis at the points

$$x_0 = a, x_1 = a + h, x_2 = a + 2h, ..., x_n = a + nh = b. \quad (5)$$

If we draw a straight line across the top of each panel, from the point $(x_0, f(x_0))$ to $(x_1, f(x_1))$, and then to the point $(x_2, f(x_2))$, etc., we will have a set of n trapezia, and we can approximate the area under $f(x)$ by the area of these trapezia.

One such trapezium is shown in Figure 16.3. The area ABCDE is

$$h(\text{AD} + \text{BE})/2 = h[f(x_i) + f(x_{i+1})]/2.$$

The area S we are after is the sum of the areas of all such trapezia, ie

$$S = h[f(x_0) + f(x_1)]/2 + h[f(x_1) + f(x_2)]/2 + ... + h[f(x_{n-1}) + f(x_n)]/2$$

$$= 0.5h[f(a) + f(b) + 2\sum_{i=1}^{n-1} f(x_i)] \quad (6)$$

Equation (6) is the **Trapezoidal Rule**. As an example, we will write a program to evaluate the integral of

$$f(x) = x^3$$

between the limits 0 and 4. The exact answer is 64. The program assumes that h will be chosen in such a way that the number of steps n will be an integer.

A new type is introduced here: **procedural** type. If you look at the procedure **Trap** below, you will see that the function being integrated is called **F**. It restricts the usefulness of the procedure if the function must also be known by that name in the calling program. The use of procedural types allows you to pass the name of any function or procedure as a procedural type parameter.

The procedural type must be declared **(Integrand)**. The syntax for a procedural type declaration is the same as for a procedure or function header, except that the identifier after the keyword **function** or **procedure** must be omitted. The parameter names in a procedural type declaration are dummy names.

The function or procedure to be passed as a parameter must be compiled in the {**$F+**} state.

To emphasise what is happening here, the function name in the calling program below is **Y**, whereas the formal procedural parameter in the declaration of **Trap** is **F**. *Any real function whose header contains a single real parameter can be passed to* **Trap.**

There is somewhat more to procedural types that is shown here (for example procedural **variables**). Please refer to the *Reference Guide* for the full treatment.

```
program Integrator;
type
  Integrand = function( X: real ): real;
var
  A, B, H, S: real;

{$F+}
function Y( X: real ): real;
{ Integrand }
begin
  Y:= X * X * X
end; { Y }
{$F-}

procedure Trap( var S: real; A, B, H: real; F: Integrand );
{ Integrates F( X ) from A to B with step-length H }
var
  I, N : word;
begin
  S:= 0;
  N:= Round( (B - A) / H );
  for I:= 1 to N-1 do
    S:= S + F( A + I * H );
  S:= H / 2 * (F( A ) + F( B ) + 2 * S)
end; { Trap }

begin
  A:= 0;
  B:= 4;
  Write( 'H? ' );
  Readln( H );
  Trap( S, A, B, H, Y );
  Writeln( 'Integral by Trapezoidal rule: ', S:8:4 )
end.
```

Table 16.1 shows the results obtained for some different values of h. It is clear that as h gets smaller, the estimated integral S becomes more accurate. You can make h as small as you like, which is not the case with differentiation (see below).

Table 16.1 Effect of different step-lengths when integrating

h	*Integral (S)*
1.00	68.0000
0.50	65.0000
0.10	64.0400
0.01	64.0004

This example assumes that $f(x)$ is a continuous function which may be calculated at any x. In practice, the function could be defined at discrete points supplied as results of an experiment. For example, the speed of an object $v(t)$ might be measured every so many seconds, and one might want to estimate the distance travelled as the area under the speed-time graph. The procedure **Trap** can be adapted if one replaces the function **F(X)** by an array

```
F: array[ 0..N ] of real;
```

into which the experimental values have been read. The references to **F(A), F(A + I * H)** and **F(B)** in Trap will have to be replaced by **F[0], F[I]** and **F[N]** respectively. Obviously, in this case a procedural type cannot be used.

16.3 NUMERICAL DIFFERENTATION

The Newton quotient for a function $f(x)$ is given by

$$[f(x + h) - f(x)]/h, \qquad (*)$$

where h is small. As h tends to zero, this quotient approaches the first derivative, df/dx. The Newton quotient may therefore be used to estimate a derivative numerically. It is a useful exercise to do this with a few functions for which you know the derivatives. This way you can see how small you can make h before rounding errors cause problems. These arise because expression (*) involves differencing two terms that eventually become equal when the limit of the computer's accuracy is reached. As an example, the following program uses the Newton quotient to estimate $f'(x)$ for

$$f(x) = x^2$$

at $x = 2$, for smaller and smaller values of h (the exact answer is 4). The results are shown in Table 16.2.

```
program Differentiator;
var
  DF, H, X: real;
  I: byte;
function F( X: real ): real;
begin
  F:= X * X
end; { F }
Begin
  X:= 2;
  H:= 1;
  for I:= 1 to 13 do
  begin
    DF:= (F( X + H ) - F( X )) / H;
    Writeln( H:8, DF:15:8 );
    H:= H / 10
  end;
end.
```

The results show that the best h for this particular problem is about 1E−6. But for h much smaller than this the estimate becomes totally unreliable. Using double type in the **{$N+}** state should improve the accuracy. Generally, the best h for a given problem can only be found by trial and error. Finding it constitutes a major problem of numerical analysis. This problem does not arise with numerical integration, because numbers are added to find the area, not subtracted.

h	df/dx
1.0E+00	5.00000000
1.0E−01	4.10000000
1.0E−02	4.01000000
1.0E−03	4.00100000
1.0E−04	4.00010002
1.0E−05	4.00001009
1.0E−06	4.00000135
1.0E−07	4.00003046
1.0E−08	4.00032150
1.0E−09	4.00177669
1.0E−10	3.92901711
1.0E−11	4.36557457
1.0E−12	0.00000000

Table 16.2 Effect of different step-length when differentiating numerically.

The next program uses the Newton quotient to draw the derivative of any given function. The function is also drawn. A procedural type is also used here. The function or its derivative can be passed to **DrawFunc**: it can draw either.

The program could be a useful aid to teaching calculus. For example, zeros of the derivative can be clearly seen when the function has a maximum or minimum. You will be surprised at the effect different values of h, between 2 and 0.0001, say, have on the numerical derivative of the particular function used here.

```
program Calculus;
uses Graph, MyGraphs;
type
  Func = function( X: real ): real;
const
  Xmin : real = 0;
  Xmax : real = 10;
  Ymin : real = -8;
  Ymax : real = 8;
var
  H, X: real;
  GrDriver, GrMode: Integer;

procedure Axes;
begin
  ScLine( Xmin, 0, Xmax, 0 );
  ScLine( 0, Ymin, 0, Ymax )
end; { Axes }
{$F+}
function F( X: real ): real;
begin
  F:= 4 * Sin( X ) + Cos( 4 * X )
end; { F }
function DF( X: real ): real;
begin
  DF:= (F( X + H ) - F( X )) / H
end; { DF }
{$F-}
procedure DrawFunc( F: Func );
begin
  X:= 0;
  ScMoveTo( X, F( X ) );
  while X < Xmax do
  begin
    ScLineTo( X, F( X ) );
    X:= X + Pi / 40
  end;
end; { DrawFunc }

begin
  GrDriver:= Detect;
  InitGraph( GrDriver, GrMode, '\tp5' );
  SetViewPort( 0, 0, GetMaxX, GetMaxY div 2 - 10, True );
  SetWindow( Xmin, Xmax, Ymin, Ymax );
  Axes;
  DrawFunc( F );

  SetViewPort(0, GetMaxY div 2-5, GetMaxX, GetMaxY-10, True);
  SetWindow( Xmin, Xmax, Ymin, Ymax );
  Axes;
  repeat
    SetViewPort( 0, GetMaxY - 8, GetMaxX, GetMaxY, True );
    ClearViewPort;
    OutText( 'H? ' );
    GrRead( H );
    SetViewPort( 0, GetMaxY div 2 - 5 , GetMaxX, GetMaxY - 10, True );
```

```
    SetWindow( Xmin, Xmax, Ymin, Ymax );
    if H <> 0 then
      DrawFunc( DF );
  until H = 0;

  CloseGraph
end.
```

Output:

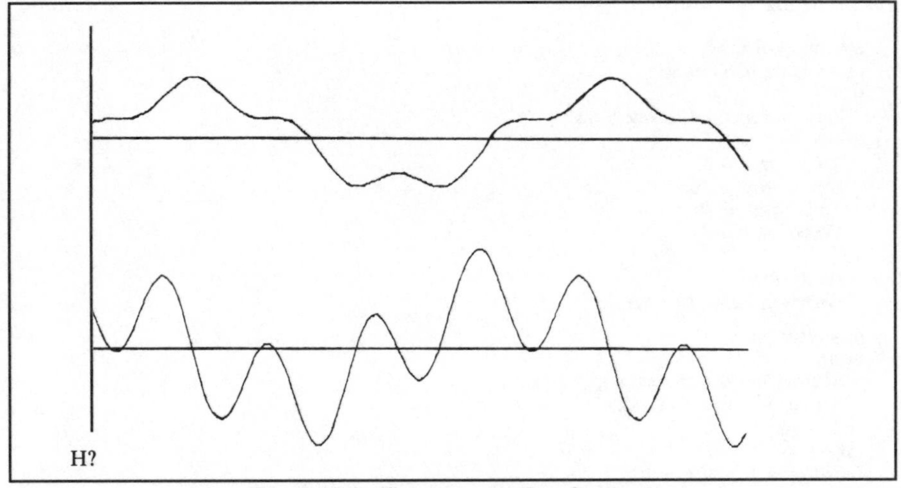

Figure 16.4 Computer produced output

16.4 FIRST-ORDER DIFFERENTIAL EQUATIONS

The most interesting situations in real life that we may want to model, or represent quantitatively, are usually those in which the variables change in time (for example biological, electrical or mechanical systems). If the changes are continuous, the system can often be represented with equations involving the derivatives of the dependent variables. Such equations are called **differential** equations. The main aim of a lot of modelling is to be able to write down a set of differential equations that describe the system being studied as accurately as possible. When one tries to solve these equations, one usually runs into difficulties pretty soon, because only a very small class of differential equations can be solved analytically. This is where numerical methods come in. We will consider only the simplest method of numerical solution in this section: Euler's method.

To illustrate it, we will take an example from Newtonian dynamics, of motion under gravity against air resistance. Suppose a parachutist steps out of a hovering helicopter, but does not open his parachute for 24 seconds. We would like to find his velocity as a function of time during this period. Assuming air resistance can not be neglected (ask any parachutist!), the man falls subject to two opposing vertical forces: gravity acting downward, and air resistance acting upward. The air resistance force is assumed to be proportional to the square of his velocity (this is fairly accurate). Applying Newton's second law to the parachutist, we have

$$ma = mg - pv^2,$$

where m is his mass, a his resultant downward acceleration, g the acceleration due to gravity, v his velocity, and p is a constant of proportionality. Dividing by m, we can rewrite this as

$$dv/dt = g - kv^2, \qquad (1)$$

where $k = p/m$. Equation (1) is the differential equation describing the motion of the parachutist under gravity. The constant k varies with shape and mass, and may be found experimentally from the **terminal velocity** of the falling object. This terminal velocity (v_T) is reached when the object stops accelerating, and may be found by equating the righthand side of equation (1) to zero. Thus

$$v_T = \sqrt{(g/k)}.$$

For a man wearing an unopened parachute, k is found to be about 0.004. Before we proceed with the numerical solution of equation (1) we should note that this particular differential equation can be solved analytically, since it is of the type called variable separable. If you know about such things, you should be able to do the integration and show that

$$v(t) = a(C - e^{-2akt})/(C + e^{-2akt}), \tag{2}$$

where $a = v_T$ and $C = [a + v(0)]/[a - v(0)]$. The basic problem to be overcome in trying to solve equation (1) numerically is the fact that a derivative (like dv/dt) can't be represented exactly on a digital computer, since the limit (as h tends to zero, where h is a small increment in t) cannot be found exactly. We therefore need to approximate the derivative, and we use the Newton quotient to do this.

Euler's method for parachutes

We now consider how to solve

$$dv/dt = g - kv^2, \tag{1}$$

numerically for $0 < t \leq 24$ seconds (since the air resistance constant k will change when the parachute is opened at $t = 24$ seconds). Euler's method consists of replacing the derivative on the lefthand side of equation (1) by its Newton quotient. If we do this we get

$$[v(t + h) - v(t)]/h = g - kv^2(t). \tag{3}$$

Making $v(t + h)$ the subject of this equation leads to

$$v(t + h) = v(t) + h[g - kv^2(t)]. \tag{4}$$

The point about equation (4) is that given v at some time t (for example $t = 0$), we can compute v at time $(t + h)$. We can then replace $v(t)$ on the righthand side of equation (4) by the $v(t + h)$ we have just found, and get $v(t + 2h)$, and so on, until we have computed v over the whole time interval.

The only thing that isn't obvious about this exercise is what value to give h. Let's try $h = 2$ seconds. Then from equation (4), starting at $t = 0$, we get

$$\begin{aligned} v(2) &= v(0) + 2[9.8 - 0.004 \times v^2(0)] \\ &= 0 + 2[9.8 - 0] \\ &= 19.6 \text{ m/s (the exact value from equation (2) is 18.64 m/s).} \end{aligned}$$

We have succeeded in integrating the differential equation numerically from $t = 0$ to $t = 2$! Putting $v(2)$ into the righthand side of equation (4) now gives us $v(4)$:

$$\begin{aligned} v(4) &= v(2) + 2[9.8 - 0.004 \times v^2(2)] \\ &= 19.6 + 2[9.8 - 0.004 \times 19.6^2] \\ &= 36.13 \text{ m/s (exact: 32.64 m/s).} \end{aligned}$$

$v(6)$ can now be computed:

$$\begin{aligned} v(6) &= v(4) + 2[9.8 - 0.004 \times v^2(4)] \\ &= 45.29 \text{ m/s (exact: 41.08).} \end{aligned}$$

We can go on like this for as long as we like. In general, equation (4) gives us Euler's rule for computing the next v^+ once we have v:

$$v^+ = v + h(g - kv^2). \tag{5}$$

It is very easy to write a program to do this, and then we can also test the accuracy of the numerical method by trying different values of h and comparing the results with the exact solution. The following program uses Euler's method as implemented in equation (4) or (5) to compute v for the first 24 seconds of the parachutist's motion.

```
program Euler { rhymes with boiler };
const
  G : real = 9.8;
  K : real = 0.004;
V : real = 0;
```

```
var
  H, T : real;
begin
  Readln( H );

  T:= H;
  while T <= 24 do
  begin
    V:= V + H * (G - K * V * V);
    Writeln( T:5:1, V:8:2 );
    T:= T + H
  end;

  Readln
end.
```

Time	*Velocity (m/s)*		
(secs)	h = *2*	h = *0.5*	*Exact*
2.0	19.60	18.94	18.64
4.0	36.13	33.45	32.64
6.0	45.29	42.00	41.08
8.0	48.48	46.22	45.50
10.0	49.28	48.11	47.65
12.0	49.45	48.92	48.65
14.0	49.49	49.26	49.11
16.0	49.50	49.40	49.32
18.0	49.50	49.46	49.42
20.0	49.50	49.48	49.46
22.0	49.50	49.49	49.48
24.0	49.50	49.49	49.49

Table 16.3 Euler's method on equation (1): parachute closed

Table 16.3 shows the results for $h = 2$ and $h = 0.5$, compared with the exact solution computed from equation (2) taking $v(0) = 0$, since the helicopter is hovering. We see from the table that the numerical solution is quite a lot better for the smaller of the two values of h, the worst error being only about 3 per cent. We also see that the parachutist's terminal velocity (49.5 m/s) is correctly computed for both values of h. The errors in fact get less and less as t approaches 24 seconds.

In a real problem, we don't usually know the exact answer, or we wouldn't be using a numerical method in the first place. The only check is to use smaller and smaller values of h until it doesn't seem to make much difference.

Now let's see what happens when the man opens his parachute at $t = 24$ seconds. The air resistance term will be different now. For an open parachute, $k = 0.3$ is quite realistic. We can use the same program as before with a few minor changes, and obviously we need to supply a new starting value of 49.49 for v. Since $h = 0.5$ worked well last time, we try the same value now. The results are rather surprising:

Time	*Velocity*
24.0	−3.130E+02
24.5	−1.500E+04
25.0	−3.378E+07
25.5	−1.712E+14
26.0	−4.395E+27
. . .	

Not only does the man fly upward, he does so with tremendous speed, and soon exceeds the speed of light! The results make nonsense physically. Fortunately, in this example our intuition tells us that something is wrong. The only remedy is to reduce h. Some experimenting will reveal that the results for $h = 0.01$ are much better. A selection of these are shown in Table 16.4. To computethe exact solution correctly from equation (2), $t = 0$ must be when the parachute opens, so $v(0) = 49.49$.

Time (*secs*)	Velocity (*m/s*) h = *0.1*	*Exact*
24.01	42.24	43.18
24.02	36.99	38.31
24.03	32.98	34.45
24.04	29.81	31.31
24.05	27.25	28.71
24.06	25.12	26.53
24.07	23.32	24.66
24.08	21.79	23.06
24.09	20.46	21.66
24.10	19.30	20.43
24.20	12.69	13.32
24.30	9.85	10.24
24.40	8.34	8.59
24.50	7.45	7.62
24.60	6.88	7.00
24.70	6.51	6.60
24.80	6.27	6.33
24.90	6.10	6.14
25.00	5.98	6.02
26.00	5.72	5.73

Table 16.4 Euler's method on equation (1): parachute open.

It is instructive to examine why the method breaks down for $h = 0.5$ with the parachute open. Euler's method basically assumes that the derivative dv/dt (ie acceleration) is constant during the interval h. The use of the Newton quotient implies this. However, a glance at the correct results in Table 16.4 shows that this assumption doesn't hold over the period from $t = 24$ to $t = 24.5$ seconds. At the beginning of this period there is an enormous deceleration of about 6 m/s^2 over an interval of 0.01 seconds, whereas by the end of the first half second, the new terminal velocity has nearly been reached. The only way to correct the problem is to go on reducing h until the results seem reasonable. The principle is that h must be small enough to make the derivative approximately constant over the interval h.

Finally, we should note that Euler's method will be just as easy to compute if the air resistance term is not kv^2, but $kv^{1.8}$ (which is more realistic), although now an analytic solution cannot be found.

Euler's method in general

In general we want to solve a first-order differential equation of the form

$$dy/dx = f(x, y), \qquad y(0) \text{ given.}$$

Euler's method replaces dy/dx by its Newton quotient, so the differential equation becomes

$$[y(x + h) - y(x)]/h = f(x, y). \tag{6}$$

Denoting $y(x)$ by y and $y(x + h)$ by y^+, we can use equation (6) to get y^+ in terms of y, starting with $y = y(0)$:

$$y^+ = y + hf(x, y). \qquad (7)$$

Equation (7) is repeated, replacing y by y^+ each time, until we have computed y over the required range of integration.

Euler's method for bacteria growth

Euler's method performs quite adequately in the parachutist problem once we have got the right value of the step-length h. In case you think that the numerical solution of all differential equations is just as easy, we will now consider an example where Euler's method doesn't do too well.

Suppose a colony of 1000 bacteria are multiplying at the rate of $r = 0.8$ per hour per individual (ie an individual produces an average of 0.8 offspring every hour). How many bacteria are there after 10 hours? Assuming that the colony grows continuously and without restriction, we can model this growth with the differential equation

$$dN/dt = rN, \qquad N(0) = 1000, \qquad (8)$$

where $N(t)$ is the population size at time t. This process is called **exponential growth**. Equation (8) may be solved analytically to give the well-known formula for exponential growth:

$$N(t) = N(0)e^{rt}. \qquad (9)$$

To solve equation (8) numerically, we apply Euler's algorithm to it by replacing dN/dt by its Newton quotient, to get

$$N(t + h) = N(t) + rhN(t).$$

Using the notation of equation (5), this can be written more concisely as

$$N^+ = N + rhN, \qquad (10)$$

where $N = 1000$ at time $t = 0$. We use equation (10) repeatedly, replacing N by N^+ each time. Taking $h = 0.5$ gives the results shown in Table 16.5, where the exact solution according to equation (9) is also given.

		Population N(t)	
time (hours)	*Euler*	*Predictor Corrector*	*Exact*
0.5	1400	1480	1492
1.0	1960	2190	2226
1.5	2744	3242	3320
2.0	3842	4798	4953
2.5	5378	7101	7389
3.0	7530	10509	11023
3.5	10541	15554	16445
4.0	14758	23019	24533
4.5	20661	34069	36598
5.0	28925	50422	54598
5.5	40496	74624	81451
6.0	56694	110444	121510
6.5	79371	163457	181272
7.0	111120	241916	270426
7.5	155568	358035	403429
8.0	217795	529892	601845
8.5	304913	784240	897847
9.0	426879	1160676	1339431
9.5	597630	1717800	1998196
10.0	836683	2542344	2980958

Table 16.5 Bacteria growth ($h = 0.5$)

This time the numerical solution (in the column headed *Euler*) is not too good. In fact, the error gets worse at each step, and after 10 hours of bacteria time it is about 72 per cent. Of course, the numerical solution will improve if we take h smaller, but there will still always be some value of t, however big, where the error exceeds some acceptable limit.

We may ask why Euler's method works so well with the parachutist, but so badly with the bacteria. The answer, as we mentioned earlier, lies in the type of numerical approximation to the derivative that is used. By using the Newton quotient each time in Euler's method, we are assuming that the derivative changes very little over the small interval h, ie that the *second* derivative is very small. Now in the case of the parachutist, by differentiating equation (1) again with respect to time, we see that

$$d^2v/dt^2 = -(2kv)dv/dt,$$

which approaches zero as the falling object reaches its terminal velocity (since dv/dt approaches zero at terminal velocity, by definition). In the bacteria case, the second derivative of $N(t)$ is found by differentiating equation (8). We get

$$d^2N/dt^2 = rdN/dt = r^2N(t).$$

This is far from zero at $t = 10$. In fact, it is approaching three million! The Newton quotient approximation gets worse at each step in this case. There are better numerical methods for overcoming these sorts of problems. Two of them are discussed below. More sophisticated methods may be found in most textbooks on numerical analysis. However, Euler's method may always be used as a first approximation as long as you realise where and why errors may arise.

A predictor-corrector method

One improvement on the solution of

$$dy/dx = f(x, y), \qquad y(0) \text{ given},$$

is as follows. Euler says compute

$$y^+ = y + hf(x, y) \tag{7}$$

repeatedly. But this formula favours the old value of y in computing $f(x, y)$ on the righthand side. Surely it would be better to say

$$y^+ = y + h[f(x + h, y^+) + f(x, y)]/2, \tag{11}$$

since this also involves the new value y^+ in computing f on the righthand side. The problem is that y^+ is as yet unknown, so we can't use it on the righthand side of equation (11). But we could use Euler to estimate (predict) y^+ from equation (7) and then use equation (11) to correct the prediction by computing a better version of y^+, say y^+. So the full procedure is:

1. Repeat as many times as required:
   1.1. Use Euler to predict:
   $y^+ = y + hf(x, y)$
   1.2. Then correct y^+ as follows:
   $y^+ = y + h[f(x + h, y^+) + f(x, y)]/2$
   1.3. Replace y by y^+.

This is called a **predictor-corrector** method. It can be applied to the bacteria growth problem as follows, and only requires one extra line in the computer program:

1. Repeat for t = 0.5 to 10.0:
   1.1. $N^+ = N + rhN$ (predictor, as before)
   1.2. $N^+ = N + rh(N^+ + N)/2$ (corrector)
   1.3. Replace N by N^+.

The results with this method are also shown in Table 16.5. The worst error is now only 15 per cent. This is much better than the uncorrected Euler algorithm, although there is still much room for improvement.

16.5 RUNGE-KUTTA METHODS

There are a variety of algorithms, under the general name of **Runge-Kutta**, of varying degrees of accuracy, which can be used to integrate almost any system of ordinary differential equations. The **fourth-order** formula is given below, for reference. A derivation of this and the other Runge-Kutta formulae can be found in most books on numerical analysis.

Runge-Kutta fourth-order formulae

The general differential equation is

$$dy/dx = f(x, y), \qquad y(0) \text{ given.} \qquad (*)$$

The fourth-order Runge-Kutta estimate y^+ at $x = h$ is given by

$$y^+ = y + (k_1 + 2k_2 + 2k_3 + k_4)/6,$$

where

$$k_1 = hf(x, y)$$
$$k_2 = hf(x + 0.5h, y + 0.5k_1)$$
$$k_3 = hf(x + 0.5h, y + 0.5k_2)$$
$$k_4 = hf(x + h, y + k_3).$$

A predator-prey model

The Runge-Kutta formulae may be adapted to integrate systems of first-order differential equations. Here we adapt the fourth-order formulae to integrate the well-known Lotka-Volterra **predator-prey** model:

$$dx/dt = px - qxy \; (= f(x, y))$$
$$dy/dt = rxy - sy \; (= g(x, y)),$$

where $x(t)$ and $y(t)$ are the prey and predator population sizes at time t, and p, q, r and s are biologically determined parameters. In this case, the values of x and y at some time t may be used to find x^+ and y^+ at time $(t+h)$ with the formulae

$$x^+ = x + (k_1 + 2k_2 + 2k_3 + k_4)/6$$
$$y^+ = y + (m_1 + 2m_2 + 2m_3 + m_4)/6$$

where

$$k_1 = hf(x, y)$$
$$m_1 = hg(x, y)$$
$$k_2 = hf(x + 0.5k_1, y + 0.5m_1)$$
$$m_2 = hg(x + 0.5k_1, y + 0.5m_1)$$
$$k_3 = hf(x + 0.5k_2, y + 0.5m_2)$$
$$m_3 = hg(x + 0.5k_2, y + 0.5m_2)$$
$$k_4 = hf(x + k_3, y + m_3)$$
$$m_4 = hg(x + k_3, y + m_3)$$

It should be noted that in this example x and y are the dependent variables, and t (which does *not* appear explicitly in the equations) is the independent variable, whereas in the general formula (*) quoted above, y is the dependent variable, and x is the independent variable.

16.6 A DIFFERENTIAL EQUATION MODELLING PACKAGE

This book concludes with an example of **interactive modelling** in Turbo Pascal. The **MiniDriver** program in this section is a very much simplified version of a general model driving program (about 122K in size) which I have written, called **Driver**. If you want a copy of **Driver**, please send a blank 5¼″ disk to me at the address in the program listing below. The disk will be returned with Driver, a fully compiled demonstration model, and a comprehensive user manual.

The basis of **MiniDriver** (and Driver) is a fourth-order Runge-Kutta procedure (which differs slightly from the one given in the previous section) to integrate a general system of first-order differential equations. The example used below is the predator-prey model of the previous section, with $x(0) = 105$, $y(0) = 8$, $p = 0.4$, $q = 0.04$, $r = 0.02$, and $s = 2$.

The state variables x and y are represented by the array **Varias**, which is an array of

```
VarType = record
            Name: Str8;
            InVal, Val, LoBound, UpBound: real
          end;
```

The **Name** field is for the variable's common or garden name (for example 'Prey' and 'Pred'). The fields **InVal** and **Val** are for the initial and current values. **LoBound** and **UpBound** are lower and upper bounds which are used in drawing the phase diagram (a graph of $x(t)$ against $y(t)$).

The parameters p, q, r and s are represented by the array **Params**, which is an array of records with only two fields: **Name** and **Val**.

The righthand sides of the model differential equations, f and g, are stored in the components **F[1]** and **F[2]** of the array **F**, which is set up in the procedure **DiffEqns**. There is in principle no limit to the number of state variables (denoted by the constant **NVar**) that can be handled by the program.

Arrays must be used for the variables and parameters so that general models of any size can be handled. This rather cumbersome notation results in coding for the righthand sides of the differential equations as follows:

```
F[1]:= Params[1].Val * Varias[1].Val - Params[2].Val * Varias[1].Val * Varias[2].Val;
F[2]:= Params[3].Val * Varias[1].Val * Varias[2].Val - Params[4].Val * X[2];
```

This is far removed from what the original model looked like! A larger model will be much worse. However, a trick known as *masquerading variables* has been used to overcome this problem of notation. This solution was suggested to me by Don Taylor, President of TUG (Turbo Users' Group).

Masquerading variables

The ideal is for us to be able to use meaningful identifiers for the variables and parameters in the formulation of the model differential equations. But Pascal's strict rules require such identifiers to be declared with a type. We get around this by declaring a whole bunch of dummy variables for each field of each record in **Params** and **Varias**. The arrays are made to share the same memory addresses as these variables by means of **absolute** clauses. So in the program below, **PN1, PV1, ..., PV4** will occupy adjacent bytes in memory. The **absolute** clause in the declaration of **Params** ensures that **Params[1].Name** occupies the same bytes as **PN1, Params[1].Val** the same bytes as **PV1**, and so on. A similar set of **absolute** declarations in the procedure **Model** lay the user's more meaningful variable and parameter names over these addresses in turn. So, for example, **Prey, V1** and **Varias[1].Val** *all occupy the same bytes of memory.* The same piece of memory therefore masquerades under three different names. (In the more general **Driver** program the **absolute** declarations in the **Model** procedure are generated automatically by an auxiliary program.) The only really messy aspect of all this is the block of dummy names **PN1, PN2, ...**, that have to be coded (the full version of **Driver** has 75 variables and parameters!).

For the masquerade to work, the **{$A−}** compiler directive must be used, to switch off **word alignment**. Under Turbo Pascal 5.5 data is word-aligned by default, ie the starting addresses of all data are even, because this makes for faster access. If a data item would normally fall on an odd-numbered address, the compiler adds a blank byte to force the new item to begin on a word boundary. However, masquerading requires data to be stored at contiguous addresses, so word alignment must be switched off.

The {**$A**} directive is not supported by Turbo Pascal 4.0 (word alignment does *not* take place), so it must be omitted for **MiniDriver** and **Driver** to run under that version.

Commands in MiniDriver

MiniDriver is driven by commands from the user. It allows you to start integrating the model equations from the initial conditions (''GO''), or from the current values (''CA'', for ''carry on''). You can display the results in table form (''TA''), or in the form of phase plane trajectories (''PH''), which results in a graph of $x(t)$ against $y(t)$. You can change (''CH'') the values of the integration step-length and the total running time, while ''IN'' enables you to set the output intervals in multiples of the step-length. The sample output below shows the initial run with the data as given.

Extensions available in Driver

MiniDriver initialises all variables and parameters in the procedure **Initial**. The full version of **Driver** stores these in a text file on disk (known as the *reference file*). The reference file is read at the start of each session. The menu has been extended to allow changes to all parameters and variables (initial or current values). These changes are automatically echoed to a text file (the *print file*) for viewing or printing at a later stage. Screen output can be optionally echoed to the print file.

Plots of a number of variables against time may be made. The list of variables being plotted at any time may be changed by the user during execution. Graphs can be superimposed or drawn alongside each other for comparison.

The present phase plane analysis is extended to allow any variable to be plotted against any other. Phase plane graphs may also be superimposed, so that, for example, the effect of different initial conditions may be seen.

Information such as the step-length, runtime, output interval and mode of output (tabular, phase plane, etc.) is also stored in the reference file. The latest graphics screen can be written to a disk file for viewing and reading at a later stage. Finally, at the end of the session there is an option to rewrite the reference file in order to save all current values.

Listing of MiniDriver

```
program MiniDriver;
{ Interactive Modelling Package                                          }
{ Send a blank 5¼" diskette for the complete version, plus user          }
{ manual, to:                                                            }
{   Brian D Hahn,                                                        }
{   Dept of Applied Mathematics,                                         }
{   University of Cape Town,                                             }
{   Rondebosch 7700,                                                     }
{   South Africa                                                         }
{   Telephone: 021-650-2341                                              }
{$A-}                     { variables not aligned on machine-word boundaries }

uses Crt, Graph, MyGraphs;
const
  First : boolean   = True;
  NVar              = 2;
  NPar              = 4;
  OutWidth          = 10;
type
  Str2     = string[2];
  Str8     = string[8];
  VarType  = record
               Name: Str8;
               InVal, Val, LoBound, UpBound: real
           end;
  ParType  = record
```

```
            Name: Str8;
            Val: real
var       end;
  Ans                         : Str2;
  T, Dt                       : real;                          { model time }
  Xmin, Xmax, Ymin, Ymax : real;
  OpIntScr                    : longint;            { output interval on screen }
  OpType                      : byte;               { 1: Table; 2: Phase plane }
  GrDriver, GrMode, I         : integer;
  RunTime, Time               : longint;                     { iteration count }
  Pic                         : pointer;                        { screen image }

  PN1: string[8]; PV1: real;                  { set up parameter masquerade }
  PN2: string[8]; PV2: real;
  PN3: string[8]; PV3: real;
  PN4: string[8]; PV4: real;

  Params: array[ 1..NPar ] of ParType absolute PN1;

  VN1: Str8; I1, V1, L1, U1 : real;             { set up variable masquerade }
  VN2: Str8; I2, V2, L2, U2 : real;

  Varias: array[ 1..NVar ] of VarType absolute VN1;

procedure Header; forward;
procedure Model; forward;
procedure Out1( Which: integer ); forward;
procedure Out2; forward;

procedure CarryOn;
{ continue running model from current values of variables }
begin
  Header;
  if (OpType = 2) and not First then
    PutImage( 0, 0, Pic^, 0 );
  First:= False;
  Model
end; { CarryOn }

procedure Change;
{ allows certain changes }
begin
  Writeln( 'Present values of RunTime and Dt are: ', Runtime, '      ', Dt:11 );
  Write(' Enter new values: ' );
  Readln( RunTime, Dt )
end; { Change }

procedure Header;
{ headings for table output }
          { sets up graphics for phase plane output }
begin
  if OpType = 1 then                                           { table output }
  begin
    Writeln; Writeln( 'Time', Varias[1].Name:OutWidth,
                      Varias[2].Name:OutWidth );
    Writeln
  end
  else if OpType = 2 then                                { phase plane output }
  begin
    SetGraphMode( GrMode );
    Xmin:= Varias[1].LoBound;
    Xmax:= Varias[1].UpBound;
    Ymin:= Varias[2].LoBound;
    Ymax:= Varias[2].UpBound;
    SetWindow( Xmin, Xmax, Ymin, Ymax );
    ScLine( Xmin, Ymin, Xmax, Ymin );
    ScLine( Xmin, Ymin, Xmin, Ymax );
    ScOutTextXY( (Xmin + Xmax) / 2, Ymin + 0.05 * (Ymax -Ymin),
```

```
Varias[1].Name );
      SetTextStyle( DefaultFont, VertDir, 1 );
      ScOutTextXY(Xmin + 0.02 * (Xmax - Xmin), (Ymin + Ymax)/ 2,
                  Varias[2].Name );
      ScMoveTo( Varias[1].Val, Varias[2].Val )
   end
end;
procedure Initial;
{ initialize everything }
begin
   Params[1].Val:= 0.4;
   Params[2].Val:= 0.04;
   Params[3].Val:= 0.02;
   Params[4].Val:= 2;
   Varias[1].Name:= 'Prey';
   Varias[2].Name:= 'Pred';
   Varias[1].InVal:= 105;
   Varias[2].InVal:= 8;
   Varias[1].Val:= 105;
   Varias[2].Val:= 8;
   Varias[1].LoBound:= 85;
   Varias[1].UpBound:= 115;
   Varias[2].LoBound:= 7;
   Varias[2].UpBound:= 13;
   Dt:= 1;
   T:= 0;
   Time:= 0;
   RunTime:= 20;
   OpIntScr:= 1;
   OpType:= 1
end; { Initial }
procedure Intervals;
{ allows change of output interval }
begin
   Writeln( 'Present screen output interval is: ', OpIntScr );
   Write( 'Enter new screen output interval (0 for no output): ' );
   Readln( OpIntScr )
end; { Intervals }

procedure Model;
var
   Itime: longint;
   F : array[ 1..NVar ] of real;

   Prey : real absolute V1;                    { the variable masquerade }
   Pred : real absolute V2;

   P : real absolute PV1;                      { the parameter masquerade }
   Q : real absolute PV2;
   R : real absolute PV3;
   S : real absolute PV4;

procedure DiffEqns;
{ model differential equations }
begin
   F[1]:= P * Prey - Q * Prey * Pred;
   F[2]:= R * Prey * Pred - S * Pred
end; { DiffEqns }

procedure Runge4;
{ fourth-order Runge-Kutta }
   var
      H, Z: real;
      A, B, C, D, X: array[ 1..NVar ] of real;         { working space }
      I : byte;

   begin
```

```
    for I:= 1 to NVar do
      X[I]:= Varias[I].Val;
    DiffEqns;
    for I:= 1 to NVar do
      A[I]:= Dt * F[I];
    for I:= 1 to NVar do
      Varias[I].Val:= X[I] + A[I] / 2;
    DiffEqns;
    for I:= 1 to NVar do
         B[I]:= Dt * F[I];
       for I:= 1 to NVar do
         Varias[I].Val:= X[I] + B[I] / 2;
       DiffEqns;
       for I:= 1 to NVar do
            C[I]:= Dt * F[I];
          for I:= 1 to NVar do
            Varias[I].Val:= X[I] + C[I];
          DiffEqns;
          for I:= 1 to NVar do
          begin
            D[I]:= Dt * F[I];
            Varias[I].Val:= X[I] + (A[I] + 2 * B[I] + 2 * C[I] + D[I]) / 6
          end
        end { Runge };

       begin { Model }
         Out1( -1 );                                          { write initial values }
     for Itime:= 1 to Runtime do
     begin
       Time:= Time + 1;                                      { total iteration count }
       T:= T + Dt;                                          { model time if we need it }
       Runge4;
       Out1( 0 )
     end;
     Out2
   end; { Model }

   procedure OpenGraphics;
   begin
     GrDriver:= Detect;
     InitGraph( GrDriver, GrMode, '\tp5' );
     GetMem( Pic, ImageSize( 0, 0, GetMaxX, GetMaxY ) )
   end;

   procedure Out1;
   { organizes output }
   var
     Screen: boolean;
     FrScr: real;
   begin
     Screen:= False;
     if Which = -1 then
       Screen:= True
     else
     begin
       FrScr:= Frac( Abs( Time ) / OpIntScr );
       if (1 - 1e-7 < FrScr) or (FrScr < 1e-7) then
         Screen:= True
     end;
     case OpType of
       1:     if Screen then Writeln( T:4:1, Varias[1].Val:OutWidth:2,
                                                Varias[2].Val:OutWidth:2 );
       2:     if Screen then ScLineTo( Varias[1].Val, Varias[2].Val )
         end
       end; { Out1 }
       procedure Out2;
                                   { tidies up at end of run }
```

```
begin
  if OpType = 2 then
  begin
    GetImage( 0, 0, GetMaxX, GetMaxY, Pic^ );
    Readln;
    RestoreCrtMode
  end;
end; { Out2 }

   procedure Run;
   { runs model from initial values }
   begin
     T:= 0;
     Time:= 0;
     for I:= 1 to NVar do
       Varias[I].Val:= Varias[I].InVal;
     Header;
     Model
   end; { Run }

   procedure Upper;
   { converts user response to uppercase }
   var
     Dum: Str2;
   begin
     for I:= 1 to 2 do
       Insert( UpCase( Ans[I] ), Dum, I );
     Ans:= Dum
   end; { Upper }
   begin { MiniDriver }
     Initial;
     ClrScr;
     OpenGraphics;
     RestoreCrtMode;
     Writeln( 'Mini Driver: the Interactive Modelling Tool' );

     repeat
       Ans:= '';
       Writeln;
           Write( 'What shall I do now? ' );
           Readln( Ans );
           Upper;
           if Ans = 'CA' then                        { carry on from current values }
         CarryOn
           else if Ans = 'CH' then                          { change RunTime or Dt }
             Change
           else if Ans = 'GO'then                            { run from initial values }
             Run
       else if Ans = 'IN' then                              { change output interval }
         Intervals
       else if Ans = 'PH' then                       { phase plane graphical output }
       begin
         OpType:= 2;
         Writeln( 'Phase plane output' )
       end
       else if Ans = 'TA' then                                       { table output }
       begin
         OpType:= 1;
         Writeln( 'Table output' )
       end
     until Ans = 'KI';                                    { KILL - end the session }

  CloseGraph;
end. { MiniDriver }
```

Sample output (initial run):

Time	Prey	Pred
0.0	105.00	8.00
1.0	110.88	9.47
2.0	108.32	11.65
3.0	98.83	12.57
4.0	91.12	11.26
5.0	90.30	9.24
6.0	95.81	7.98
7.0	104.30	7.99
8.0	110.45	9.34
9.0	108.61	11.48
10.0	99.58	12.52
11.0	91.65	11.37
12.0	90.33	9.39
13.0	95.37	8.07
14.0	103.63	7.99
15.0	110.00	9.23
16.0	108.83	11.31
17.0	100.29	12.46
18.0	92.20	11.47
19.0	90.40	9.53
20.0	94.97	8.17

SUMMARY

- A numerical method is an approximate computer method for solving a mathematical problem which often has no analytical solution.
- A numerical method is subject to two distinct types of error: rounding error in the computer solution, and **truncation error**, where an infinite mathematical process, like taking a limit, is approximated by a finite process.
- Procedural type may be used to pass a function or procedure name as a parameter.

EXERCISES

16.1 Write down Newton's algorithm to find the cube root of 2. Taking 1 as the starting value, use a calculator to do the first few iterations, and observe how fast they converge.

16.2 Use Newton's method in a program to solve some of the following (you may have to experiment a bit with the starting value):

(a) $x^4 - x = 10$ (two real roots)

(b) $e^{-x} = \sin(x)$ (infinitely many roots)

(c) $x^3 - 8x^2 + 17x - 10 = 0$ (three real roots)

(d) $\log(x) = \cos(x)$

(e) $x^4 - 5x^3 - 12x^2 + 76x - 79 = 0$ (two real roots near 2)

16.3 Use the Bisection method by hand to find the square root of 2, taking 1 and 2 as initial values of x_L and x_R. Continue bisecting until the maximum error is less than 0.05 (use inequality (3) of section 16.1 to determine how many bisections are needed).

16.4 Write a procedure **Root(var X: real; F: Func; A, B, Acc: real)** which uses the Bisection method to find the root **X** of a given function $f(x)$. **A** and **B** are the starting limits for the bisection (supplied by the user through the calling program) and **Acc** is the maximum acceptable error. **F** is a procedural type parameter for passing the name of $f(x)$, which must be declared in the calling program. Write a program which uses **Root** to solve one of the equations in Exercise 16.2.

16.5 Use the Trapezoidal rule by hand to evaluate

$$\int_0^4 x^2 dx,$$ using a step-length of $h = 1$.

16.6 Consider the differential equation

$dx/dt = 1 - x, \quad x(0) = 0.$

Use Euler's method by hand to estimate $x(1)$, using (a) two steps of length $h = 0.5$, and (b) four steps of length $h = 0.25$.

16.7 Use Euler's method by hand to evaluate the integral in Exercise 16.5 using the same step-length.

16.8 A human population of 1000 at time $t = 0$ grows at a rate given by

$$dN/dt = aN,$$

where $a = 0.025$ per person per year. Use Euler's method to project the population over the next 30 years, working in steps of (a) $h = 2$ years, (b) $h = 1$ year and (c) $h = 0.5$ years. Compare your answers with the exact mathematical solution.

16.9 Radio-active substance A decays into substance B at a rate given by the equation

$$dx/dt = -rx,$$

where x is the amount of A present at time t, and r is a constant called the decay rate.

(a) Solve for x as a function of t (analytically).

(b) Show that the initial amount of A present is reduced by half in time $T = 0.693/r$. (T is the half-life of A.)

(c) If y is the amount of B present at time t, and if $y = 0$ at time $t = 0$, deduce an expression for y as a function of t.

(d) Given $r = 0.0033$ per year, and $x = 10$ at time $t = 0$, use Euler's method to find x as a function of time for a period of 450 years. Work in steps of $h = 15$ years, and compare your answers with the exact solution.

16.10 Some radio-active substances decay into other radio-active substances, which in turn also decay. For example, Strontium 92 ($r_1 = 0.256$ per hr) decays into Yttrium 92 ($r_2 = 0.127$ per hr), which in turn decays into Zirconium. Write down a pair of differential equations for Strontium and Yttrium to describe what is happening.

Starting at $t = 0$ with 5×10^{26} atoms of Strontium 92 and none of Yttrium, use the Runge-Kutta formulae to solve the equations up to $t = 8$ hours in steps of 1/3 hr. Also use Euler's method for the same problem, and compare your results.

16.11 Solve numerically

$$dy/dx = x - y, \quad y(0) = 1,$$

over the domain [0; 1] using $h = 0.2$.

16.12 The impala population $x(t)$ in the Kruger National Park in South Africa may be modelled by the equation

$$dx/dt = [r - bx \sin(at)]x,$$

where r, b, and a are constants. Write a program which reads values for r, b, and a, and initial values for x and t, and which uses Euler's method to compute the impala population at monthly intervals over a period of two years.

16.13 Simpson's rule is a method of numerical integration which is a good deal more accurate than the Trapezoidal rule. The step-length h must be chosen so that there are an even number ($2n$) of panels. Using the notation of section 16.2, the formula for Simpson's rule is

$$(h/3)[f(a) + f(b) + 2\sum_{i=1}^{n-1} f(x_{2i}) + 4\sum_{i=1}^{n} f(x_{2i-1})].$$

Write a procedure to implement this formula. Try it out on the function $f(x) = x^3$ between any limits. You may find your answers surprising when you compare them with the exact mathematical solution.

16.14 The luminous efficiency (ratio of the energy in the visible spectrum to the total energy) of a black body radiator may be expressed as a percentage by the formula

$$E = 64.77T^{-4} \int_{4\times10^{-5}}^{7\times10^{-5}} x^{-5}(e^{1.432/Tx} - 1)^{-1}dx,$$

where T is the absolute temperature in degrees Kelvin, x is the wavelength in cm, and the range of integration is over the visible spectrum. Taking $T = 3500$°K, use Simpson's rule to compute E, firstly with 10 intervals ($n = 5$), and then with 20 intervals ($n = 10$), and compare your results.

16.15 Van der Pol's equation is a second-order non-linear differential equation which may be expressed as two first-order equations as follows:

$$dx_1/dt = x_2$$
$$dx_2/dt = a(1 - x_1 2)x_2 - b^2 x_1.$$

The solution of this equation has a stable limit cycle, which means that if you plot the phase trajectory of the solution (the plot of x_1 against x_2) starting at any point in the positive x_1-x_2 plane, it always moves continuously into the same closed loop. Use the Runge-Kutta method to solve this system numerically, with $h = 0.1$, $x_1(0) = 0$, and $x_2(0) = 1$. Draw the phase trajectory for $b = 1$ and a ranging between 0.01 and 1.0.

Epilogue
Program Style

Throughout this book the emphasis has been on writing clear, coherent programs to solve interesting problems. A program which is written any old how, although it may do what is required, is going to be difficult to understand when you go through it again after a month or two. Serious programmers therefore pay a fair amount of attention to what is called programming style, in order to make their programs clearer and more readable both to themselves, and to other potential users. You may find this irritating, if you are starting to program for the first time, because you will naturally be impatient to get on with the job. But a little extra attention to your program layout will pay enormous dividends in the long run, especially when it comes to debugging.

Some hints on how to improve your programming style are given below:

1. You should make liberal use of comments, both at the beginning of a program/-function/procedure, to describe briefly what it does and any special methods that may have been used, and also throughout the coding to introduce different logical sections. Any restrictions on the size and type of data that may be used as input should be stated clearly in the comments (for exampe, maximum sizes of arrays), and formal parameter types in functions/procedures should be prominently displayed.
2. The meaning of each variable should be described briefly in a comment at its declaration. You should declare variables systematically, for example in alphabetical order by type.
3. Blank lines should be freely used to separate sections of coding (for example before and after loop structures).
4. Coding inside structures (loops, decisions, **begin-end**) should be indented a few columns to make the logic more apparent.
5. Blanks should be used in statements in the following places:

   - on either side of operators;
   - after the equal sign in assignment statements;
   - after punctuation marks like commas and semi-colons.

   However, blanks may be omitted in places in complex expressions, where this may make the structure clearer.
6. It is strongly recommended that the **goto** statement ***never be used***, under any circumstances.
7. Functions and procedures should be arranged in alphabetical order with at least one blank line between them. Use a forward clause to achieve this, if necessary.

Appendix A
Quick Reference

A.1 Syntax Summary

Formal definitions of Pascal statements are given in terms of **syntax diagrams**, but these tend to be of more interest to the connoisseur (*the Reference Guide* abounds in them). What follows here is a collection of the most common examples of the syntax used in this book. Anything in angled brackets (for example **Read<ln>**) is optional. The angled brackets should not be typed literally.

```
absolute $0040:$0049;                  { segment and offset where var must go }
array[ 1..100 ] of real;
array[ 1..3, 1..3 ] of integer;                                  { 3x3 matrix }
begin                    { compound statement - no semi-colon needed before end }
  ...
end;
case Ch of                                                       { ordinal type }
  ‘a’, ‘e’, ‘i’, ‘o’, ‘u’: Writeln( ‘Vowel’ );
  ‘.’, ‘’‘’, ‘“’, ‘;’, ‘!’: Writeln( ‘Punctuation’ )
else
  Writeln( ‘Consonant’ )
end;
case I of
  2, 4, 6: statement1;
  10..25 : statement2
else
  statementE
end;
const                                   { untyped – may be a simple expression }
  C  = 150;
  C  = GetMaxX div 2;
  C  = Chr( 224 );
  C  = ‘File does not exist’;                                { string constant }
  C  = [‘a’..‘z’, ‘A’..‘Z’];                                    { set constant }
  C  = [ ];                                                        { empty set }
const                                      { typed: initialised at compilation }
  C  : array[ 1..4 ] of char = ‘ABCD’;
  C  : array[ 1..4 ] of char = (‘A’, ‘B’, ‘C’, ‘D’ );
  C  : array[ 1..3 ] of real = ( 7, 4, 7 );
  C  : array[ 1..2, 1..2 ] of integer = ((1, 2), (3, 4))             { by rows }
  C  : integer = 99;
  C  : set of ‘0’..z’ = [‘0’..‘9’, ‘A’..‘F’];
  C  : string[3] = ‘Yes’;
file of integer;
file of type;
for control:= first to last do statement;
for control:= first downto last do statement;
function Plonk( X, Y: real; N, M: integer ): type; <forward>;
if (X <= Y) and not (Y >= Z) then statement;
if condition then statement1< else statement2>;
```

```
if condition1 then
  statement1
else if condition2 then
  statement2
else if . . .
  . . .
else
  statementE;
procedure Plink( var X, Y: real; N, M : word ); <forward;>
record                          { fixed fields - see under type for variant records }
  Name      : string;
  ID        : array[ 1..10 ] of char
end;
repeat
  statement
until condition;
set of 'a'..'z';
type
  T  = (club, diamond, heart, spade );                    { enumerated }
  T  = ^array[1..20000] of byte;                          { pointer }
  T  = ^BaseType;                                         { pointer }
  T  = 0..99;                                             { subrange }
  T  = 'a'..'e';                                          { subrange }
  T  = array[ index type (ordinal) ] of type;
  T  = array[ 1..3, 1..3 ] of real;
  T  = array[ index1 ] of [ index2 ] ... of type;
  T  = file;                                              { untyped }
  T  = file of integer;
  T  = file of type;                                      { any type except file }
  T  = function( dummy parameters ): type;
     T  = procedure( dummy parameters );
     T  = record                                          { all fields fixed }
            Name : string;
            ID   : array[ 1..10 ] of char
        end;
     T  = record
            name : string;                                { fixed field }
            case person : boolean of                      { variant fields }
              True : ( BirthDate : string[6];
                       BirthPlace : string[20] );
              False : ( ExpiryDate : string[6] )
          end;
     T  = record
              case byte of                                { no tag field: free union variant }
                0 : ( Full : word );
                1 : ( Low : byte;
                      High : byte )
            end;
     T  = set of char;
     T  = set of 1..10;
     T  = set of ordinal type;                            { ordinal value 0 .. 255 }
     T  = string<[73]>;                                   { default length is 255 bytes (max) }
   uses units;
   var
     X:  boolean;          { False .. True }
     X:  byte;             { 0 .. 255}
     X:  char;             { single characters in extended ASCII set }
     X:  comp;             { -2^63+1 .. 2^63 - 1 }
     X:  double;           { 5.0e-324 ..1.7e308 }
     X:  extended;         { 3.4e-4932 .. 1.1e4932 }
     X:  integer;          { -32768 .. 32767 }
     X:  longint;          { -2147483648 .. 2147483647 }
     X:  pointer;          { generic pointer }
```

X: real;	**{ 2.9e−39 .. 1.7e38 }**
X: shortint;	**{ −128 .. 127 }**
X: single;	**{ 1.5e−45 ..3.4e38 }**
X: text;	**{ text file }**
X: type;	**{ any standard or user-defined type }**
X: type absolute $45:$42;	**{ specifies X's address in hex }**
X: type absolute ident;	**{ X starts at same address as ident }**
X: word;	**{ 0 .. 65535 }**

while ***condition*** **do** ***statement*;**
with ***record variable*** **do** ***statement*;**

A.2 EDITOR COMMANDS

Basic movement commands

Character left	**Ctrl-S** or **Left arrow**
Character right	**Ctrl-D** or **Right arrow**
Word left	**Ctrl-A** or **Ctrl-Left arrow**
Word right	**Ctrl-F** or **Ctrl-Right arrow**
Line up	**Ctrl-E** or **Up arrow**
Line down	**Ctrl-X** or **Down arrow**
Scroll up	**Ctrl-W**
Scroll down	**Ctrl-Z**
Page up	**Ctrl-R** or **PgUp**
Page down	**Ctrl-C** or **PgDn**

Extended movement commands

Beginning of line	**Ctrl-QS** or **Home**
End of line	**Ctrl-QD** or **End**
Top of window	**Ctrl-QE** or **Ctrl-Home**
Bottom of window	**Ctrl-QX** or **Ctrl-End**
Beginning of file	**Ctrl-QR** or **Ctrl-PgUp**
End of file	**Ctrl-QC** or **Ctrl-PgDn**
Beginning of block	**Ctrl-QB**
End of block	**Ctrl-QK**
Last cursor position	**Ctrl-QP**
Last error position	**Ctrl-QW**

Insert and delete commands

Insert compiler directives	**Ctrl-OO**
Insert line	**Ctrl-N**
Insert mode on/off	**Ctrl-V** or **Ins**
Delete block	**Ctrl-KY**
Delete line	**Ctrl-Y**
Delete to end of line	**Ctrl-QY**
Delete character left of cursor	**Ctrl-H** or **Backspace**
Delete character above cursor	**Ctrl-G** or **Del**
Delete word right of cursor	**Ctrl-T**

Block commands

Mark beginning of block	**Ctrl-KB**
Mark end of block	**Ctrl-KK**
Mark single word	**Ctrl-KT**
Print block	**Ctrl-KP**
Copy block	**Ctrl-KC**
Delete block	**Ctrl-KY**
Hide/display block	**Ctrl-KH**
Move block	**Ctrl-KV**
Read block from disk	**Ctrl-KR**
Write block to disk	**Ctrl-KW**

Indent block	**Ctrl-KI**
Unindent block	**Ctrl-KU**

Miscellaneous commands

Abort operation	**Ctrl-U**
Autoindent mode on/off	**Ctrl-OI** or **Ctrl-QI**
Control character prefix	**Ctrl-P**
Exit editor (no save)	**Ctrl-KD** or **Ctrl-KQ**
Fill mode on/off	**Ctrl-OF**
Find	**Ctrl-QF**
Find and replace	**Ctrl-QA**
Find *n*th place marker	**Ctrl-Q***n*
Go to last error position	**Ctrl-QW**
Invoke main menu	**F10**
Language help	**Ctrl-F1**
Load file	**F3**
Pair matching forward	**Ctrl-Q[**
Pair matching backward	**Ctrl-Q]**
Repeat last find	**Ctrl-L**
Restore line	**Ctrl-QL**
Save and remain in editor	**Ctrl-KS** or **F2**
Set *n*th place marker	**Ctrl-K***n*
Tab	**Ctrl-I** or **Tab**
Tab mode on/off	**Ctrl-OT** or **Ctrl-QT**
Unindent mode on/off	**Ctrl-OU**

A.3 HOT KEYS

F1	Calls up context-sensitive help
F2	Saves the file currently in the editor
F3	Loads a file
F4	Executes to the cursor location
F5	Zooms/unzooms the active window
F6	Switches the active window
F7	Traces into subroutines (functions/procedures)
F8	Steps over subroutine calls
F9	Performs a ''Make'' – recompiles updated units
F10	Toggles between main menu and active window
Alt-F1	Calls up last help screen you were reading
Alt-F3	Lets you pick a file to load
Alt-F5	Switches to the User screen
Alt-F6	Switches the contents of the active window
Alt-F9	Compiles the current program
Alt-B	Takes you to the **B**reak/Watch menu
Alt-C	Takes you to the **C**ompile menu
Alt-D	Takes you to the **D**ebug menu
Alt-E	Puts you in the **E**dit window
Alt-F	Takes you to the **F**ile menu
Alt-O	Takes you to the **O**ptions menu
Alt-R	Takes you to the **R**un menu
Alt-X	Quits Turbo Pascal and takes you to DOS
Ctrl-F1	Gives language help while in editor
Ctrl-F2	Terminates a debugging session
Ctrl-F3	Displays call stack when debugging
Ctrl-F4	Evaluates or modifies a variable
Ctrl-F7	Adds an expression to the Watch window
Ctrl-F8	Toggles breakpoint
Ctrl-F9	Runs the current program
Shift-F10	Displays the version screen

A.4 LAYOUT OF A TURBO PASCAL PROGRAM

PROGRAM *identifier*;
USES *unitnames*;
LABEL *declarations*;
CONST *declarations*;
TYPE *declarations*;
VAR *declarations*;
PROCEDURE *declarations*;
FUNCTION *declarations*;
BEGIN
 statements
END.

A.5 SPECIAL KEY COMBINATIONS

Ctrl-Alt-Del	Reboots the system
Ctrl-NumLock	Suspends execution (press any key to continue)
Ctrl-ScrollLock	Terminates execution
Ctrl-Break	

Appendix B
Standard Functions and Procedures

A summary of the standard functions and procedures used in this book follows. The unit is indicated where appropriate. A complete description of all functions and procedures appears in the *Reference Guide.* Angled brackets indicate optional parameters.

B.1 FUNCTIONS

Abs(X): real

returns the absolute value of *X*, which is real or integer type.

ArcTan(X): real

returns the principal value, in radians, of the arctangent of *X*, which is real type.

Chr(X): char

returns the character with ordinal value (ASCII code) *X*, which is an integer expression.

Concat(S1, S2, S2, ..., Sn): string

concatenates its string arguments.

Copy(S, Start, Number): string

returns *Number* characters from the string *S* starting with the *Start*th character of *S*.

Cos(X): real

returns the cosine of *X*, assumed to be an angle in radians.

Eof(<F>): boolean

returns the end-of-file status of a file. *F* is a typed or untyped file variable. If *F* is omitted, the standard file variable **Input** is assumed. **Eof** is True only if the current file position is beyond the last component of the file, or if the file is empty.

Eoln(<F>): boolean

returns the end-of-line status of a text file. *F* is a text file variable. If *F* is omitted, the standard file variable **Input** is assumed. **Eoln** is True only if the current file position is at an end-of-line marker, or if Eof is true.

Exp(X): real

returns the exponential of *X*, ie e^X.

FilePos(F): longint

returns the current file position of the file associated with the file variable *F.* The file *may not* be a text file. If the current file position is at the beginning of the file, **FilePos** returns 0. If the current file position is at the end of the file, **FilePos(F)** is equal to **FileSize(F).**

FileSize(F): longint

returns the current number of components in *F,* where *F* is a file variable. The file *may not* be a text file. If the file is empty, **FileSize** returns 0.

Frac(X): real

returns the fractional part of *X*.

GetBkColor: word

(**Graph** unit) returns the current background colour, in the range 0 to 15.

GetColor: word

(**Graph** unit) returns the current drawing colour in the palette.

GetGraphMode: integer

(**Graph** unit) returns the current graphics mode, in the range 0 to 5.

GetMaxColor: word

(**Graph** unit) returns the highest colour that can be passed to **SetColor.**

GetMaxMode: word

(**Graph** unit) returns the maximum mode number for the currently loaded graphics driver.

GetMaxX: integer

(**Graph** unit) returns the maximum horizontal pixel co-ordinate for the current graphics driver and mode, for example in a 320 × 200 mode **GetMaxX** returns 319. **GetMaxX** is *never viewport relative.*

GetMaxY: integer

(**Graph** unit) returns the maximum vertical pixel co-ordinate for the current graphics driver and mode, for example in a 320 × 200 mode **GetMaxY** returns 199. **GetMaxY** is *never viewport relative*.

GetPaletteSize: integer

(**Graph** unit) returns the number of palette colours in the current graphics mode.

GetPixel(X, Y): word

(**Graph** unit) returns the pixel colour at the point (*X*, *Y*), where *X* and *Y* are integer type.

GetX: integer

(**Graph** unit) returns the *X* co-ordinate of the current position (CP). **GetX** is *viewport relative*.

GetY: integer

(**Graph** unit) returns the *Y* co-ordinate of the current position (CP). **GetY** is *viewport relative*.

GraphErrorMsg(ErrorCode): string

(**Graph** unit) returns a string describing the error indicated by the integer parameter *ErrorCode*. *ErrorCode* is the latest value returned by **GraphResult**.

GraphResult: integer

(**Graph** unit) returns an error code for the last graphics operation. A value of 0 means no error.

Hi(X): byte

returns the high-order byte of *X*, which is integer or word type.

ImageSize(X1, Y1, X2, Y2): word

(**Graph** unit) returns the number of bytes required to store the rectangular region of the graphics screen bounded by the points (*X*1, *Y*1) and (*X*2, *Y*2). The arguments are all integers.

Int(X): real

returns the integer part of its real argument.

IOResult: word

returns the status of the last I/O (input/output) operation. I/O checking must be off – **{$I–}** – to trap I/O errors with **IOResult**. A value of 0 means no error.

KeyPressed: boolean

returns True only if a key has been pressed on the keyboard. The character(s) is (are) left in the keyboard buffer. **KeyPressed** does not detect shift keys, like **Shift**, **Alt**, **NumLock**, etc.

Length(S): integer

returns the dynamic length of its string argument.

Ln(X): real

returns the natural logarithm of its real argument.

Lo(X): byte

returns the low-order byte of *X*, which is integer or word type.

MaxAvail: longint

returns the size of the largest contiguous free block in the heap. This is the size of the largest dynamic variable that can be allocated at that time.

MemAvail: longint

returns the sum of all free blocks in the heap.

Odd(X): boolean

returns True if *X* is an odd number and False if it is even. *X* is a longint type expression.

Ofs(X): word

returns the offset part of the address of *X*, which may be any variable, procedure or function identifier.

Ord(X): longint

returns the ordinality of its ordinal type argument.

Pi: real

returns the value of π (3.1415927...).

Pos(Substr, S): byte

returns the position of the first character of the string *Substr* within the string *S*. If *Substr* is not found, 0 is returned.

Pred(X)

returns the predecessor of its ordinal type argument. The result is of the same type as the argument.

Random(<Range>)

returns a random number. If *Range* is omitted, a real type random number in the range [0; 1) is returned. If *Range* is specified, it must be of integer type, and the result is a word type random number in the range [0; *Range*). If *Range* is zero, a value of 0 is returned.

Random is intialised according to the system time by a call to **Randomize**.

ReadKey: char

reads a character, which is not echoed to the screen, from the keyboard. If **KeyPressed** was True before the call to **ReadKey**, the character that made **KeyPressed** True is returned immediately. Otherwise **ReadKey** waits for a key to be typed.

The **special keys** on the keyboard (function keys, cursor control keys, **Alt** keys, etc.) return **extended key codes** (see Appendix C). When a special key is pressed, a call to **ReadKey** first returns a null character (#0). The next call to **ReadKey** returns the extended key code. Since null characters cannot be generated any other way, you are guaranteed that the next character will be an extended key code. See section 13.5 for an example.

Round(X): longint

rounds its real argument to the nearest whole number. For example, 1.5 is rounded to 2, but 1.499 is rounded to 1.

SeekEof(<F>): boolean

returns the end-of-file status of a **text** file. It is similar to **Eof** except that it skips all blanks, tabs, and end-of-line markers before returning the end-of-file status. It is useful when reading numeric values from a text file.

SeekEoln(<F>):boole

returns the end-of-line status of a *text* file. It is similar to **Eof** except that it skips all blanks and tabs before returning the end-of-line status. It is useful when reading numeric values from a text file.

Seg(X): word

returns the segment part of the address of *X*, which may be the identifier of any variable, procedure or function.

Sin(X): real

returns the sine of its real argument, which is assumed to be an angle in radians.

SizeOf(X): word

returns the number of bytes of memory occupied by its argument, which is either a variable or type identifier.

Sqr(X)

returns the square of its argument in the same type.

Sqrt(X): real

returns the square root of its real argument.

Succ(X)

returns the successor of its ordinal type argument. The result is the same type as *X*.

Swap(X)

swops the high- and low-order bytes of its integer or word argument.

Trunc(X): longint

truncates its real argument to a whole number by *discarding* the fractional part. For example, 1.999 truncates to 1.

UpCase(Ch): char

converts its char argument to uppercase. Characters not in the range ‘a’..‘z’ are unaffected.

WhereX: byte

(**Crt** unit) returns the current horizontal position (column) of the cursor relative to the current text window.

WhereY: byte

(**Crt** unit) returns the current vertical position (row) of the cursor relative to the current text window.

B.2 PROCEDURES

Append(F)

opens an existing *text* file for appending. If an end-of-file marker (**Ctrl-Z,** ASCII 26) is present, it is overwritten. In this way, text can be added on at the end of a text file without losing the current contents.

Arc(X, Y, Start, Finish, Radius)

(Graph unit) draws a circular arc, centre (*X, Y*) (integers) from *Start* angle to *Finish* angle, with the specified radius (words).

Assign(F, Name)

assigns the external file *Name* (string) to the file variable *F* (any file type).

AssignCrt(F)

(**Crt** unit) associates the text file variable *F* with the monitor (CRT). It works just like **Assign** except that no file name is specified. Instead, the file is associated with the CRT. This allows faster output and input than would normally be possible.

BlockRead(F, Buf, Count <, Result>)

reads *Count* or less records from the file *F* into memory, starting at the first byte occupied by *Buf*.

BlockWrite(F, Buf, Count <, Result>)

writes *Count* or less records to the file *F* from memory, starting at the first byte occupied by *Buf*.

ChDir(S)

changes the current directory to a path specified by the string *S*. If *S* specifies a drive letter, the current drive is also changed.

Circle(X, Y, Radius)

(**Graph** unit) draws a circle centre (*X*, *Y*) (integers). *Radius* is word type.

ClearDevice

(**Graph** unit) clears the graphics screen using the background colour, and moves the current pointer to (0, 0).

ClearViewPort

(**Graph** unit) clears the current viewport.

Close(F)

closes an open file.

CloseGraph

(**Graph** unit) shuts down the graphics system and restores the original screen mode in force before graphics was initialised.

ClrEol

(**Crt** unit) sets all characters from the cursor to the end of the line to blanks with the currently defined text attributes.

ClrScr

(**Crt** unit) sets all characters in the active window to blanks with the currently defined text attributes, and places the cursor in the top left corner.

Dec(X <, N>)

decrements the ordinal type variable *X* by *N* (longint), or by 1, if *N* is omitted. **Dec** generates optimized code.

Delay(Ms)

(**Crt** unit) delays execution by *Ms* milliseconds (word).

Delete(S, Start, Number)

deletes *Number* characters from the string *S*, starting at the *Start*th position.

DelLine

(**Crt** unit) deletes the line containing the cursor. All lines below it are moved up, and a new line, with all its characters set to blanks with the currently defined text attributes, is added at the bottom.

DetectGraph(GrDriver, GrMode)

(**Graph** unit) determines which graphics driver and mode to use, and returns the appropriate values in *GrDriver* and *GrMode* for passing to **InitGraph**. If no graphics hardware is detected, *GrDriver* and the function **GraphResult** return a value of −2.

Dispose(P)

releases the memory allocated to the dynamic variable *P^* and returns it to the heap.

DrawPoly(NumPoints, PolyPoints)

(**Graph** unit) draws the outline of a polygon with *NumPoints* (word) vertices. *PolyPoints* is an untyped parameter containing the co-ordinates of each vertex (the first and last pairs of co-ordinates must coincide for the polygon to close). See Section 13.5 for an example.

Ellipse(X, Y, Start, Finish, Xradius, Yradius)

(**Graph** unit) draws an elliptical arc from *Start* angle to *Finish* angle with (*X*, *Y*) as the centre and *Xradius* and *Yradius* as the horizontal and vertical axes.

Erase(F)

erases (deletes) the external file to which the file variable *F* is assigned.

Exit

exits immediately from the current block, ie causes an immediate return to the calling block.

FillChar(X, Number, Value)

fills *Number* (word) contiguous bytes of memory with the ordinal type expression *Value*, starting at the first byte occupied by the variable *X* (any type). No range checking is performed, so this operation can overwrite data unintentionally if you are not careful.

FillEllipse(X, Y, XRadius, YRadius)

(**Graph** unit) is similar to **Ellipse** except that the ellipse is completed and filled with the current fill colour and style.

FillPoly(NumPoints, PolyPoints)

(**Graph** unit) is similar to **DrawPoly** except that the polygon is filled with the current fill colour and style.

FloodFill(X, Y, Border)

(**Graph** unit) fills a region containing the point (*X*, *Y*) and bounded by *Border* colour with the current fill pattern.

Flush(F)

flushes the buffer of the text file associated with *F*.

FreeMem(P, Size)

disposes the dynamic variable *P^*. *Size* must be the exact number of bytes allocated to the variable by **GetMem**. *P* is a pointer variable of any pointer type.

GetAspectRatio(Xasp, Yasp)

(**Graph** unit) returns its parameters in such a way that the ratio *Xasp*:*Yasp* is the ratio of the width of a pixel to its height in the current graphics driver and mode.

GetDate(Year, Month, Day, DayOfWeek)

(**Dos** unit) returns the current date set in the operating system. *DayOfWeek* is in the range 0..6 where 0 is Sunday. All the parameters are word type.

GetDir(D, S)

returns the current directory *S* (string) and drive *D* (byte: 0 means the current drive, 1 means drive A, etc.).

GetImage(X1, Y1, X2, Y2, BitMap)

(**Graph** unit) saves a bit image of the rectangular region of the graphics screen defined by the points (*X1*, *Y1*) and (*X2*, *Y2*) in *BitMap*, which is an untyped parameter. Use **ImageSize** to determine the size of *BitMap*.

GetMem(P, Size)

creates a new dynamic variable *P^* occupying *Size* (word) bytes on the heap. *P* is a pointer variable of any pointer type.

GetTime(Hour, Minute, Second, Sec100)

(**Dos** unit) returns the current time set in the operating system. *Sec100* is hundredths of a second. All the parameters are word type.

GetViewSettings(ViewPort)

(**Graph** unit) returns a variable of predeclared type **ViewPortType:**

```
type
  ViewPortType = record
                   x1, y1, x2, y2: integer;
                   Clip: boolean
                 end;
```

(*X1*, *Y1*) and (*X2*, *Y2*) define the current viewport in *absolute screen co-ordinate. Clip* determines whether clipping is active. The current viewport parameters are set by **SetViewPort**.

GoToXY(X, Y)

(**Crt** unit) moves the cursor to column *X* and row *Y* of the current text window. Both parameters are byte type.

Halt

stops execution and returns to the operating system.

HighVideo

(**Crt** unit) selects high intensity characters. Normal intensity is restored with *NormVideo.*

Inc(X <, N>)

increments the ordinal type variable *X* by *N* (longint), or by 1, if *N* is omitted. **Inc** generates optimized code.

InitGraph(GrDriver, GrMode, Path)

(**Graph** unit) initialises the graphics system.

If a value of **Detect** (0) is passed to **InitGraph** through *GrDriver*, an attempt is made to detect the graphics device installed. If graphics hardware is detected, the appropriate graphics driver is initialised, and the graphics mode with the highest resolution for that device is selected.

If *GrDriver* is not equal to 0 on calling **InitGraph**, a driver is selected according to the value of *GrDriver* (Table 13.1), and the system is put into the mode specified by *GrMode* (Table 13.2). *Path* (string) specifies the directory path where the graphics drivers are to be found.

Insert(Source, Target, Start)

inserts the string *Source* into the string *Target*, starting at the *Start*th position (integer) in *Target*.

InsLine

(**Crt** unit) inserts an empty line at the cursor position. The new line consists of blanks displayed with the currently defined text attributes. All lines below the inserted line are moved down, and the bottom line scrolls off the screen.

Line(X1, Y1, X2, Y2)

(**Graph** unit) draws a line from (*X1*, *Y1*) to (*X2*, *Y2*). All parameters are integer type. The current pointer is *not* updated.

LineRel(Dx, Dy)

(**Graph** unit) draws a line from the current point to the point (*Dx*, *Dy*) (integer) *relative to the current pointer* (CP). The CP is updated by **LineRel**.

LineTo(X, Y)

(**Graph** unit) draws a line from the current pointer (CP) to the point (*X*, *Y*). LineTo updates the CP.

LowVideo

(**Crt** unit) selects low-intensity characters. Normal intensity is restored with **NormVideo**.

MkDir(S)

creates a new subdirectory with the path specified by the string *S*.

Move(Source, Target, Number)

copies a block of *Number* (word) contiguous bytes, starting from the first byte occupied by *Source* in such a way that the copy starts at the first byte occupied by *Target*. *Source* and *Target* are variables of any type. No range checking is performed, so this operation can overwrite data unintentionally if you are not careful.

MoveRel(Dx, Dy)

(**Graph** unit) moves the current pointer (CP) to the point (*Dx*, *Dy*) (integer) *relative to the CP.*

MoveTo(X, Y)

(**Graph** unit) moves the current pointer to the point (*X*, *Y*).

New(P)

creates a new dynamic variable *P^* of size corresponding to the size of the type that the pointer *P* points to.

NormVideo

(**Crt** unit) restores the original text attribute selected when the program started.

NoSound

(**Crt** unit) turns off the speaker.

OutText(S)

(**Graph** unit) displays the string *S* in the current viewport. Various output options are set by **SetTextJustify**. The default is that *S* is output so that the current pointer (CP) is roughly at the left top corner of an imaginary box containing the text. The CP is updated in the default state.

OutTextXY(X, Y, S)

(**Graph** unit) is similar to **OutText** except that the string *S* is output relative to the point (*X*, *Y*) (integer), and the current pointer is *not* updated.

PutImage(X, Y, BitMap, BitBlt)

(**Graph** unit) puts the bit image stored in *BitMap* onto the screen in the rectangular region with the point (*X*, *Y*) (integer) at its top left corner. *BitMap* is an untyped parameter. *BitBlt* (word) determines how the bit image is put on the screen. It can take the following values: **CopyPut** (0), **XORPut** (1), **OrPut** (2), **AndPut** (3) and **NotPut** (4).

PutPixel(X, Y, Colour)

(**Graph** unit) plots a point at (*X*, *Y*) (integers) in the specified colour (word).

Randomize

initialises (seeds) the random number generator (**Random**) using the system clock. The random number generator's seed is stored in a predeclared longint variable called **RandSeed**. By assigning a specific value to **RandSeed**, a specific sequence of random numbers can be generated repeatedly by **Random**.

Read <ln> (<F,> V1, V2, ..., Vn)

reads one or more values from the *text* file associated with *F* into one or more variables, which must be of type char, integer, real or string. If *F* is omitted, the standard file variable **Input** is assumed, and values are then generally read from the keyboard. To understand clearly how the different types are handled you should carefully study the description of **Read** in the *Reference*

Guide.

Readln executes **Read** and then skips to the next line of the file.

Read(<F,> V1, V2, ..., Vn)

reads one or more file components from the typed file associated with *F* into one or more variables. *F* is a file variable of any type except text, and each variable *V* is of the same type as the component type of *F.*

Rectangle(X1, Y1, X2, Y2)

(**Graph** unit) draws a rectangle with the points (*X1*, *Y1*) and (*X2*, *Y2*) (integers) at opposite corners.

Rename(F, NewName)

renames to *NewName* (string) the external file associated with *F.*

Reset(F <, Recsize >)

opens an existing file. *F* is a file variable of any file type, which must have been associated with an external file with **Assign**. The current file position is set to the beginning of the file. If *F* is a text file, it becomes read-only until closed.

If *F* is an untyped file, the optional parameter *Recsize* specifies the record size to be used in data transfers (the default record size is 128 bytes).

RestoreCrtMode

(**Crt** unit) restores the text screen to its state before graphics was initialised.

Rewrite(F<, Recsize >)

creates a new external file with the name assigned to *F* using **Assign**. *F* is a file variable of any file type. If an external file of the same name already exists, it is deleted, and a new empty file is created in its place. The current file position is set to the beginning of the file. If *F* is a text file, it becomes write-only until closed.

If *F* is an untyped file, the optional parameter Recsize specifies the record size to be used in data transfers (the default record size is 128 bytes).

RmDir(S)

removes the empty subdirectory with path *S* (string).

Seek(F, Number)

moves the current position of the file associated with *F* to component *Number* (longint). *F* is any file variable type except text. The number of the first component of a file is 0. It is necessary to seek one component beyond the last component of a file in order to expand it.

SetAspectRatio(Xasp, Yasp)

(**Graph** unit) changes the default aspect ratio to *Xasp*:*Yasp*. This is the ratio of the width of a pixel to its height in the current grahpics driver and mode.

SetBkColor(ColourNum)

(**Graph** unit) sets the background colour to *ColourNum* (word), according to the values in Table 13.3 (Section 13.4).

SetColor(ColourNum)

(**Graph** unit) sets the drawing colour to the *ColourNumth* colour in the current palette. *ColourNum* is word type.

SetDate(Year, Month, Day)

(**Dos** unit) sets the current date in the operating system. All the parameters are word type, with ranges as follows: *Year* 1980..2099, *Month* 1..12, *Day* 1..31.

SetFillStyle(Pattern, ColourNum)

(**Graph** unit) sets the fill pattern (word) and colour (word). *Pattern* can take on the following predeclared values (see GRAPH.DOC):

```
{Fill patterns for Get/SetFillStyle: }
EmptyFill        = 0;  { fills area in background color }
SolidFill        = 1;  { fills area in solid fill color }
LineFill         = 2;  { --- fill }
LtSlashFill      = 3;  { /// fill }
SlashFill        = 4;  { /// fill with thick lines }
BkSlashFill      = 5;  { \\\ fill with thick lines }
LtBkSlashFill    = 6;  { \\\ fill }
HatchFill        = 7;  { light hatch fill }
XHatchFill       = 8;  { heavy cross hatch fill }
InterleaveFill   = 9;  { interleaving line fill }
WideDotFill      = 10; { Widely spaced dot fill }
CloseDotFill     = 11; { Closely spaced dot fill }
UserFill         = 12; { user defined fill }
```

The default pattern is solid, and the default colour is the maximum colour in the palette.

You can define your own fill pattern with **SetFillPattern**, as described in the *Reference Guide*.

SetGraphMode(GrMode)

(**Graph** unit) sets the system to graphics mode and clears the screen. It can be used in conjunction with **RestoreCrtMode** to switch back and forth between graphics and text.

SetLineStyle(Style, Pattern, Thickness)

(**Graph** unit) sets the current line style and width for all lines drawn by **Line, LineTo, DrawPoly,** etc. The meanings of the parameters are described in the *Reference Guide*.

SetTime(Hour, Minute, Second, Sec100)

(**Dos** unit) sets the current time in the operating system. All parameters are word type. *Sec100* is hundredths of a second.

SetViewPort(X1, Y1, X2, Y2, Clip)

(**Graph** unit) sets the current viewport for graphics output to a rectangle with the points.

(*X*1, *Y*1) and (*X*2, *Y*2) (integer) at opposite corners. *Clip* is boolean. If it is True, drawing is clipped at the viewport boundaries.

Sound(Hz)

(**Crt** unit) makes the speaker emit a sound of frequency *Hz* hertz. The noise continues unabated until switched off with **NoSound**.

Str(X <:Width <:Decimals>>, Stg)

converts the integer or real value in *X* to its string representation in the string *Stg*. If *Width* and *Decimals* are present they format *X* in exactly the same way as **Write**.

TextBackground(ColourNum)

(**Crt** unit) sets the background colour in text mode. *ColourNum* is a byte variable. It can take on the following predeclared values (see CRT.DOC):

```
Black      = 0;
Blue       = 1;
Green      = 2;
Cyan       = 3;
Red        = 4;
Magenta    = 5;
Brown      = 6;
LightGray  = 7;
```

TextColor(ColourNum)

(**Crt** unit) sets the foreground character colour in text mode. *ColourNum* is a byte variable. It can take on the predeclared values allowed with **TextBackground** as well as the following:

```
DarkGray      =  8;
LightBlue     =  9;
LightGreen    =  10;
LightCyan     =  11;
LightRed      =  12;
LightMagenta  =  13;
Yellow        =  14;
White         =  15;
```

The colour will blink if 128 is added to it. The current video attribute is stored in the predeclared **Crt** variable **TextAttr**, which is discussed in section 11.10.

TextMode(Mode)

(**Crt** unit) selects a text mode. *Mode* is a word variable which can take on the following predeclared values:

```
BW40     =  0;      { 40x25 B/W on Color Adapter }
CO40     =  1;      { 40x25 Color on Color Adapter }
BW80     =  2;      { 80x25 B/W on Color Adapter }
CO80     =  3;      { 80x25 Color on Color Adapter }
Mono     =  7;      { 80x25 on Monochrome Adapter }
Font8x8  =  256;    { Add-in for ROM font }
C40      =  CO40;   { for 3.0 compatibility }
C80      =  CO80;   { for 3.0 compatibility }
```

Truncate(F)

truncates the file associated with the file variable *F* at the current file position. All subsequent records are deleted. **Truncate** does not work on text files.

Val(S, Value, Code)

converts the string value in the string expression *S* to its numeric equivalent *Value* (integer or real). *S* must be a sequence of characters that form a valid *signed whole number.* If the string is invalid, the position of the offending character is returned in *Code*, which is otherwise set to zero.

Window(X1, Y1, X2, Y2)

(**Crt** unit) defines a text window on the screen with *X1* (column) and *Y1* (row) as the co-ordinates of the upper left corner, and *X2*, *Y2* as the co-ordinates of the lower right corner. The upper left corner is (1, 1). All parameters are byte type.

The current window definition is stored in the low- and high-order bytes of the **Crt** variables **WindMin** and **WindMax**, as described in section 11.10.

Write<ln>(<F,> V1, V2, ..., Vn)

writes the values of one or more expressions of type char, integer, real, string or boolean, to the *text* file associated with *F.* If *F* is omitted, the standard file variable **Output** is assumed, and values are then generally displayed on the screen. There is a full description of Write and its formatting parameters in the *Reference Guide.*

Writeln executes **Write** and then writes an end-of-line marker to the file.

Write(<F,> V1, V2, ..., Vn)

writes one or more variables into the file components of the typed file associated with *F. F* is a file variable of any type except text, and each variable *V* is of the same type as the component type of *F.*

Appendix C
Character Codes

C.1 ASCII CODES

The ASCII (American Standard Code for Information Interchange) codes are 7-bit binary codes for control characters (codes 0 to 31) and printable characters (codes 32 to 255). The standard function **Chr** converts a code into the character it represents.

You can display the characters directly with the **Alt** key. For example, to display π on the screen, hold down the **Alt** key while typing its code (227) using the numeric keys on the righthand keypad. The symbol appears on the screen after you release the **Alt** key.

The names of the characters with codes 0 to 31 hark back to the old days of teletype machines. So LF means line feed, BS means backspace, VT means vertical tab, and so on.

The ASCII codes are as follows:

Dec	*Hex*		*Char*	*Dec*	*Hex*	*Char*	*Dec*	*Hex*	*Char*	*Dec*	*Hex*	*Char*
0	00		NUL	32	20		64	40	@	96	60	‘
1	01	☺	SOH	33	21	!	65	41	A	97	61	a
2	02	☻	STX	34	22	“	66	42	B	98	62	b
3	03	♥	ETX	35	23	#	67	43	C	99	63	c
4	04	♦	EOT	36	24	$	68	44	D	100	64	d
5	05	♣	ENQ	37	25	%	69	45	E	101	65	e
6	06	♠	ACK	38	26	&	70	46	F	102	66	f
7	07	•	BEL	39	27	’	71	47	G	103	67	g
8	08	◘	BS	40	28	(	72	48	H	104	68	h
9	09	○	HT	41	29	)	73	49	I	105	69	i
10	0A	◙	LF	42	2A	*	74	4A	J	106	6A	j
11	0B	♂	VT	43	2B	+	75	4B	K	107	6B	k
12	0C	♀	FF	44	2C	,	76	4C	L	108	6C	l
13	0D	♪	CR	45	2D	-	77	4D	M	109	6D	m
14	0E	♫	SO	46	2E	.	78	4E	N	110	6E	n
15	0F	☼	SI	47	2F	/	79	4F	O	111	6F	o
16	10	►	DLE	48	30	0	80	50	P	112	70	p
17	11	◄	DC1	49	31	1	81	51	Q	113	71	q
18	12	↕	DC2	50	32	2	82	52	R	114	72	r
19	13	‼	DC3	51	33	3	83	53	S	115	73	s
20	14	¶	DC4	52	34	4	84	54	T	116	74	t
21	15	§	NAK	53	35	5	85	55	U	117	75	u
22	16	▬	SYN	54	36	6	86	56	V	118	76	v
23	17	↨	ETB	55	37	7	87	57	W	119	77	w
24	18	↑	CAN	56	38	8	88	58	X	120	78	x
25	19	↓	EM	57	39	9	89	59	Y	121	79	y
26	1A	→	SUB	58	3A	:	90	5A	Z	122	7A	z
27	1B	←	ESC	59	3B	;	91	5B	[	123	7B	{
28	1C	∟	FS	60	3C	<	92	5C	\	124	7C	¦
29	1D	↔	GS	61	3D	=	93	5D	]	125	7D	}
30	1E	▲	RS	62	3E	>	94	5E	^	126	7E	~
31	1F	▼	US	63	3F	?	95	5F	_	127	7F	△

Dec	Hex	Char	Dec	Hex	Char	Dec	Hex	Char	Dec	Hex	Char
128	80	Ç	160	A0	à	192	C0	└	224	E0	α
129	81	ü	161	A1	ì	193	C1	┴	225	E1	β
130	82	é	162	A2	ó	194	C2	┬	226	E2	Γ
131	83	â	163	A3	ù	195	C3	├	227	E3	π
132	84	ä	164	A4	ñ	196	C4	─	228	E4	Σ
133	85	á	165	A5	Ñ	197	C5	┼	229	E5	σ
134	86	ǎ	166	A6	a̲	198	C6	╞	230	E6	μ
135	87	ç	167	A7	o̲	199	C7	╟	231	E7	τ
136	88	ê	168	A8	¿	200	C8	╚	232	E8	Φ
137	89	ë	169	A9	⌐	201	C9	╔	233	E9	θ
138	8A	é	170	AA	¬	202	CA	╩	234	EA	Ω
139	8B	Ï	171	AB	½	203	CB	╦	235	EB	δ
140	8C	î	172	AC	¼	204	CC	╠	236	EC	∞
141	8D	ì	173	AD	i	205	CD	═	237	ED	φ
142	8E	Ä	174	AE	≪	206	CE	╬	238	EE	ε
143	8F	Å	175	AF	≫	207	CF	╧	239	EF	∩
144	90	É	176	B0	░	208	D0	╨	240	F0	≡
145	91	æ	177	B1	▒	209	D1	╤	241	F1	±
146	92	Æ	178	B2	▓	210	D2	╥	242	F2	≥
147	93	ô	179	B3	│	211	D3	╙	243	F3	≤
148	94	ö	180	B4	┤	212	D4	╘	244	F4	⌠
149	95	ò	181	B5	╡	213	D5	╒	245	F5	⌡
150	96	û	182	B6	╢	214	D6	╓	246	F6	—
151	97	ù	183	B7	╖	215	D7	╫	247	F7	≈
152	98	ÿ	184	B8	╕	216	D8	╪	248	F8	°
153	99	Ö	185	B9	╣	217	D9	┘	249	F9	·
154	9A	Ü	186	BA	║	218	DA	┌	250	FA	·
155	9B	¢	187	BB	╗	219	DB	█	251	FB	√
156	9C	£	188	BC	╝	220	DC	▄	252	FC	n
157	9D	¥	189	BD	╜	221	DD	▌	253	FD	2
158	9E	Pt	190	BE	╛	222	DE	▐	254	FE	■
159	9F	ƒ	191	BF	┐	223	DF	▀	255	FF	

C.2 EXTENDED KEY CODES

Certain keys and key combinations that are not represented by the standard ASCII codes in section C.1 return two codes, called **extended key codes**. The first code returned is the null character (#0), and the second is given in the table below. (See the description of **ReadKey** in Section B.1 for how to determine if an extended key has been pressed.)

Second Code	*Meaning*
3	**NUL** (null character)
15	**Shift-Tab**
16-25	**Alt-Q/W/E/R/T/Y/U/I/O/P**
30-38	**Alt-A/S/D/F/G/H/J/K/L**
44-50	**Alt-Z/X/C/V/B/N/M**
59-68	**F1** to **F10** (disabled as softkeys)
71	**Home**
72	**Up arrow**
73	**PgUp**
75	**Left arrow**
77	**Right arrow**
79	**End**
80	**Down arrow**
81	**PgDn**
82	**Ins**
83	**Del**
84-93	**F11** to **F20** (**Shift-F1** to **Shift-F10**)
94-103	**F21** to **F30** (**Ctrl-F1** to **Ctrl-F10**)
104-113	**F31** to **F40** (**Alt-F1** to **Alt-F10**)
114	**Ctrl-PrtSc**
115	**Ctrl-Left arrow**

116	**Ctrl-Right arrow**
117	**Ctrl-End**
118	**Ctrl-PgDn**
119	**Ctrl-Home**
120-131	**Alt-1/2/3/4/5/6/7/8/9/0/-/=**
132	**Ctrl-PgUp**
133	**F11**
134	**F12**
135	**Shift-F11**
136	**Shift-F12**
137	**Ctrl-F11**
138	**Ctrl-F12**
139	**Alt-F11**
140	**Alt-F12**

Appendix D
Reserved Words

Reserved words may not be used as identifiers. They are as follows:

absolute
and
array
begin
case
const
constructor
destructor
div
do
downto
else
end
external
file
for
forward
function
goto
if
implementation
in
inline
interface
interrupt
label
mod
nil
not
object
of
or
packed
procedure
program
record
repeat
set
shl
shr
string
then
to
type
unit
until
uses
var
virtual
while
with
xor

Appendix E
Compiler Directives

Compiler directives are specific instructions to the compiler embedded in your program code. This can also be done through the Options menu, but sometimes it is more convenient to have the directives in the code.

Strictly speaking, the compiler directives are special comments, so they are enclosed in comment symbols. Their first character is always a $ symbol, and *there must be no spaces between the opening comment symbol(s) and the dollar symbol*, for example,

```
{$I MyGraphs}
(*$R-*)
```

There are three types of compiler directives: switch directives, parameter directives and condition directives.

E.1 SWITCH DIRECTIVES

Switch directives turn some condition on or off with "+" or "–". Several switch directives may be included in the same comment, separated by commas, in which case only the first directive need be preceded by a dollar symbol. There should be no spaces after the commas, for example,

```
{$I-,R-,V+}
```

Some commonly used switch directives are discussed below briefly.

Align Data: {$A+} or {$A–} (default: **{$A+}**)

$A+ specifies word alignment, ie forces data storage to start at even-numbered addresses.

$A– disables word alignment.

Boolean Evaluation: {$B+} or {$B–} (default: **{$B–}**)

$B– makes the compiler generate code that short-circuits the evaluation of Boolean expressions, ie stops evaluation of the expression as soon as its value is determined.

$B+ forces complete evaluation of Boolean expressions.

Emulation of 8087: {$E+} or {$E–} (default: **{$E+}**)

Emulation enables linking at runtime to software which emulates the action of the 8087 maths co-processor. This allows you to use the IEEE floating point types (single, double, extended and comp), even if an 8087 chip is not installed in your machine. Turbo Pascal links with the full emulator if you compile in the **{$N+,E+}** states. The resulting code will run on any machine, whether or not an 8087 is present.

Compiling in the **{$N+,E–}** states results in code which is substantially smaller, but which will only run on a machine with an 8087 present.

Force FAR Calls: {$F+} or {$F–} (default: **{$F–}**)

This directive controls which call model to use for subsequently compiled functions and procedures. Procedures and functions that are passed as procedural type parameters must be compiled in the **{$F+}** state, ie using the FAR call model. The default is that NEAR is always used unless the procedure or function is in the interface section of a unit. See the *Reference Guide* for more details.

Input/Output Checking: {$I+} or {$I−} (default: **{$I+}**)

If I/O checking is on, errors are trapped and the program crashes. If I/O checking is off, errors are merely reported by the IOResult function, and execution continues. In this case, you should test for errors, and take appropriate action.

Numeric Co-processing: {$N+} or {$N−} (default: **{$N−}**)

In the **{$N+}** state you can use the IEEE floating point types (single, double, extended and comp) if your machine has an 8087 co-processor installed. If you don't have an 8087 chip, you can still use these types if you compile in the **{$E+}** state, which emulates the action of the 8087 chip, although the code generated is considerably slower and larger.

In the **{$N−}** state, you cannot use the IEEE 8087 types in your code, even if an 8087 is present.

An 8087 chip can speed up execution considerably, depending on the code. A benchmark test I have used to test execution speed is discussed below in section E.4.

Range Checking: {$R+} or {$R−} (default: **{$R−}**)

Turbo Pascal does not usually check whether an array or string is indexed outside its legal bounds, but this can cause other data to be overwritten. In the **{$R+}** state, such checks are made, at the expense of slightly slower and larger code. It's a good idea to switch range checking on while a program is being developed, but to switch it off when the final version is compiled.

Var String Checking: {$V+} or {$V−} (default: **{$V+}**)

Normally, when a string is passed to a procedure or function as a parameter, the declared physical length of the actual parameter must be the same as that of the formal parameter, which can be a nuisance. In the **{$V−}** state, you can pass actual string parameters of any length to a given formal string parameter.

Note that passing a string which is *larger* than the formal parameter could cause data to be overwritten.

E.2 PARAMETER DIRECTIVES

The most commonly used of these is **Include File: {$I}**. This has nothing to do with the I/O checking switch directive above. Rather it enables you to include coding from another file at compile time. For example,

```
{$I Globals }
```

means that the file GLOBALS.PAS will be included at that point during compilation, but without being read into memory. This is a way of breaking your code up into smaller pieces. This facility was very useful under version 3.0 of Turbo Pascal, which did not support units.

Include files may be nested to a depth of 15 levels.

$I may not appear inside any **begin-end** block.

E.3 CONDITION DIRECTIVES

A **condition directive** enables you to produce different compiled code from the same source code, depending on the value of conditional symbols. For example,

```
var
  X, Y: {$IFDEF CPU87} double {$ELSE} real {$ENDIF};
```

This is very like the **if-then-else** statement. If the 8087 chip is present, **X** and **Y** are compiled with type double, otherwise with type real.

CPU87 is a standard **conditional symbol**, which is defined if an 8087 numeric co-processor is present at compilation.

{**$IFDEF** *Name*} compiles the code that follows if *Name* is defined. You can define your own conditional symbols with the **O/C/**Conditional Defines menu.

There are examples of condition directives in a complete program in the next section.

E.4 USING THE 8087 NUMERIC CO-PROCESSOR

The 80x86 family of microprocessors are designed to handle integers very efficiently, but they require a lot more effort to handle reals. Since real arithmetic is the basis of most number crunching, this design feature can reduce execution speed considerably.

The 80x87 co-processors (known severally as the maths co-processors, the floating point chips, the numeric co-processors, etc.) have been designed to improve the situation with special hardware to handle floating point (real) arithmetic. If you do a lot of number crunching you should consider installing an 8087. Table 1.2 (in Chapter 1) shows that an 8087 chip makes a Turbo Pascal 5.5 benchmark test (listed below) run about three times faster.

If you have an 8087 installed, Turbo Pascal 5.5 supports the IEEE floating point types (single, double, extended and comp – see section 2.17 for specifications) as long as you compile in the {**$N+**} state.

You may not have an 8087 chip (or you may want to compile code to run on a machine which does not have an 8087), but may still want to use the IEEE floating point types for reasons of accuracy. Turbo Pascal 5.5 handles this situation by loading (by default) some special software to *emulate* the action of the 8087 chip, *as long as you still compile in the* {**$N+**} *state.*

The emulation software uses more memory (at least 10K more), and there is no need to use it if indeed you do have an 8087 chip. If you want to save memory, you can switch off emulation with {$E–} Code compiled in this state will then not run on a machine without an 8087 present.

A Benchmark Test for Execution Time

The use of condition directives is illustrated in the following program which can be used to test execution on different machines, in different states. The program computes 1000 terms of the Taylor series for cos(*x*) in steps of one degree. Execution time is displayed for every group of 10 degrees.

The program as it stands will report the fastest time for a machine as long as it is compiled on that machine.

Note that in the {**$N+**} state a "real" type is defined which is actually the IEEE double type. Omitting this type declaration, ie using genuine real type in the {**$N+**} state, interestingly slows down execution by a factor of almost two on a machine with the 8087 present, although this is still faster than code compilied in the {**$N–**} state. So for the fastest execution in general number crunching, it is probably best to use double type (with an 8087).

Incidentally, execution also slows down considerably if you replace **X * X** by **Sqr(X)** in the calculation of **Term** below.

```
{ Computes 1000 terms of Taylor series for cos(x) in              }
{ steps of 1 degree. Times reported every 10 degrees.             }
{$N+}
{$IFDEF CPU87}
  {$E-}
{$ELSE}
  {$NE+}
```

```
{$ENDIF}
uses
   Crt, Dos;
 {$IFOPT N+}
 type
   Rreal = double;
 {$ENDIF}
 var
   Index, I, A                  : integer;
   Hour, Min, sec, sec100       : word;
   Tstart, Tend                 : real;
   Term, Coz, X                 : real;
   Ans                          : Char;
 procedure Timer( var TimeInSecs: real );
 { System time in seconds }
 begin
   GetTime( Hour, Min, Sec, Sec100 );
   TimeInSecs:= 3600 * Hour + 60 * Min + Sec + Sec100 / 100
 end {Timer};
 begin
   ClrScr;
   Writeln( 'Bench mark test in Turbo Pascal 5.5 ' );
   Writeln;
   {$IFDEF CPU87}
     Writeln( '8087 co-processor present' );
   {$ENDIF}
   {$IFOPT N+}
     Writeln( '$N+ state' );
   {$ELSE}
     Writeln( '$N- state' );
   {$ENDIF}
   {$IFOPT E+}
     Writeln( 'Emulation on' );
   {$ELSE}
     Writeln( 'Emulation off' );
   {$ENDIF}
   Writeln;
   Timer( Tstart );
   for a:= 1 to 90 do
   begin
     Term:= 1;
     Coz:= 0;
     X:= A * Pi / 180;
     for I:= 1 to 1000 do
     begin
       index:= I;
       Coz:= Coz + Term;
       Term:= - Term * X * X / (2.0 * Index) / (2.0 * Index - 1.0)
     end;
     if A mod 10 = 0 then
     begin
       Timer( Tend );
       Writeln( A, ' Taylor: ', Coz, ' Turbo:',
                Cos(x), Tend - Tstart:8:2 );
       Tstart:= Tend
     end
   end;

   Readln
 end.
```

Appendix F Solutions to Selected Problems

CHAPTER 1

1.1
```
program One_1;
var
   A, B, Diff, Prod, Quot, Sum: real;
begin
   Readln( A, B );
   Sum:= A + B;
   Diff:= A - B;
   Prod:= A * B;
   Quot:= A / B;
   Writeln( 'The sum is:           ', Sum:8:1 );
   Writeln( 'The difference is:    ', Diff:8:1 );
   Writeln( 'The product is:       ', Prod:8:1 );
   Writeln( 'The quotient is:      ', Quot:8:1 )
end.
```

1.2
```
program One_2;
var
   C, E, V: real;
begin
   Readln( C, V );
   E:= C * V * V / 2;
   Writeln( 'Energy on the condenser: ', E:8:2 )
end.
```

CHAPTER 2

2.2 (b) zero must precede decimal point
(d) comma should be decimal point
(e) asterisk should be omitted
(f) decimal point not allowed in exponent
(h) comma should be decimal point

2.3 (b) first character must be a letter
(c) dollar symbol not allowed
(e) **for** is a reserved word
(f) asterisk not allowed
(g) plus sign not allowed
(h) space not allowed
(j) periods not allowed
(k) exclamation mark not allowed

2.4 Display the following expressions with **Writeln**:

(a) **Sqrt(2))**
(b) **(5 + 3) / (5 * 3))**
(c) **Exp((1 / 3) * Ln(2.3 * 4.5)))**
(d) **Sqr(2 * Pi))**
(e) **2 * Sqr(Pi))**
(f) **1000 * Exp(60 * Ln(1 + 0.15 / 12)))**

```
2.5  (a)  P + W / U
     (b)  P + W / (U + V)
     (c)  (P + W / (U + V)) / (P + W / (U - V))
     (d)  X * X
     (e)  Exp( 2.5 * Ln( X ) )
     (f)  Sqrt( X )
     (g)  Exp( (Y + Z) * Ln( X ) )
     (h)  Exp( Z * Ln( Exp( Y * Ln( X ) ) ) )                    { X <> 0 }
     (i)  Exp( Exp( Z * Ln( Y ) ) * Ln( X ) )                    { X, Y <> 0 }
     (j)  X - X*X*X / (3*2) + X*X*X*X*X / (5*4*3*2)

2.6  (a)  I:= I + 1;
     (b)  I:= I * I * I + J;
     (c)  if E > F then
            G:= E
          else
            G:= F;
     (d)  if D > 0 then
            X:= - B;
     (e)  X:= (A + B) / (C * D);

2.7  program Two_7;
     var
       Km, KmpL, L, Lp100Km, Petrol: real;
     begin
       Readln( Km, L );
       KmpL:= Km / L;
       Lp100Km:= L / (Km / 100);
       Writeln( 'Distance':12, 'Litres':12, 'Km/L':12, 'L/100Km':12 );
       Writeln;
       Writeln( Km:12:2, L:12:2, KmpL:12:2, Lp100Km:12:2 )
     end.

2.8  program Two_8;
     var
       A, B, C, X: real;
     begin
       Read( A, B, C );
       X:= (-B + Sqrt( B * B - 4 * A * C) ) / (2 * A);
       Writeln( X:8:1 )
     end.

2.9  program Two_9;
     var
       G, L, P: real;
     begin
       Readln( G, P );
       P:= P + 8 * G;                       { convert everything to pints }
       L:= P / 1.76;                                     { then to litres }
       Writeln( L:10:2 )
     end.

2.10a  program Two_10a;
       var
         C, F: real;
         begin
           Write( 'Enter Celsius temperature: ' );
           Readln( C );
           F:= 9 * C / 5 + 32;
           Writeln( 'Fahrenheit temperature:          ', F:6:1 )
         end.

2.10b  program Two_10b;
       var
         C: integer;                        { control variable of for loop }
```

```
    F: real;
  begin
    Writeln( 'Celsius              Fahrenheit' );
    Writeln;

    for C:= 20 to 30 do
    begin
      F:= 9 * C / 5 + 32;
      Writeln( C, F:13:1 )
    end

  end.
```

2.12b
```
  program Two _ 12b;
  var
    I, N: integer;
  begin
    Readln( N );
    for I:= 1 to N do
      Write( '*' );
    Writeln
  end.
```

2.12c
```
  program Two _ 12b;
  var
    I: integer;
  begin
    for I:= 1 to 5 do
      Writeln( ' ':I, '*' )
  end.
```

2.14
```
  program Two _ 14;
  var
    I, Sum: integer;
  begin
    Sum:= 0;

    for I:= 1 to 100 do
      Sum:= Sum + 2 * I;

    Writeln( Sum )
  end.
```

2.15
```
  program Two _ 15;
  var
    I, Sum: longint;
  begin
    Sum:= 0;

    for I:= 1 to 256 do
      Sum:= Sum + I * I;

    Writeln( Sum )
  end.
```

2.16
```
  program Two _ 16;
  const
    Num = 10;
    Pass: word = 0;
  var
    F: text;
    Stu: word;
       Mean, Mk: real;
     begin
       Assign( F, 'MARKS.' );
       Reset( F );

       for Stu:= 1 to Num do
       begin
      Read( F, Mk );
      Mean:= Mean + Mk;
```

```
    if Mk >= 5 then                                    { this is for 2.17 }
        Pass:= Pass + 1
  end;

    Mean:= Mean / Num;
    Writeln( 'Mean:', Mean:8:2, ' Passed: ', Pass );
    Close( F )
  end.
```

2.18
```
program Two_18;
const
  N = 10;
  More: word = 0;
  Less: word = 0;
var
  I: word;
begin
  Randomize;

  for I:= 1 to N do
    { probability that Random = 0.5 exactly is almost zero! }
    if Random > 0.5 then
      More:= More + 1
    else
      Less:= Less + 1;

  Writeln( 'More: ', More, ' Less: ', Less )
end.
```

2.19 (d) Solve the quadratic in t:

$$0.5gt^2 - ut + s = 0.$$

Part (c) is the special case $s = 0$.

2.20
```
T:= A;
A:= B;
B:= T;
```

2.21
```
A:= A - B;                                     { Try it out with some numbers! }
B:= B + A;
A:= B - A;
```

2.22 $A = 4; X = 1 + 1/2 + 1/3 + 1/4.$

2.23
```
X:= 0;
for A:= 1 to 4 do
  X:= X + 1 / A;
```

2.24 The limit is π.

2.31
```
program Slosh;
var
  Name, Street, Town: string;
  Number: word;
  Data : text;
begin
  Assign( Data, 'Slosh.dat' );
  Reset( Data );
  Readln( Data, Name );
  Readln( Data, Number, Street );
  Readln( Data, Town );
  Writeln( 'Dear Mr ', Name, ',' );
  Writeln( 'We will paint your house with Sloshon at half price!' );
  Writeln( 'You can have the smartest house in', Street );
  Writeln( 'if not in the whole of ', Town );
  Writeln( 'The ', Name, ' family will be able to walk tall again.' );
  Writeln( 'Your neighbours at number ', Number + 2, ' will be amazed!' );
  readln;
  close( Data );
end.
```

CHAPTER 3

3.1 You should get a picture of tangents to a curve. See section 13.3 for a graphics program to draw this construction.

3.2 (a) 4; (b) 2

(c) The algorithm (attributed to Euclid!) finds the HCF (Highest Common Factor) of two numbers by using the fact that the HCF divides exactly into the difference between the two numbers, and that when the numbers are equal, they are equal to their HCF.

3.3 The program is similar to the solution to Exercise 2.10.

3.4
```
program Three_4;
const
  RunTot: real = 0;
var
  F, I, M: real;
  P: word;
  Data: text;
begin
  Assign( Data, 'PLANKS.' );
  Reset( Data );
  Writeln( 'Feet':10, 'Inches':10, 'Metres':10 );
  Writeln;

  for P:= 1 to 5 do
  begin
    Readln( Data, F, I );
    M:= 0.3048 * F + 0.0254 * I;
    RunTot:= RunTot + M;
    Writeln( F:10:2, I:10:2, M:10:2 )
  end;

  Writeln;
  Writeln( 'Total length: ', RunTot:10:3 );
  Close( Data )
end.
```

3.5
```
program Three_5;
var
  X, Y: real;
begin
  Readln( X, Y );
  if X > Y then
    Write( X )
  else
    Write( Y );
  Writeln( ' is larger' )
end.
```

3.6
```
program Three_6;
var
  I, Posn: word;
  Max, X: real;
  F: text;
begin
  Assign( F, 'MARKS.' );
  Reset( F );
  Read( F, Max );                    { first one may be largest }
  Posn:= 1;

  for I:= 2 to 10 do
  begin
    Read( F, X );
    if X > Max then
    begin
```

```
        Max:= X;
        Posn:= I
      end
    end;

    Writeln( 'Largest is', Max:10:2, ' at position ', Posn )
  end.
```

3.7
```
program Three_7;
var
  N: word;
  Sum: real;
begin
  Sum:= 0;

  for N:= 1 to 100 do
  begin
    Sum:= Sum + 1 / N;
    if N mod 10 = 0 then
      Writeln( N:3, Sum:10:5 )
  end

end.
```

3.8
```
program Three_8;
var
  Hours, Mins, Secs: word;
begin
  Readln( Secs );
  Hours:= Secs div 3600;
  Secs:= Secs mod 3600;                     { no. of seconds left }
  Mins:= Secs div 60;
  Secs:= Secs mod 60;
  Writeln( Hours:4, Mins:4, Secs:4 )
end.
```

CHAPTER 4

4.1
```
program Four_1;
var
  Ft, Inch, Yd: integer;                    { word may not be big enough }
  FracIn, RealIn, M: real;
begin
  Write( 'Metric:            ' );
  Readln( M );
  RealIn:= 39.37 * M;
  FracIn:= Frac( RealIn );                  { the decimal part }
  Inch:= Trunc( RealIn );                   { the integer part }
  Yd:= Inch div 36;
  Inch:= Inch mod 36;
  Ft:= Inch div 12;
  RealIn:= Inch mod 12 + FracIn;
  Writeln( 'Imperial: ', Yd:4, Ft:4, RealIn:6:2 )
end.
```

4.2
```
(a) C:= Sqr( A * A + B * B );
(b) Theta:= Theta * Pi / 180;               { Convert to radians }
    C:= Sqr( A * A + B * B - 2 * A * B * Cos( Theta ) );
```

4.3
```
(a) Ln( X + X * X + A * A )
(b) (Exp( 3 * T) + T * T * Sin( 4 * T )) * Sqr( Cos( 3 * T ) )
(c) 4 * ArcTan( 1 )
(d) 1 / Sqr( Cos( X ) ) + Cos( X ) / Sin( X )
(e) ArcTan( Abs( A / X ) )
```

4.5
```
program Four_5;
var
  F, L, P, R: real;
  N: word;
```

```
function Power( A, B : real ): real;
{ raises A to the power B }
begin
  Power:= Exp( B * Ln( A ) )
end; { Power }

begin
  R:= 0.15;
  Write( 'Enter L and N: ' );
  Readln( L, N );
  F:= Power( 1 + R / 12, 12 * N );
  P:= L * R * F / 12 / (F - 1);
  Writeln( 'P:', P:8:2 )
end.
```

4.6

```
program Four_6;
var
  L, N, P, R: real;
begin
  R:= 0.15;
  Write( 'Enter L and P: ' );
  Readln( L, P );
  N:= Ln( P / (P - L * R / 12) ) / Ln( 1 + R / 12 ) / 12;
  Writeln( 'N:', N:8:2 )
end.
```

CHAPTER 5

5.1

```
program Five_1;
var
  X, Y: real;
begin
  Readln( X, Y );
  if X > Y then
    Writeln( X, ' is larger' )
  else if X < Y then
    Writeln( Y, ' is larger' )
  else
    Writeln( 'Numbers are equal' )
end.
```

5.2

1. Repeat 10 times
   - 1.1. Input number
   - 1.2. If number < 0 then
     - 1.2.1. Increase negative counter
       otherwise if number = 0 then
     - 1.2.2. Increase zero counter
       otherwise
     - 1.2.3. Increase positive counter
2. Print counters

```
program Five_2;
const
  Neg : word = 0;
  Pos : word = 0;
  Zer : word = 0;
var
  I, N: integer;
begin

  for I:= 1 to 10 do
  begin
    Read( N );
    if N < 0 then
      Neg:= Neg + 1
    else if N = 0 then
      Zer:= Zer + 1
    else
      Pos:= Pos + 1;
```

```
{     case N of                                    (* alternative method with case *)
        -MaxInt .. -1 : Neg:= Neg + 1;
                    0 : Zer:= Zer + 1;
         1 .. MaxInt : Pos:= Pos + 1
      end; }
  end;

  Writeln( Neg, ' are negative' );
  Writeln( Zer, ' are zero' );
  Writeln( Pos, ' are positive' )
end.
```

5.3
1. Let C be the amount of change in cents
2. Number of \$5 notes = **Trunc**(C / 500)
3. Replace C by C **mod** 500 (the remainder)
4. Print number of \$5 notes
5. Number of \$2 notes = **Trunc**(C / 200)
6. Replace C by C **mod** 200
7. Print number of \$2 notes
8. Etc., etc., etc.

5.5
1. Input a, b, c, d, e, f
2. Let $u = ae - db$
   $v = ec - bf$
3. If $u = 0$ and $v = 0$ then
   3.1. Lines coincide
   otherwise if $u = 0$ and $v <> 0$ then
   3.2. Lines are parallel
   otherwise
   3.3. Let $x = v/u$
   $y = (af - dc)/u$
   3.4. Print x, y
4. Stop.

```
program Five_5;
var
  A, B, C, D, E, F, U, V, X, Y: real;
begin
  Readln( A, B, C, D, E, F );
  U:= A * E - D * B;
  V:= E * C - B * F;
  if (U = 0) and (V = 0) then
    Writeln( 'Lines coincide' )
  else if (U = 0) and (V <> 0) then
    Writeln( 'Lines are parallel' )
  else
  begin
    X:= (E * C - B * F) / U;
    Y:= (A * F - D * C) / U;
    Writeln( 'X: ', X:10:2 );
    Writeln( 'Y: ', Y:10:2 )
  end
end.
```

CHAPTER 6

6.1

```
program Six_1;
var
  I, Sum: word;
begin
  I:= 2;
  Sum:= 0;
  while I <= 200 do
  begin
    Sum:= Sum + I;
    I:= I + 2
  end;
```

```
   Writeln( Sum )
end.
```

6.3
```
program Six_3;
var
   Bal, R: real;
   Mon, Yr: word;
begin
   R:= 0.01;
   Bal:= 1000;

   for Yr:= 1 to 10 do
   begin
      for Mon:= 1 to 12 do
         Bal:= (1 + R) * Bal;
      Writeln( Yr:2, Bal:12:2 )
   end
end.
```

6.4a
```
program Six_4a;
{$N+}                                  { speeds things up if you have an 8087 }
var
   Pi: double;                                           { Pi isn't reserved }
   K, N, Sign: longint;
begin
   Pi:= 1;
   Sign:= 1;
   Write( 'Number of terms: ' );
   Readln( N );

   for K:= 1 to N do
   begin
      Sign:= - Sign;                                       { reverse the sign }
      Pi:= Pi + Sign / (2 * K + 1)
   end;
   Pi:= 4 * Pi;
   Writeln( Pi:12:6 )
end.
```

6.4b
```
program Six_4b;
{$N+}                                  { speeds things up if you have an 8087 }
var
   Pi: double;                                           { Pi isn't reserved }
   K, N: longint;
begin
   Pi:= 0;
   Write( 'Number of terms: ' );
   Readln( N );

   for K:= 1 to N do
      Pi:= Pi + 1 / (4 * K - 3) / (4 * K - 1);

   Pi:= 8 * Pi;
   Writeln( Pi:12:6 )
end.
```

6.6
```
program Six_6;
var
   F, H, X: real;
begin
   Readln( H );

   X:= -1;
   while X <= 1 do
   begin
      F:= X * Sin( Pi * (1 + 20 * X) / 2 );
      Writeln( X:8:2, F:8:2 );
      X:= X + H
   end

end.
```

6.7
```
program Six_7;
uses Crt, Graph;
var
  Left, Right, Bottom, Top: real;
  I: word;

{$I GrScale}

begin
  Randomize;
  SetGraphics;
  Left:= 0;
  Right:= 1;
  Bottom:= 0;
  Top:= 1;

  for I:= 1 to 100 do
  begin
    SetColor( I mod 3 + 1 );                    { see section 13.4 for colour }
    LineTo( ScaleH( Random ), ScaleV( Random ) );
        Delay( 100 )
      end;

      Readln;
      CloseGraph
    end.
```

6.8
```
program Six_8;
{$N+}
var
  E, X: double;                                  { for greater accuracy }
  I: word;

begin
  X:= 0.1;

  for I:= 1 to 10 do
  begin
    E:= 1 / Exp( (1 / X) * Ln( 1 - X ) );
    Writeln( X:10, E:14:10 );
    X:= X / 10
  end

end.
```

6.9
```
program Six_9;
var
  Four, T: real;
  K, N: word;
begin
  Readln( N );

  T:= 0;
  while T <= 1 do
  begin
    Four:= 0;
    for K:= 0 to N do
      Four:= Four + Sin( (2 * K + 1) * Pi * T ) / (2 * K + 1);
    Four:= 4 * Four / Pi;
    Writeln( T:8:1, Four: 10:4 );
    T:= T + 0.1
  end

end.
```

6.10
```
program Six_10;
var
  A, R, V: real;
  I, K, N: longint;                              { N gets very big very quickly! }
```

```
function Power( A, B : real ): real;
{ raises A to the power B }
begin
  Power:= Exp( B * Ln( A ) )
end; { Power }

begin
  Write( 'Enter A, R(%), K: ' );
  Readln( A, R, K );
  N:= 1;
  R:= R / 100;

  for I:= 1 to 20 do
  begin
    V:= A * Power( (1 + R / N), (N * K) );
    Writeln( N:2, V:10:2, A * Exp( R * K):10:2 );
    N:= 2 * N
  end

end.
```

6.11
```
program Six_11;
var
  Ans, I, NumTerms, Sum: word;
begin
  I:= 0;
  Sum:= 0;

  while Sum < 100 do
  begin
    Ans:= Sum;                          { since Sum will go over 100 }
    NumTerms:= I;
    I:= I + 1;
    Sum:= Sum + I
  end;

  Writeln( 'Sum:           ', Ans );
  Writeln( 'Integers used: ', NumTerms )
end.
```

6.12 For a given interest rate, the time to double is always the same, no matter what the initial balance is. This is a feature of what is called **geometric** or **exponential** growth.

6.13
```
  program Six_13;
var
  M, N: longint;
begin
  Read( M, N );

  while M <> N do
  begin
    while M > N do
      M:= M - N;
    while N > M do
      N:= N - M
  end;

  Writeln( 'HCF is ', M )

end.
```

6.15 The final payment is $157.75 in the 54th month (don't forget the interest in the last month!)

6.16 See section 13.3 for a graphics version.

6.18 K is the stable equilibrium population, ie if $x(t) > K$, $x(t)$ decreases, whereas if $x(t) < K$, it increases. See section 8.5 for a solution.

6.21
```
program Six_21;
{$N+}
uses Graph;
var
  R, X, Left, Right, Bottom, Top : real;
  I : integer;

{$I GrScale}

begin
  SetGraphics;
  Left:= 0;
  Right:= 1;
  Bottom:= 4;
  Top:= 2.95;
  R:= Top;

  while R <= 4 do
  begin
    X:= 0.1;

    for I:= 1 to 300 do
      X:= R * X * (1 - X);

    for I:= 1 to 100 do
    begin
      X:= R * X * (1 - X);
      PutPixel( ScaleH( X ), ScaleV( R ), 1 )
    end;
    R:= R + 0.005;
  end;

  Readln;
  CloseGraph;
end.
```

CHAPTER 8

8.2
```
program MyExpo;
var
  X: real;

function Ex( X: real ): real;
var
  Sum, Term: real;
  K: word;
begin
  Sum:= 1;
  K:= 1;
  Term:= 1;
  while Abs( Term ) >= 1e-6 do
  begin
    Term:= Term * X / K;
    Sum:= Sum + Term;
    K:= K + 1
  end;

  Ex:= Sum
end; { Ex }

begin
  Readln( X );
  Writeln( 'Taylor series:      ', Ex( X ):10:6 );
  Writeln( 'Standard function:  ', Exp( X ):10:6)

end.
```

8.5
```
program Normal;
var
  X: real;
function Phi( X: real): real;
const
  A = 0.4361836;
```

```
   B = -0.1201676;
   C = 0.937298;
var
   R, T: real;
begin
   R:= Exp( -0.5 * X * X ) / Sqrt( 2 * Pi );
   T:= 1 / (1 + 0.3326 * X);
   Phi:= 0.5 - R * (A * T + B * T * T + C * T * T * T)
end; { Phi }

begin
   X:= 0;

   while X <= 4 do
   begin
      Writeln( X:4:1, Phi( X ):10:4 );
      X:= X + 0.1
   end

end.
```

8.6

```
function F( N: word ): longint;
begin
   if (N = 0) or (N = 1) then
      F:= 1
   else
      F:= F( N - 1) + F( N - 2)
end; { F }
```

8.7

```
function Time: real;
var
   Hours, Mins, Secs, Sec100: word;
begin
   GetTime( Hours, Mins, Secs, Sec100 );
   Time:= 3600 * Hours + 60 * Mins + Secs + Sec100 / 100
end; { Time }
```

8.9

```
program React;
uses Crt, Dos;
var
   Finish, Start: real;
   Ch: char;

function Time: real;
var
   Hours, Mins, Secs, Sec100: word;
begin
   GetTime( Hours, Mins, Secs, Sec100 );
   Time:= 3600 * Hours + 60 * Mins + Secs + Sec100 / 100
end; { Time }

begin
   Randomize;
   Delay( Round( 1000 * (1 * 10 * Random) ) );
   Writeln( #7 );
   Start:= Time;

   repeat
   until KeyPressed;

   Ch:= Readkey;        { reads the key }
   Finish:= Time;
   Writeln( 'Your reaction time is ', Finish - Start:4:2 );
   readln
end.
```

CHAPTER 9

9.1a

```
for I:= 1 to 100 do
   Num[I]:= I;
```

9.1b
```
for I:= 1 to 50 do
  Num[I]:= 2 * I;
```

9.1c
```
for I:= 1 to 100 do
  Num[I]:= 101 - I;
```

9.2
```
program Fibo;
var
  F: array[1..100] of word;
  I: word;
begin
  F[1]:= 1;
  F[2]:= 1;

  for I:= 3 to 100 do
    F[I]:= F[I-1] + F[I-2]

end.
```

9.3
```
program Salaries;
const
  NumScales = 7;
var
  NumEmps: array[1..NumScales] of longint;
  Scales: array[1..NumScales] of real;
  Above, Below, I, People: longint;
  F: text;
  AvLev, AvSal: real;
begin
  Assign( F, 'data.' );
  Reset( F );
  AvLev:= 0;
  People:= 0;
  Above:= 0;
  Below:= 0;
  AvSal:= 0;

  for I:= 1 to NumScales do
  begin
    Read( F, Scales[I] );
    AvLev:= AvLev + Scales[I]
  end;

  AvLev:= AvLev / NumScales;

  for I:= 1 to NumScales do
  begin
    Read( F, NumEmps[I] );
    People:= People + NumEmps[I]
  end;

  for I:= 1 to NumScales do
    if Scales[I] < AvLev then
      Below:= Below + NumEmps[I]
    else
      Above:= Above + NumEmps[I];
  for I:= 1 to NumScales do
    AvSal:= AvSal + Scales[I] * NumEmps[I];

  AvSal:= AvSal / People;
  Writeln( 'Average salary level: ', AvLev:6:2 );
  Writeln( 'Employees above average level: ', Above );
```

```
    Writeln( 'Employees below average level: ', Below );
    Writeln( 'Average salary earned: ', AvSal:6:2 )
  end.
```

9.4

```
program DecToBin;
var
  Bits: array[1..5] of byte;
  Dec, I, Num: word;
begin
  Readln( Num );
  Dec:= Num;      { keep a copy of the number }

  for I:= 5 downto 1 do      { low bits first }
  begin
    Bits[I]:= Num mod 2;
    Num:= Num div 2
  end;

  Writeln( 'Decimal: ', Dec );

  for I:= 1 to 5 do { high bits first now }
    Write( Bits[I] );

  Writeln
end.
```

9.5

1. Initialise: $N = 3$; $P_1 = 2$; $j = 1$ (prime counter)
2. While $N < 1000$ repeat:
   - 2.1. $i = 1$
   - 2.2. $Rem = N \textbf{ mod } P_i$
   - 2.3. While Rem <> 0 and $P_i < \sqrt{N}$ repeat:
     - 2.3.1. Increase i by 1
     - 2.3.2. $Rem = N \textbf{ mod } P_i$
   - 2.4. If Rem <> 0 then
     - 2.4.1. Increase j by 1 (that's another prime!)
     - 2.4.2. $P_j = N$
   - 2.5. Increase N by 2 (even numbers can't be prime)
3. Print all the P_j's
4. Stop.

9.7

```
program Zeller;
const
  DayOfWeek: array[0..6] of string =
        ('Sunday', 'Monday', 'Tuesday', 'Wednesday', 'Thursday', 'Friday', 'Saturday');
var
  Cent, Day, F, Mon, Month, Year, Yr: word;
begin
  Write( 'Enter day month year: ' );
  Readln( Day, Month, Year );
  Yr:= Year;
  Mon:= Month - 2;
  if Mon <= 0 then
    Mon:= Mon + 12;
  if Mon >= 11 then
    Yr:= Yr - 1;
  Cent:= Yr div 100;
  Yr:= Yr mod 100;
  F:= Trunc( 2.6 * Mon - 0.2 ) + Day + Yr + Yr div 4 + Cent
      div 4 - 2 * Cent;
  F:= F mod 7;
  Writeln( Day:3, Month:3, Year:5, ' : ', DayOfWeek[F] )
end.
```

CHAPTER 10

10.1

```
program BackString;
var
  Sentence: string;
```

```
   I, L: word;
begin
   Readln( Sentence );
   L:= Pos( '.', Sentence );

   for I:= L-1 downto 1 do
      Write( Sentence[I] );

   Writeln
end.
```

10.2

```
program BinToDec;
var
   Bin: string;
   Dec, I, L: longint;
   V, Code: integer;
begin
   Readln( Bin );
   L:= Length( Bin );
   Dec:= 0;

   for I:= 1 to L do
   begin
      Val( Bin[I], V, Code );
      Dec:= Dec + Round( V ) * Round( Exp( (L - I) * Ln( 2 ) ) )
   end;
   Writeln( 'Decimal: ', Dec )
end.
```

CHAPTER 11

11.1

```
procedure UpperCase( Name: string );
const
   Scratch = '$$$$$$.###';
var
   InFile, OutFile: text;
   Ch: char;
begin
   Assign( InFile, Name );
   Reset( InFile );
   Assign( OutFile, Scratch );
   Rewrite( OutFile );
   repeat
      Read( InFile, Ch );
      Write( OutFile, UpCase( Ch ) )
   until Eof( InFile );

   Close( InFile );
   Close( OutFile );
   Assign( InFile, Name );
   Erase( InFile );        { never erase an open file! }
   Assign( OutFile, Scratch );
   Rename( OutFile, Name );
end; { UpperCase }
```

11.2

```
program Transmit;
var
   F: text;
   Ch: char;
   CharCount: byte;
begin
   Assign( F, 'Jabber.' );
   Reset( F );
   CharCount:= 0;

   repeat
      Read( F, Ch );
      if (Ch <> ' ') and (Ord( Ch ) > 31) then
      { don't write the EOLN marker }
      begin
         Write( UpCase( Ch ) );
```

```
            CharCount:= CharCount + 1;
            if CharCount = 5 then
            begin
               Write( ' ' );
               CharCount:= 0
            end
         end
      until Eof( F );

      Close( F );
      Writeln
   end.
```

CHAPTER 12

12.1
```
procedure ReverseCase( Name: string );
const
   Upper = ['A'..'Z'];
   Lower = ['a'..'z'];
   Scratch = '$$$.&&&';
var
   InFile, OutFile: text;
   Ch: char;
begin
   Assign( InFile, Name );
   Assign( OutFile, Scratch );
   Reset( InFile );
   Rewrite( OutFile );

   repeat
      Read( InFile, Ch );
      if Ch in Upper then
         Write( OutFile, Chr( Ord( Ch ) + 32 ) )
         { 32 is distance in ASCII codes between upper and lower }
      else if Ch in Lower then
         Write( OutFile, UpCase( Ch ) )
      else
         Write( OutFile, Ch )
   until Eof( InFile );

   Close( InFile );
   Close( OutFile );
   { Rename and dispose as in Ex. 11.1 }
end; { ReverseCase }
```

CHAPTER 13

13.1
```
program Graphs;
uses Graph, MyGraphs;
var
   H, X: real;
   GrDriver, GrMode: integer;

function F( X: real ): real;
begin
   F:= X * Sin( Pi * (1 + 20 * X) / 2 )
end; { F }

begin
   GrDriver:= Detect;
   Initgraph( GrDriver, GrMode, ' \ tp5' );
   SetWindow( -1, 1, -2, 2 );

   repeat
      SetViewPort( 0, 0, GetMaxX, 10, True );
      ClearViewPort;
      OutText( 'Enter value of H: ' );
      GrRead( H );
      SetViewPort( 0, 0, GetMaxX, GetMaxY, True );
      X:= -1;
      ScMoveTo( X, F( X ) );
```

```
    if H <> 0 then

      while X <= 1 do
      begin
        ScLineTo( X, F( X ) );
        X:= X + H
      end

  until H = 0;

  Readln;
  CloseGraph;
end.
```

13.2
```
program Archimedes;
uses Graph, MyGraphs;
var
  GrDriver, GrMode: integer;
  A, R, T, X, Y: real;
begin
  GrDriver:= Detect;
  InitGraph( GrDriver, GrMode, '\tp5' );
  SetWindow( -10, 10, -10, 10 );
  A:= 0.1;
  T:= 0;
  ScMoveTo( 0, 0 );

  while T <= 150 do
  begin
    R:= A * T;
    X:= R * Cos( T );
    Y:= R * Sin( T );
    ScLineTo( X, Y );
    T:= T + 0.1
  end;

  Readln;
  CloseGraph;
end.
```

CHAPTER 14

14.1
```
program Bingo;
var
  Bing: array[1..99] of byte;
  I, R, Temp: byte;
begin
  for I:= 1 to 99 do
    Bing[I]:= I;
  for I:= 1 to 99 do                          { 2nd method of section 14.5 }
  begin
    R:= Trunc( 99 * Random + 1 );
    Temp:= Bing[R];
    Bing[R]:= Bing[I];
    Bing[I]:= Temp
  end;

  for I:= 1 to 99 do
  begin
    Write( Bing[I]:4 );
    if I mod 10 = 0 then
      Writeln
  end;

  Writeln
end.
```

14.2
```
program MonteCarlo;
{ Centre the square and circle at the origin }
var
  I, N: longint;
  Pi, X, Y: real;
```

```
begin
  Randomise;
  Readln( N );
  Pi:= 0;

  for I:= 1 to N do
  begin
    X:= -1 + 2 * Random;      { -1 to 1 }
    Y:= -1 + 2 * Random;      { same    }
    if X * X + Y * Y < 1 then
      Pi:= Pi + 1
  end;

  Pi:= 4 * Pi / N;
  Writeln( ' π is very roughly:', Pi:10:4 )
end.
```

14.4 Theoretically (from the binomial distribution), the probability of a DFII crashing is 1/4, while that of a DFIV crashing is 5/16; more can go wrong with it, since it has more engines!

14.5 On average, *A* wins 12 of the possible 32 plays of the game, while *B* wins 20, as can be seen from drawing the game tree. Your simulation should come up with these proportions. (However, it can be shown from the tree that B can always force a win, if he plays intelligently.)

CHAPTER 15

15.1

```
procedure Trans( var A: Mat; N, M: byte );
{ A will be M x N on return }
var
  I, J: byte;
  T: real;
begin

  for I:= 1 to N do
    for J:= I to M do
    { start at I to avoid swopping back }
    begin
      T:= A[I,J];
      A[I,J]:= A[J,I];
      A[J,I]:= T
    end

end; { Trans }
```

15.4

```
procedure RowSwop( var A: Mat; I, J, M: byte );
var
  K: byte;
  T: real;
begin
  for K:= 1 to M do
  begin
    T:= A[I,K];
    A[I,K]:= A[J,K];
    A[J,K]:= T
  end
end; { RowSwop }
```

15.5

```
procedure Sum( A: Mat; var Row,Col: real; I,J,N,M: byte );
var
  K: byte;
begin
  Row:= 0;
  Col:= 0;

  for K:= 1 to M do { run across columns }
    Row:= Row + A[I,K];
```

```
    for K:= 1 to N do { run down rows }
      Col:= COl + A[K,J]
  end; { Sum }
```

CHAPTER 16

16.1 $x_0 = 1; x_1 = 1.333; x_2 = 1.2639; x_3 = 1.2599; x_4 = 1.2599$ ..

16.2 (a) The real roots are 1.856 and −1.697.
(b) 0.589, 3.096, 6.285 ... (roots get closer to multiples of π).
(c) 1; 2; 5
(d) 1.303
(e) There are real roots at 1.768 and 2.241. The other two roots may also be real, but I couldn't find them. Perhaps you can?

16.3 Successive bisections are: 1.5, 1.25, 1.375, 1.4375 and 1.40625. The exact answer is 1.414214..., so the last bisection is within the required error.

16.5 22 (the exact answer is 21.3333...)

16.6 $x(1)$ = (a) 0.75, (b) 0.6836 (0.6321 exactly).

16.7 ie solve $dy/dx = x^2$ numerically. The answer is 14 (this is effectively the rectangular rule for integration).

16.8 The exact answer is 2117 (ie 1000 e^{rt}).

16.10 The differential equations to be solved are

$$dS/dt = -r_1 S,$$

$$dY/dt = r_1 S - r_2 Y.$$

Using the Runge-Kutta procedure of section 16.6 gives S = 6.4496E25 and Y = 2.3124E26 after 8 hours (the same as the exact solution). However, Euler gives S = 4.1373E23 and Y = 3.7282E25 after 8 hours, which is way out. In fact, the Euler solution gets *worse* as h gets smaller!

16.12
```
program Impala;
var
  A, B, H, R, T, X: real;
begin
  Readln( R, B, A, X );
  H:= 1;
  T:= 0;

  while T <= 24 do
  begin
    T:= T + H;
    X:= X + H * (R - B * X * Sin( A * T )) * X;
    Writeln( T:4:0, X:10:0 )
  end

end.
```

16.14 WITh 10 intervals (n = 5), the luminous efficiency is 14.512725%. With 20 intervals, it is 14.512667%. These results justify the use of 10 intervals in any further computations involving this problem. This is the standard way of testing the accuracy of a numerical integration or differentiation: halve the step-length and see how much the solution changes.

References

Duntemann J *Complete Turbo Pascal* (Third edition), Scott Foresman, 1989.

Knuth D E *The Art of Computer Programming*, Volume 2: *Seminumerical Algorithms*, Addison-Wesley, 1981.

Kruse R L *Data Structures and Program Design* (Second edition), Prentice-Hall International, 1987.

Peitgen H O, Richter P H *The Beauty of Fractals*, Spring-Verlag, 1986.

Starfield A M, Bleloch A L *Building Models for Conservation and Wildlife Management*, MacMillan, 1986.

Index